Reading

for Christian Schools® 5

Bob Jones University Press, Greenville, South Carolina 29614

This textbook was written by members of the faculty and staff of Bob Jones University. Standing for the "old-time religion" and the absolute authority of the Bible since 1927, Bob Jones University is the world's leading Fundamentalist Christian university. The staff of the University is devoted to educating Christian men and women to be servants of Jesus Christ in all walks of life.

Providing unparalleled academic excellence, Bob Jones University prepares its students through its offering of over one hundred majors, while its fervent spiritual emphasis prepares their minds and hearts for service and devotion to the Lord Jesus Christ.

> If you would like more information about the spiritual and academic opportunities available at Bob Jones University, please call
> *1-800-BJ-AND-ME* (1-800-252-6363).
> www.bju.edu

READING for Christian Schools® 5

Produced in cooperation with the Bob Jones University School of Education and Bob Jones Elementary School.

for Christian Schools is a registered trademark of Bob Jones University Press.

© 1986, 1999 Bob Jones University Press
Greenville, South Carolina 29614

Printed in the United States of America
All rights reserved

ISBN 0-89084-293-0

15   14   13   12   11   10   9   8

Acknowledgments

Of the following publishers, authors, and other holders of copyright material:

Charles Scribner's Sons: "His First Bronc" by Will James. From *Young Cowboy*. Copyright 1935 by Charles Scribner's Sons; copyright renewed ©1963 by Auguste Dufault. Reprinted by permission of Charles Scribner's Sons.

Doubleday & Company, Inc.: "The Wonderful Words." From *Words, Words, Words* by Mary O'Neill. Copyright ©1966 by Mary O'Neill. Reprinted by permission of Doubleday & Company, Inc.

E. P. Dutton: "Mijbil—Iraq to London" by Gavin Maxwell. Adapted from *The Otter's Tale*. Copyright ©1960 by Gavin Maxwell. Reprinted by permission of the publisher, E. P. Dutton, a division of New American Library.

Harcourt Brace Jovanovich, Inc.: "Rufus and the Fatal Four" by Eleanor Estes. From *Rufus M.*, copyright ©1943, 1971 by Eleanor Estes. Reprinted by permission of Harcourt Brace Jovanovich, Inc.

Harper & Row, Publishers, Inc.: "Sissa and the Troublesome Trifles" retold by I. G. Edmonds. From *Trickster Tales* by I. G. Edmonds (J. B. Lippincott Co.). Copyright ©1966 by I. G. Edmonds. Reprinted by permission of Harper & Row, Publishers, Inc.

"The Quarrel" by Eleanor Farjeon. From *Eleanor Farjeon's Poems for Children* (J. B. Lippincott Co.). Copyright 1933, 1961 by Eleanor Farjeon. Reprinted by permission of Harper & Row, Publishers, Inc.

Holiday House: "The Leaves Rustle" by Jim Kjelgaard. Copyright 1945 by Jim Kjelgaard. Copyright © renewed 1973 by Edna Kjelgaard. Reprinted from *Big Red* by permission of Holiday House.

Holt, Rinehart and Winston: "Race" by Millicent Vincent Ward, appearing without other copyright citation in *Sounds of a Distant Drum* by Bill Martin, Jr. Copyright ©1967 by Holt, Rinehart and Winston, Publishers. Used by permission. All rights reserved.

Houghton Mifflin Company: Glossary material based on the lexical database of the *Children's Dictionary*, copyright ©1981 by Houghton Mifflin Company. No part of this book may be reproduced or transmitted in any form or by any means, electronic or mechanical, including photocopying and recording, or by any information storage or retrieval system, except as may be expressly permitted by the 1976 Copyright Act or with prior written permission from both Houghton Mifflin Company and the Bob Jones University Press.

New American Library: "Tolstoy's Stories" by Leo Tolstoy. From *Fables and Fairy Tales* by Leo Tolstoy, translated by Ann Dunnigan. Copyright ©1962 by Ann Dunnigan. Reprinted by arrangement with New American Library.

The Paternoster Press: "The Monkey, The Mirror and the Red Paint" by Paul White. Reprinted by permission of The Paternoster Press.

A careful effort has been made to trace the ownership of selections included in this reader in order to secure permission to reprint copyright material and to make full acknowledgment of their use. If any error of omission has occurred, it is purely inadvertent and will be corrected in subsequent editions, provided written notification is made to the publisher.

Contents

LESSONS

VIEWPOINTS

REGIONS

CREATURES
GREAT AND SMALL

ENDEAVORS

OTHER DAYS

LESSONS

Adventure on Gull Island

Milly Howard

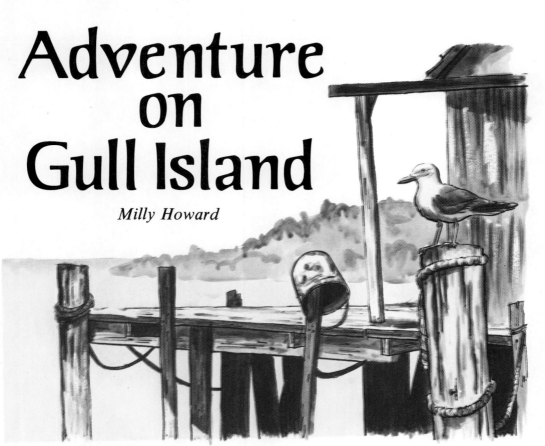

Jennifer stretched out face down on the dry boards of the dock and peered through one of the cracks. Below her, the shadowed water swirled around the posts. Slashes of sunlight poured through the cracks and rode the tiny ripples of seawater. A huge splash of water over her brought her to her feet.

"Jeremy!" she shrieked at her twin as he headed down the beach with his empty pail. "If you don't quit sneaking up on me, I'll . . . !"

"You'll what?" Jeremy's gray eyes sparkled as she caught up

with him. With a whoop, Jennifer grabbed his pail. She filled it in the surf and drenched his sunbleached hair. Jeremy called them even, and they sat down on the edge of the dock, watching the mild surf.

Without looking up, Jeremy said, "They're not here yet."

His words pricked their frail bubble of peace.

Jennifer sighed as she tossed a shell into the water. "How come Aunt Helen married a widower with an eleven-year-old son?" She didn't expect an answer. "And

2

why does he have to spend the summer with Gramps just because we do?"

After many summers alone with Gramps, the twins didn't want to share this one with a newcomer. But both Jennifer and Jeremy remembered what Gramps had said before he left to meet the plane.

"You two make Anthony welcome, you hear? Remember, he's a guest, just as you two are." He had stopped to give them a piercing look out from under his white, bushy brows. "He may not be your real cousin, but he loves the Lord and has the same heavenly Father. That makes him more than a cousin. He's your Christian brother." Gramps's keen blue eyes had not wavered as he looked at each in turn. "Anthony might seem a little different because he's city-born, but he'll get used to our ways soon enough."

A flash of sun on a white sail caught Jennifer's eye. "Here they come," she said quietly.

By the time the day sailer had reached the dock, the twins were ready to help secure the boat and stow the sails. Only when the work was done did Gramps take time to introduce the boy.

"This is Anthony, twins," Gramps said. "Anthony, the one with short hair is Jeremy; the one with long hair is Jennifer."

"Nice to meet you, Anthony," Jeremy said. He thrust out a hand.

Sunlight glinted off the newcomer's glasses, hiding his eyes. "I'd rather be called Tony." He shook Jeremy's hand rather stiffly and nodded at Jennifer.

"Hi," she said, a little too brightly.

"Hello."

"Jennifer, why don't you and Tony talk while Jeremy and I take the suitcases up to Tony's room?" Gramps and Jeremy headed for the summer house with Tony's things.

The silence was awkward. Tony shifted uneasily. His eyes followed the white curve of sand and water that formed the cove. "It's called Mangrove Cove," Jennifer said, watching him. "We're protected from the ocean here, but we're still on it."

"Why?"

Startled, Jennifer stared. "Why?"

Tony took off his glasses to clean away specks of ocean spray. Without the glasses, his face lost its owlish look. "Why is it called Mangrove Cove?"

"Look down there." She pointed. Tony replaced his glasses

and looked toward the left curve of the cove. "Those are mangroves." She pointed to the right. "There too, and over there past the palmettos are more. The cove is named for them."

Jeremy ran down the porch steps in time to overhear Jennifer's comments about the mangroves.

"Gramps says the mangroves may have started the island," Jenny said. "Their roots catch sand and mud and finally form a landmass. The island grows from that."

"How old is this island, then?" Tony asked. Keen interest lit his features.

"Gramps says some of the mangroves are hundreds of years old," Jeremy replied. "Gull Island has been on the charts since the seventeenth century," he added. "You ought to see some of the old maps Gramps has!"

Tony forgot his awkwardness. "Wow," he exclaimed, "Like pirate maps and all? I'd like that!"

Jennifer groaned inside. "Not those maps again!"

The three children turned up the grassy slope to the house. Jeremy turned to Jennifer and whispered, "He's not so bad."

Jennifer shrugged.

Jennifer set the table on the screened porch. The railing along the bottom of the porch held dozens of old bottles that they had collected along the beaches of the island. The wind blew softly over the bottles, making a hollow tune. Down in the cove the breakers boomed the deep bass for the melody of the bottles. Dinner music, Gramps called it.

Jennifer sighed in satisfaction. "It's ready!"

Jeremy and Tony took their seats quickly. "Your Mom's told me you can swim pretty well, Tony," Gramps said. "I won't be worried about you when you go off with the twins now. They've explored some on their own the last two summers. They can teach you how to handle a boat, too."

"Thank you, sir." Tony grinned.

"And by the way, call me Gramps."

Jennifer muttered, "Soup's getting cold, Gramps."

Jeremy glanced at his sister's troubled face, but ignored it. "I don't know about anybody else, but I'm hungry!"

They bowed their heads as Gramps took his seat at the head of the table. He smiled and made his blessing just a bit shorter than usual.

The sky went crimson as dusk crept over the sea. The breeze off the cove became cooler, and the cry of gulls faded away. They finished the meal, and Gramps pushed back his chair. He reached for the big Bible that lay on a side table. Then he lit the hurricane lamp on the table and turned the old pages until he found the passage he wanted to read. There was the usual "harumphing" as he cleared his throat and fumbled for his reading glasses. His strong voice rose and fell as he read aloud. Around them the song of the bottles rose with the wind and flowed with the familiar verses.

Later, Gramps and the children sat on the porch and talked. Then as the sunset faded, Gramps began to tell his sea stories. The three children listened to old tales of shipwreck, pirate maps, and treasure. Finally Gramps stopped, smiling at Tony, who was propped up against the railing. "Tony's had a long day, twins, and I suspect tomorrow will be as full as you three can pack it. How about early to bed?"

They groaned but moved inside willingly enough. When Jennifer began to stack the dishes, Gramps said, "My turn tonight. To bed with you too!"

In the tower bedroom Jennifer stretched and yawned. Sleepily, she changed and climbed into her alcove bed. She reached across the bed to swing the casement window open. The beam from the lighthouse on the northern tip of the island silvered the leaves of the tallest palm trees along the shore. Jennifer stopped to watch the play of light on the trees. As the light swept past, she looked down toward the water beyond the curve of Mangrove Cove. Just offshore a tiny light moved steadily along the shoreline. For a moment she stared, but then a yawn overtook her curiosity. "Probably just a night trawler." Before she leaned back in bed she looked out again. Now not even a flicker of light showed against the dark. Jennifer shrugged, pulled up her sheet, and closed her eyes.

Usually the sound of the surf and the tangy scent of the salt sea mist roused Jennifer with the dawn. She was nearly always the first one up. This morning was different. A restless night filled with pirates, maps, and boats running without lights had made her weary. When she awoke the sun was streaming through her window. She got to her knees and sat, elbows on the sill, looking out. She watched the ocean and tried to recall the wild dreams of the past night. Along the shore the ocean boomed as waves crashed against the sand.

In the morning light, the sand gleamed white against the dark green of the trees. As Jennifer watched, two figures moved into sight. They headed toward the house, carrying a basket. Ever so often the taller figure bent over and picked up something from the sand. As he turned toward the house, Jennifer saw the sparkle of sunlight on his glasses. She stared at the other figure in disbelief. Jeremy! Outrage choked her. Jeremy and Tony!

She bounced off the bed, straw-colored hair flying as she yanked open a drawer to find clean clothes. Quickly she pulled on an old tee shirt and culottes. She balanced on one foot as she thrust the other into a sneaker, and she glanced back out the window. The boys had just entered the cove and were looking at something. They were chattering to each other just like old friends. Angrily, Jennifer snatched the other sneaker and clumped down the stairs. She found Gramps in the kitchen cooking breakfast.

"Is that the latest style?" He grinned and raised a bushy eyebrow.

Caught by surprise, Jennifer blinked. "What?"

"The hair," he said calmly. He didn't mention the bare foot. "Looks like you tangled with an electric eel."

Jennifer ran her hands through her tangled hair. "I forgot to brush it."

"In a hurry to catch the boys, eh?"

"Jeremy left without me!" Jennifer exploded. "Just wait until I get my hands on him!"

"Hold on, Jenny." Gramps took the pan off the stove. "You were sleeping late, so I asked Jeremy to take Tony shell hunt-

ing. High tide last night probably gave them good pickings. Now, why don't you run up and fix your hair before breakfast? And there's enough time for you to spend a few minutes with your Bible."

Speechless, Jennifer turned and went back upstairs. In her room she fought back her tears. "You'd think Gramps would understand. Instead, he seems to think it's just fine that I'm the odd one out! And how does he always know when I've skipped my quiet time?"

After breakfast Gramps took Tony into the study to show him the maps. The twins were left alone to do the dishes.

"Say, Tony sure knows a lot about shells!" Jeremy exclaimed as they worked. "He was telling me about the collection he started last year in school. Why, I guess he knows just about as much as Gramps does."

At Jennifer's outraged look, Jeremy mumbled, "Well, almost. He is good, Jen. Loosen up, will you? After all, we just could have gotten stuck with a real loser."

Lips tight, Jennifer reached for another plate.

Jeremy went on uneasily. "You know something? Tony thinks there may be pirate treasure on the island too."

"So does half the rest of the world!" Jennifer snapped. "All those legends about Gull Island bring treasure hunters from all over. And no one's found anything in all these years!"

"Well," Jeremy shrugged. "They don't have Gramps's maps, and we do."

"Jeremy, you said we wouldn't be slogging all over the swamp looking for clues again this year!" Jennifer said, near tears once more. "I'd rather go sailing any time."

"One more year?" Jeremy pleaded as Jennifer let out the dishwater. "Just think of all those places we discovered last year while we were exploring! Remember all the things we found—the turtle shell, the hermit crab, the Seminole axehead on the lighthouse cliff—"

"Okay, okay!" Jennifer said as she wiped her hands. It would be useless to argue. After all, it wasn't Jeremy's fault that Tony was here.

Soon the boat was loaded with their gear and the picnic basket, and they were ready to cast off. Gramps took his place in the stern beside the tiller. Jeremy and Tony headed forward to man the sails. Jennifer cast off the mooring lines and leaped in. One quick glance told her that her usual job was taken. She slumped against the side of the boat and stared glumly at her sneakers.

"Come and sit by me, Jen girl," Gramps said. "When we get past the breakers, you can take over."

Jennifer's face lit up. Taking the tiller when Gramps was in the boat was a special treat.

"Watch out for the boom," Jeremy warned Tony. "It'll swing over when Gramps changes tack. Watch."

"It's like flying," Tony shouted. Jeremy shook the hair out of his eyes and laughed. As Gramps changed tack again, they scrambled to the other side. The boat cut cleanly through the breakers and headed out to sea. Then after a final tack, they headed downshore and ran alongside the island.

Gramps moved over, and Jennifer squeezed in between him and the tiller. Gramps's hand pressed gently on hers as they guided the boat together along the island coastline. Jennifer glanced down at his brown hand, gnarled and wrinkled with age. Gramps loved her, and yet he also had enough love for a new grandson. She hated herself for the way she felt toward the newcomer. Gramps's hand pressed gently on hers as they guided the boat together along the coastline.

"There aren't as many people down on this end of the island." Tony's voice broke into her thoughts. "Why not?"

"It's the old part of the island. Most of it belongs to three or four families. They've been here for ages." Jeremy raised his voice to be heard. "Gramps's land was one of the first three holdings on the island. His family settled here in the late 1700s. He came from a seafaring family—that's why he has the maps."

Gramps pointed toward the shore. "I thought we'd anchor in Sebastian Cove and explore Catfish Inlet. We started to explore there last summer, but a storm blew up and we had to leave."

Gramps took the tiller again and guided the boat past some outcroppings of coral reef. When the bottom touched sand, Jeremy and Tony leaped overboard, holding the bowline. They hauled the boat onto shore and held it steady as Gramps climbed out with the anchor. He wrapped the line around a tree and jerked.

"She'll hold," Gramps decided. "Let's go!" He unrolled his map and led the way around the sandy shoreline.

"Come on, Jen," Jeremy called, as Tony splashed ahead. Jennifer passed Gramps and ran after her twin. They rounded the bend to find that the inlet widened. It formed a small protected cove. At one end of the cove was a high, white mound, half covered with rough bushes.

"A shell mound!" Jeremy exclaimed. "The Seminoles must have had a village here!"

The boys charged across the cove and climbed the mound. Jennifer waited for Gramps to catch up. By the time they reached the bottom of the mound, the boys had reached the top.

"Just look at that!" Jeremy said.

"Come on up!" Tony called to the other two. Jennifer and Gramps struggled to the top and stood silently beside the boys. Beyond the mound the inlet curved into an open stretch of water.

"A land-locked harbor!" Gramps exclaimed. "This isn't on the map!"

"We're not the first to find it, though," Jeremy said suddenly. "Look over there!"

On the other side of the stretch of water, a boat rode at anchor. Long and lean, it looked as powerful as any Coast Guard cutter the children had seen.

"How'd it get in here?" Tony asked, puzzled.

Gramps rubbed his chin. He watched the boat. It lay motionless, not a sign of life on board. "Probably came up the inlet during high tide when the water was deep enough. The question is, why? What would people who own a boat like that want here unless they're treasure hunters?"

As Jennifer looked at the boat, something tugged at her memory—something about lights and darkness. Shrugging, she gave up and turned away. "I'm going down—" she began. Suddenly, they heard the crunch of footsteps below them.

Startled, they turned to see a burly, heavy-shouldered man approaching. He thrust his way up the mound. Scowling, he brandished a rifle at them.

"What're you doing here?" he shouted.

Gramps's eyes narrowed. His weather-beaten face tensed. "Exploring. What about you?" he said quietly.

"None of your business. You're on private property. Off!" Face flushed with anger, the man gestured down the mound.

"Private prop—!" Jennifer began angrily. A motion from Gramps cut her off.

"Just hold your peace, stranger," Gramps said firmly. "We'll leave."

Wide-eyed, the children scrambled down after Gramps. The man stood, legs apart, and watched them as they headed back across the cove. Gramps didn't let them speak until he was sure they were out of hearing.

"Whose property?"

"What right does he have to this end of the island?"

Gramps brushed away their indignant outbursts. "Now, hold on. You're reacting just like the stranger did. What kind of testimony is that?" He glanced down at them. "Besides, it's never

wise to argue with an angry man holding a loaded gun."

When they reached the boat, Gramps inspected the map again. He held it so the others could see. "No sign of deep water. The inlet ends in the cove. The map was made in 1806, but it's been accurate so far. Sorry, kids, it probably wasn't on our property."

"Well, it's on somebody's!" Jeremy insisted, still annoyed at the man's threatening manner.

"What's this?" Tony asked. He touched a sun drawn on the map.

Jeremy looked over his shoulder. "It's the lighthouse."

Gramps added, "Old Cap'n Trevor had it built in 1798. Too many ships were lost along these beaches. Since the lighthouse was built, only a few wrecks have been recorded. Didn't you see the light last night?" he asked, as he drew his finger across the map. "It's about a mile from our house."

"So that's the light I saw last night," Tony said. "I thought there must be a lighthouse somewhere. I just didn't know it was that close. Will we go see it?" Tony asked Gramps.

"Well, we can walk to it from the house, but I'll have to arrange a visit to get inside because it's kept locked. The Coast Guard owns and operates it now. There's no caretaker anymore. The Coast Guard put in a newfangled light that pretty nigh takes care of itself. I'll check on it when we get home. For right now, though, let's find a beach where we can eat our lunch."

Just before bedtime, Gramps put his arm around Jennifer and gave her a little piece of paper with a Scripture verse written on it. When she got to her room, she opened her Bible and sat on her big windowsill and looked up the verse. In I John 1:7a she read, "If we walk in the light, as he is in the light, we have fellowship one with another." Jennifer knew Gramps wanted to help her see Tony as a Christian brother. Well, she'd try. She really would.

That night not one dream dared enter Jennifer's head. She slept soundly and was the first to wake the next morning. She read Gramps's verse again and determined to be friends with Tony. A little later she went quietly to the kitchen and began making breakfast. The smell of sizzling bacon brought Gramps and the boys downstairs.

"Where are we going today, Gramps?" Jeremy asked as his grandfather forked a pancake onto his plate.

Gramps spread butter generously on the pancake before he answered. "Haven't heard from the Coast Guard yet. I telephoned my friend over there. He said he'd check on that hidden harbor and that boat. We'd better stick close to home until we know more."

By that afternoon Jennifer's good mood had evaporated. Tony didn't try to keep her out of any of the games, and he didn't do anything to annoy her. He and Jeremy just enjoyed each other's company so much that Jennifer felt left out.

She wandered into the study. The boys were stretched out on the carpet, playing checkers. Jennifer sat down on the arm of Gramps's old chair to watch.

"Gotcha," Tony said. He jumped three of Jeremy's men. Jennifer grinned, waiting for the explosion that usually came when she beat Jeremy. It didn't come. Instead, Jeremy set up a new game and laughed, saying, "Just wait. This time I'll win." Jennifer watched sullenly. "They could have asked if I wanted a turn," she thought crossly. Deep into a new game, the boys seemed not to know she was even there. Jennifer gave the stool beside the boys a vicious kick. It fell across the game and scattered the pieces.

Tony looked up. Jeremy scrambled around on the floor to catch the pieces and yelled, "Jennifer, go away!"

Jennifer spun around and ran through the kitchen. The screen door slammed behind her. Tears stung her eyes as she plunged through the underbrush. The grasses stung her legs as she pounded up the path to the shadows of the live oaks. She looked at their wide branches but decided to keep going. Out of the trees, she found herself on the path to the lighthouse. She climbed the rocks on the northern tip of the island.

The lighthouse stood like a sentinel on the cliff. Jennifer walked slowly along the gravel path, around the tall tower and the deserted house that leaned against it. She tipped her head back to watch a gull calling from a ledge near the top. The verse from her morning Bible time came to her mind again. She kicked at a shell on the path and continued toward the lighthouse keeper's house. Then she stopped. The padlock on the door hung from the broken hasp, and the door wasn't completely closed. She looked back and saw Jeremy and Tony scrambling up the rocks after her. Quickly she pushed on the door and it swung open. Jennifer stepped inside. She waited until her eyes became used to the darkness and then made her way past stacks of wooden crates. Through the gloom she could see the broad barred door that led into the lighthouse tower.

"Jennifer! Jennifer-r! Wait for us!"

The boys shoved the door open and stepped inside. "Jennifer?" Jeremy whispered. "Is that you?"

For a moment, Jennifer considered not answering, but finally she said, "Who else?"

"Hey, Jennifer, I'm sorry," Jeremy said quietly. "I'm sorry I yelled. Come on, you know we aren't supposed to be in here without permission."

"Yeah, let's play pirates in the live oaks. You can be captain," Tony suggested.

"I thought we had to stay around the house," Jennifer reminded him.

"The Coast Guard just called." Jeremy replied. "They said the boat was gone, and Gramps said we could play in the live oaks. Okay, Jen?"

"Okay." Jennifer moved forward and banged her shin against a crate. "What *is* this stuff?"

Tony moved over to look at the one closest to the door. "The lid's broken on this one. It has some metal rods in it."

"Better not touch it. Hey, let's get out of here." Jeremy insisted.

"Jeremy," Jennifer called in a small voice. She was standing by the door and staring out toward the path that led to the sea. "Here comes that man we saw at the mound! Someone's with him!"

"Get back inside," Tony whispered. "Follow me!"

They rushed across the room to the door inside that led into the lighthouse tower. Crouched behind the wooden staircase, the three hardly dared to breathe.

The front door was shoved open, and two men entered. "I thought I told you to shut that door!" the first man said angrily. "Any fool could see the lock's broken!"

"I did close it, Lee," his companion answered. "The wind must have blown it open."

"Always some excuse," Lee growled. "I'll be glad when this shipment is delivered. That old graybeard will have the Coast Guard on us before we know it."

"Aw, he won't do anything. He didn't give you any trouble, did he? I don't see why we even had to move the stuff."

"You know what the sentence is for selling guns? I sure do, and I don't aim to spend my life behind bars!"

"Well, the deal's over tonight. By nine we'll be on our way to Bermuda. Relax, Lee."

Lee lit a hurricane lamp as the children shrank further back. He checked the broken crate and then held the lamp high to check the other boxes. With a cry of annoyance, he crossed the room to study the crate beside the tower door. "Another cracked one! Can't you do anything right?"

He leaned down to run his hand across the far end of the crate, and the lamp slipped forward. As he tried to keep the oil from spilling out of the lamp, he lurched into the tower door. It slammed and the bar fell solidly into place.

The children stared at each other in the dim light that filtered down from the narrow slits in the tower. "What'll we do?" Jennifer whispered.

Tony put his finger to his lips and leaned against the door. After a while he straightened up. "They're gone," he said grimly, "and we're locked in!"

"Gramps will never find us," Jeremy said. He pushed desperately against the barred door. "We're not supposed to be in here."

"He thinks we're playing in the live oaks," Tony agreed. "That's where we told him we'd be."

Jennifer groaned. "I got us into this."

"It wasn't your fault. And don't worry; we'll find a way out," Tony said. "Jeremy, why don't you go up and see how big those slits are?"

"Okay. Come on, Jen."

Tony inspected the materials stacked under the stairs until the twins came clumping back down. "The slits are hardly wide enough for a cat to get through," Jeremy said glumly.

"I thought so," Tony replied quietly, "but we have to do something!"

Jeremy noticed that Tony had been rummaging through the materials under the stairs. "Did you find anything?" Jeremy asked.

"Two empty paint cans, a brush, an old tarp, and two ladders," Tony answered.

"What good are they?" Jennifer asked. She was still frightened.

Tony didn't answer. "Let's all go upstairs. Maybe there'll be something we can use in the lamp room."

At the top of the winding stairs, the children pulled the heavy door open.

A search around the circular room yielded nothing of any use. "We'll have to wait, then," Jeremy said. "The smugglers might get away, but Gramps will find us. He'll come looking when we don't show up for supper."

They went back into the tower and sat down on the steps. "There ought to be some way we could warn the Coast Guard about those gun smugglers. They shouldn't get away. Who knows who they're selling those guns to!" Jeremy muttered, his usually cheerful face grim and tense.

"At home," Tony said hesitantly, "we pray for God's help."

Jennifer smiled. "So do we. You want to start, Tony?"

Sometime later, Tony said suddenly, "I know a way to warn the Coast Guard. But we'll have to wait until dark."

"What? What?" Jennifer asked eagerly.

"That tarp downstairs is big enough to block one side of the lamproom," Tony said.

"And?" Jennifer asked.

"And the light wouldn't show through on that side!" Jeremy interrupted. "We could block the one toward the mainland where the Coast Guard station is located. That wouldn't get any ships into trouble, but the dispatcher would send someone to check on the lamp!"

"You've got it, Tony!" Jennifer said excitedly. "You're all right!"

By late afternoon they were ready. It had taken some time to carry the ladders up the stairs to the lamproom. The tarp wasn't easy to carry either. The three of them pushed, shoved, and dragged it up, stair after stair. At the top they stopped to rest.

"Okay," Jeremy puffed. "Just a little more."

When the tarp was finally in place it covered an entire block of windows. "It'll do," Jennifer said with satisfaction. "It's actually going to work!"

They went downstairs to wait. Jennifer's stomach rumbled. "Gramps must really be worried by now," she sighed, leaning against the wall. "What's for supper?"

"Don't mention food," Jeremy groaned. "I could eat an alligator right now!"

For a while they sat without speaking. The dim light from the slits faded, and finally they were left in darkness. Jennifer said quietly, "Jeremy, why don't you tell some of Gramps's stories? Tony hasn't heard most of them."

A sudden scrape and bump interrupted the stories. The children got to their feet and leaned against the door. The crates were being moved!

"The smugglers came by sea,

or they would have seen the blocked light," Tony whispered. "The big boat is probably anchored offshore. They'll be taking the crates out in a rowboat," Jeremy added. He grinned with satisfaction. "It'll take them a long time."

Minutes dragged into an hour. The scraping and thudding continued. Suddenly a crash sounded from the other side of the door.

"Someone else is here!" Tony exclaimed as they heard shouts from the house. A gunshot echoed in the night, and scuffling sounds came from outside. Then all was quiet.

The children listened tensely. The door creaked. Then they heard footsteps in the room. The bar lifted and the door slowly opened. They blinked as a figure holding a flashlight appeared in the doorway.

"Gramps!" Jennifer shouted and launched herself into his arms.

"So this is where you three were," Gramps said. "If you only knew how worried I was—but never did it cross my mind that you were trapped by smugglers!"

The bulky figure of a Coast Guard lieutenant entered the room. "Kids! What are kids doing here?"

"We got locked in," Jeremy began.

"And we heard the smugglers talking about the guns," Jennifer interrupted.

"So we tried to warn the Coast Guard." Tony finished.

"One at a time," the lieutenant said, amazed. "Don't tell me—*you* blocked the light!"

"Only toward the mainland," Tony said hastily. "We knew you would come and check on it, and you did."

"Yes, we made a fine haul tonight," the lieutenant said. "We've heard about this group, but we didn't know they were operating this far up. Good thinking, kids."

Jennifer looked up at Gramps.

"You aren't mad, are you, Gramps? It's all my fault—I ran away mad."

Gramps gave her a comfortable hug. "I just thank the Lord you're okay. How about supper?"

He grinned at the enthusiastic replies. "How about you, lieutenant?"

"After I fix this light," the lieutenant said, starting up the stairs. He teased, asking, "I don't suppose it'll be an easy job?"

"We just put that old tarp over the windows," Tony said. "It'll come right down."

The lieutenant burst into laughter.

Jennifer beamed. "It was Tony's idea."

Gramps ushered them out the door, all chattering at once again. "Hold on, you three," he said. "Looks like you have an adventure tale to beat all. After supper you can tell me the whole story!"

Jennifer grabbed Gramps's big hand. "Thank you for the verse, Gramps. Being together there in the lighthouse . . . I guess we learned what fellowship is."

"If we walk in the light, as he is in the light, we have fellowship one with another."—I John 1:7

BEACONS AND BELLS

Becky Davis

In "Adventure on Gull Island," Jennifer, Jeremy, and Tony explored a lighthouse that was over 150 years old. The children saw the keeper's house too, but nobody lived there anymore.

Ever since men first started traveling by water, rocky coasts and dangerous shoals have taken the lives of sailors who were driven into them by storms or who didn't see them soon enough. Long ago someone thought of the idea of constructing a tall building with a light to warn sea travelers of the dangers ahead.

One of the first—and definitely the most famous—lighthouses was built over 2,000 years ago in Egypt. Thousands of the Pharaoh's slaves worked over twenty years to build it. The

lighthouse, called the Pharos, stood over 400 feet high, with a huge fire burning on top. Mirrors made the fire seem even brighter. Stories say that the light could be seen for over thirty miles! The Pharos was one of the Seven Wonders of the Ancient World.

But after the Pharos was destroyed, no other lighthouse quite as splendid was ever built. For one thing, lighthouses were hard to construct because of *where* they had to be built. One of the most fearsome places was the Eddystone rocks, which jutted out of the English Channel. These rocks were not quite high enough to be seen from a distance, but high enough to wreck many a passing ship. Since many seamen lost their lives on these rocks, the English government finally hired Mr. Henry Witstanley to build a lighthouse in 1698.

The Eddystone rocks curved and jutted so much that no one thought a lighthouse could be built there. Besides, Henry Witstanley had a reputation—as a "kook"! He had an inventor's mind, but he used it in strange ways. In his own house he had so many weird contraptions and trick devices that he charged admission for people to walk through. You won't be surprised to learn that the lighthouse that he built had extra balconies, flagpoles, odd fixtures, and other gadgets, just right for a man like Henry. But it did stand—for almost four years. No ships crashed into the rocks during that whole time. Then a storm hit, one of the worst that the Eddystone rocks had ever known. Henry was killed in the lighthouse when the storm destroyed it.

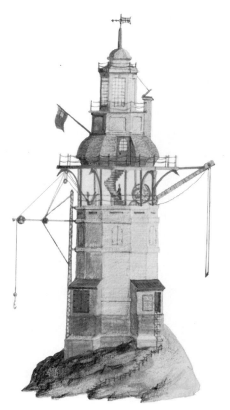

A new lighthouse was erected on the Eddystone rocks, and then another, and then another. The last one, finished in 1882, still stands, partly because of the many improvements that have been made in lighthouse construction.

One improvement that has been made over the centuries is in the light itself. In the Pharos a huge bonfire burned at the top. In later lighthouses hundreds of candles were tended by the lighthouse keeper. Then oil lamps with reflectors were used. But it wasn't until Thomas Edison invented the light bulb that lighthouses became really effective and required less maintenance, or care, by the lighthouse keeper.

The lighthouse keeper is the faithful man who makes sure that the lighthouse is operating constantly to warn passing seamen of possible dangers. If a lighthouse is built on land, like the one in "Adventure on Gull Island," the keeper's house may be built alongside the lighthouse tower. A door leads right from the keeper's house to the tower. But if you wanted to visit a lighthouse that has been constructed on a solitary rock, you would have to get there by boat. As you climbed the many steps up to the light, you would pass each room of the lighthouse

keeper's home on your way. At the very top you'd find the thousand-watt bulb—about the size of a volleyball—and the huge rotating lenses that send the strong beacons of light over the water.

But during a thick fog, even the powerful beacon from the lighthouse can't be seen by passing fishermen. Hundreds of years ago, seamen realized that some sort of warning sound was needed for foggy days and nights. They tried cannons for a while, but the short blasts couldn't tell them much about how far they were from the rocks. Then huge fog bells were used. But the fog bells were hard for the lighthouse keepers to work; so they became unpopular. Finally someone realized that if steam were channeled just the right way, it would make a very loud noise. And thus the foghorn was invented—a huge machine powered by steam that sends out a long, low sound over the water.

You read in "Adventure on Gull Island" that the keeper's house had long ago been abandoned. New electronic devices and other inventions allow many lighthouses to work almost by themselves. In many cases it's no longer necessary for one man to live next to or inside the tower

and carefully maintain it every day. The Coast Guard, which is always stationed near the lighthouse tower, can watch the lighthouse and visit it if the bulb needs to be changed, if the foghorn needs to be activated, or if something seems to be wrong.

A lighthouse keeper's life has always been thought of as a lonely one, and it's true that it used to be solitary. But since electricity has brought the radio, telephone, and other electrical conveniences, a lighthouse keeper's life doesn't have to be as lonely. Motorboats can take him to the mainland much faster than boats of the old days, too. Most lighthouse keepers now live with their families on their little rocky islands year round. They seem to love the beautiful ocean and quiet privacy.

As lighthouses are improved, there will be even less need for full-time lighthouse keepers. But for centuries seamen have owed their safety near the shores to the faithfulness of the lighthouse keepers.

The Story of a Gospel Song

Becky Davis

More than a hundred years ago, men used oil-lamp light-houses to warn pilots of dangerous coastlines. In the dark and for a great distance, the lighthouse would send out its warning. But if a sea captain had to navigate his ship close to that ragged shore, the lighthouse keeper placed smaller oil lamps along the coast to lead the pilot to the harbor.

Lorraine Harbor along the great Lake Erie had this kind of coastline. But one night in the late 1800s the lighthouse keeper of Lorraine Harbor was feeling tired. He decided that since no ship had ever navigated that treacherous coastline at night, no one would need the lower lights along the coast that night. He didn't feel like trimming the lamps along the shore and filling up their oil reservoirs. So he went to bed.

But while he slept, a terrible storm blew up. And indeed a ship did come along, tossing and plunging, trying to enter the harbor, watching the lighthouse, and searching desperately for the lower lights. Because they had not been lit, the ship crashed into the jagged rocks and sank. Only a few men survived.

When Mr. Philip P. Bliss heard this story, he was angry that such a terrible thing had happened simply through careless neglect. But the more he thought about it, the more he realized that he—and other Christians—were just like the lighthouse keeper. Lost souls in the night are often dashed along the coastline even while the

light of Christ's love is shining. This tragedy occurs because Christians, who are the lower lights to lead people to Christ, do not have their lamps trimmed and bright. Mr. Bliss promptly wrote a song. His metaphors compared our heavenly Father to the great lighthouse and Christians to the lower lights along the shore. He hoped that his song would remind Christians all over the world of their responsibility to lead souls to Christ.

Let The Lower Lights Be Burning

Skill Lesson:
Reference Books

Libraries provide resource materials on hundreds of subjects. A person could look up anything from *aardvarks* to *zithers*. He could find out about places as different from each other as Arizona and New Zealand. But if a person wanted to understand a subject well, he would have to consult several reference books before he could be satisfied.

• **Encyclopedias and Dictionaries**

If you were planning to visit or move to Florida, you might want to find out what the state has to offer. You would check an *encyclopedia*. Encyclopedias provide informative articles on many subjects. Suppose you checked the entry "Florida" in the encyclopedia. You would discover

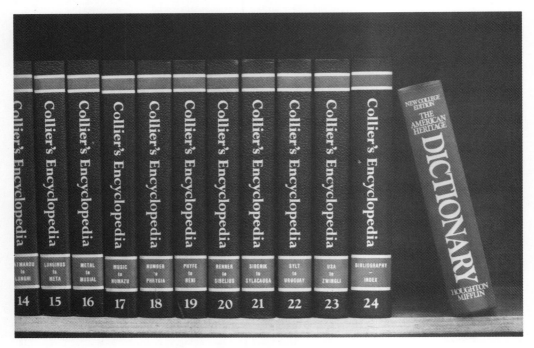

that one of Florida's biggest industries is mining. Florida is rich in phosphate and zircon. What easy reference book could you check to find out what zircon and phosphate are?

A dictionary provides short definitions. Like the encyclopedia, the dictionary lists its entries in alphabetical order. The dictionary would define *phosphate* as a sedimentary rock used to make fertilizer. It would define *zircon* as a mineral which can be made into jewelry or ground up for use in ceramics. One difference between encyclopedias and dictionaries is that dictionaries usually have more entries. But encyclopedias provide complete explanations and more illustrations instead of just a few sentences. Both sources are valuable for research.

- **The Atlas**

As you did more research about Florida, you would discover that Florida has more coastline than any other state except Alaska. A large *atlas* would provide you with several detail maps of Florida. You could check an atlas to trace the turnpikes and major highways in Florida and to find the big airports and cities. A good atlas would provide a map to show the transportation systems of the state such as roads, railroads, and waterways, and a map to show the physical features such as the everglades, uplands, lakelands, swamps, and coastal plains. Some atlases would include maps to show rainfall and climate in the state throughout the year.

A person doing research for any reason, whether for travel plans or for a homework assignment, can start his project with three sources. He can use the encyclopedia for informative articles, the dictionary for brief, accurate definitions, and the atlas for geography and description.

Lessons
from
Mr. Lee

Jeri Massi

The martial art tae kwon do *was developed over a thousand years ago by the royal bodyguard of the Korean emperor. At the time, the people called it* hwarang-do, *which means "the way of the flower of manhood." People in nearby China and Japan had also developed their own martial arts and sometimes used them to help in the study of pagan religions like Zen and Taoism. These religions demanded stern physical training and discipline, and for this reason the martial arts have sometimes been used by pagan priests to assist them in their training. Many good karate and tae kwon do teachers conduct schools without any association with pagan beliefs, and as Billy learns in this story, sometimes a karate teacher can teach a boy one of the most important lessons he will ever learn.*

The sun was setting. I hurried on my way up Clover Road, past the quiet houses and neat lawns. I walked as fast as I could.

A front door slammed. Two boys came out of one of the houses. They saw me and looked away. But after I was past them, I heard them laughing. I looked back and saw one of them imitating me, holding his left hand clenched against his chest.

I looked down at my feet and kept going. Soon I couldn't hear them anymore.

Clover Road led to the highway. I walked past a bakery and a dry cleaner's, then came to a one-story building that was marked by a single sign. The sign said

LEE'S TAE KWON DO SCHOOL
MR. LEE, HEAD INSTRUCTOR
FIFTH-DEGREE BLACK BELT

An oriental man stood in the doorway, looking up at the pink and orange sky. Then he looked down at me.

"Can I help you?" he asked. His eyes were black and sparkling like dark oil.

"I want to learn karate," I told him.

"Lot of people want to learn that," he said. "Why come here to learn?"

I pointed down the highway with my good arm. "I live a few blocks away. I can walk here," I said. "At least until the days start getting shorter."

"Huh. Sensible," he agreed, putting his long slim hands on his hips. His skin was a smooth tan color and contrasted sharply against the snowy whiteness of his

karate uniform. "You come here and sit down," he said. "Watch a while." He pointed to a row of folding chairs that were lined up against the wall inside. "You are how old?"

"Ten."

"Okay."

I did as he told me. He walked away. I rubbed my bare toe into the rough carpet and watched the other students. They looked like genies, strolling across the room in their billowy white uniforms.

Mr. Lee stepped into his tiny private office. He came out with a long cloth strip in his hands. It was his black belt, but years of use had worn it to gray. He wrapped it twice around his hips, knotted it, and waited while the students lined up to face him.

An American and a Korean flag were hanging on the wall behind Mr. Lee. He and his students said the Pledge of Allegiance to the American flag. Then the students bowed to him. He bowed to them, clapped his hands, and class began.

The students groaned and toiled through calisthenics, sit-ups, and stretching exercises. Many of the people had white belts, and many had green belts. Some had brown belts. Only two wore black belts. Mr. Lee told one

of the men with a black belt to take over.

"You come with me," he said to me. We went into his office.

"So," he said to me. "You take karate from me because you live close. Any other reason?"

I shrugged.

"You like sports? Play football?"

"No."

"Baseball?"

"No . . . sir."

"You don't play baseball?" he asked, his shining dark eyes getting wide. "What kind of American boy are you?" He smiled a strong white smile at me.

For an answer, I offered him my left arm. I knew that look, always of surprise and fear, that came into people's eyes when they saw my arm. They usually tried not to stare at it.

His smile faded, and he took hold of my babyishly tiny left hand in his big brown one. "Hurt you?" he asked.

"No. It's just too small." I felt my eyes stinging with tears. I swallowed a couple times and said, "My other one is normal. Can I still learn karate here?"

"Yes." He leaned across his desk and pulled a sheaf of papers from a basket. "You promise to work hard for me?"

"Yes sir."

"You good boy? Obey law? Go to school every day?"

"Yes sir."

"Take papers to your parents. If they sign, I let you come to my school."

"Okay."

"I see you tomorrow night. Your name is?"

"Bill."

He shook hands with me. "I am Mr. Hyong Lee. Maybe you knew that."

"Yes sir. Good-bye."

I learned how to wear a *gi* and tie my white belt the right way. I was the newest student; so I always stood at the end of the line when we pledged allegiance and bowed to Mr. Lee.

The exercises stretched my legs and my back and pulled at my stomach until I felt like a rubber band. Mr. Lee made us do sit-ups very slowly, with our feet in the air and our toes pointed straight up.

One of the men with a black belt taught me how to punch. It was hard, because in tae kwon do students don't throw their shoulders forward like boxers would. They use their hips instead. At first I felt awkward about punching with my left arm, but Mr. Lee told me to do it.

"Other people think that arm no good," he said. "You make it take them by surprise. Work on it."

One evening when I was walking up to the karate school— or tae kwon do school as we called it—some of the older kids were out playing stickball on the street.

"Hey, let's see you chop down that tree!" one of them called out to me. I pulled my folded-up *gi* closer and tried to ignore them as I passed. Some of them imitated me doing karate, clenching their arms to their chests and yelling, "Hiyah! Hiyah!"

I was almost running by the time I got to Mr. Lee's.

"Hello Billy," Mr. Lee called as I ducked past him into the training hall, or *dojo*.

"You okay, Billy?" he asked.

I threw my *gi* onto a folding chair and asked, "When am I going to learn how to fight?"

He bent down. "Only been three weeks. Still early."

"But when? How long does it take?"

He shrugged. "I study karate all my life. I still not a fighter. Never wanted to be one."

"You can fight," I said. "I've seen you."

"Spar, maybe. Fighting means hurting. I not hurt other people."

I looked down and didn't say anything.

He straightened up and put his hands on his hips. "Somebody picking on you, Billy?"

I nodded.

"Older boys?" he asked.

"Junior high boys."

"What they say?"

"They laughed at me for my arm and for taking karate."

"Huh," he said, then added, "Many people fear what they not understand. They think martial art is fight, fight, fight; yell and scream and break board. Maybe you thought that too, at first."

I nodded.

"Some people," he continued, "think we meditate and pray. But

we not do that in my *dojo*. We practice hard, be good citizens, learn discipline. But some people make fun. That is same with your arm. People fear it a little bit. It look strange to them."

"I'm tired of people laughing at me," I told him. "I want to be somebody."

He squatted down so that he could see me face to face. His glittering dark eyes were serious. "You somebody now," he said. "Mr. Lee cannot give new arm; he give skill instead. Mr. Lee cannot make older boys leave you alone; he make you see how foolish they are. Someday you see, it not the arm or leg that make you somebody. It is what you have inside. Fighting not help you."

Then he stood up and walked away.

I learned how to do the basic kicks. At first when I practiced them, I nearly fell over each time I tried. My legs got tired. My feet got tired. My ankles and knees felt like they'd been twisted and turned every which way. After class I could barely get into my street clothes, and my short walk home seemed like a long hike.

One night it started to rain during the lesson. By the time I had struggled back into my clothes, it was pouring outside.

Mr. Ryan, the man who had taught me to punch, called me over. "Hey, Billy, I can give you a ride home. I live over by Clover Road," he said. "Call your folks and ask if it's all right."

There was a phone in Mr. Lee's office. I called quickly and got permission.

I folded my damp *gi* together and followed him out to his little Volkswagen. Mr. Lee smiled and waved to us.

We climbed in and pulled out with a jerk as the little car jumped forward.

"Tired out?" Mr. Ryan asked, squinting at the windshield as he guided the car onto the highway.

"Uh-huh."

"You always push yourself hard in class. That's good. Where's your house?"

"All the way down to the end of the street."

"You always walk to class?"

"My dad works at night and he takes our car. I don't mind so long as it's light outside."

He turned the car onto Clover Road. A few of the older kids were still out. They moved aside for us as we rumbled through. A few of them saw me and pointed. He ignored them.

"I can start picking you up for class," he told me.

"Thank you."

"You're a hard worker, a good student. This your house?"

"Yes. Thanks."

My mother was hurrying down the driveway with an umbrella. "Thank you so much for bringing Billy home," she called to him as I scrambled out. I winced at the name Billy. When Mr. Lee used it, it wasn't so bad, but when Mom said it, I felt like a kid.

"Are you Mr. Ryan?" she asked.

"Yes, I am. I enjoy working with your son. If it's all right, I can pick him up for class," he called over the rumbling of the car.

"Oh, that would be fine. Billy talks so much about you and Mr.

Lee." I felt my face burning, but Mr. Ryan didn't even seem to notice.

"Very nice meeting you, ma'am. I better let you get in out of the rain. Bill, I'll see you tomorrow night."

"Good-bye."

I felt a lot better going to class with Mr. Ryan. The kids up the street stared at us when we drove past. They pointed at me a couple times at first, but Mr. Ryan always ignored them. After a while they stopped. Mr. Ryan was tall and looked like a mountain climber. He had thick curly hair and dark eyes. Although he was not old, his face was craggy and he rarely smiled. He wasn't the sort of man that people laugh at.

I learned how to do jump kicks and spinning kicks. At first all the turning and spinning made me dizzy, but I worked on keeping my balance. Mr. Lee could leap through the air, twirl around in a blur, and touch his foot against my ear as lightly as though I were made of porcelain and he were afraid of breaking me. But I also saw him leap through the air and drive his foot through three pine boards. Sometimes he would toss a board into the air and then break it with a punch or kick before it hit the ground.

The school year started; I continued my lessons from Mr. Lee. The air outside was crisp and clear, but it was still hot inside the *dojo* when we trained.

"You ready for green-belt test?" he asked me one night.

My mouth went dry. I nodded, waiting for him to name a day.

"I think I test you next week. You very good student. Older boys still pick on you?'"

I shrugged. "I come with Mr. Ryan now, so they don't have a chance to."

"You could walk to class," he observed. "Then drive home with Mr. Ryan."

"I like driving with him both ways."

He nodded and looked down at me. "When you first come here," he said gently, "you carried left arm way up here, like this." He pressed his left arm to his chest. "Seemed like you were afraid people should see it. Now you do not care anymore. You swing arms a lot now."

"Nobody here makes fun of it," I said.

"You not ashamed of it in here anymore. I make you punch with it and you do. You are used to it; they are used to it."

"But other people outside the *dojo* will make fun of it."

He cocked his head. "Those boys still so important?"

I didn't know what to say. Finally he said, "Okay, okay, enough of that. Let me see you punch."

I punched for him a couple times. "More?" I asked.

"No. Let me see you kick. Try a side kick." I snapped out a side kick for him. He nodded and asked to see more. It was the first time he had ever tutored me. I supposed it was to get me ready for my green-belt test. Mr. Ryan and a couple of older students strolled across the *dojo* and watched us. Mr. Lee went through all the kicks with me. We practiced self-defense together, and I showed him the first *kata,* a routine of karate techniques that's sort of like a drill. He did not say much. When we were finished, he nodded.

"You coming along pretty well," he said. "You very good student. Wish all my students work as hard as you."

He walked away. Mr. Ryan looked down at me. "Mr. Lee doesn't say that to many people," he told me.

After class when Mr. Ryan was driving me home, I said, "Some of the older kids on the street laugh at me for my arm."

"I noticed that," he replied. "Do you let it bother you?"

"It always has."

"Some day you'll grow out of thinking so much of what other people say. Nobody can do it for you."

"Would you mind," I asked, "if I walked to class next time?"

"Nope. I'll drive you home afterwards."

"Thanks."

On Monday night after dinner I folded up my *gi* and set off for the *dojo* while it was still light outside. I tucked my *gi* under my left arm.

The boys up the street were sitting on the curb, talking. My heart beat harder, but I thought about Mr. Lee. Everything he had to say was a million times more important than jeers and catcalls from these boys.

They stopped talking and watched me. Some of them started laughing. I kept walking with my head up. I could sense that they were imitating me, but I didn't look back at them this time. Some day you'll grow out of thinking so much of what other people say, Mr. Ryan had told me. He was right. It was time to stop being afraid of older kids who picked on me. I just wanted to get to the karate school, test for my green belt, and tell Mr. Lee I had walked to class.

I passed the boys and walked on to Mr. Lee's. He was standing in the doorway. His hands were clasped behind his back.

"You early Billy," he called.

"I started early," I said. "I walked."

"Boys pick on you?"

"I just kept walking, Mr. Lee. I never looked back." I swung my *gi* into my hand and looked up at his sparkling black eyes. "You were right. It wasn't important anymore."

"You make a big step," he said. "I have something for you." He pulled a green belt from behind his back and put it into my hand.

"But I haven't tested!" I exclaimed.

"You tested last week with me," he replied. "And now tonight I know you ready for green belt from Mr. Lee."

The belt was new and stiff, folded up and held together with rubber bands. I knew that tonight I would be standing with all the green-belted students, no longer last in line. I thanked him and ducked past him.

"Where you go so fast?" he called.

"To put it on, to show Mr. Ryan!"

Mr. Wolf Makes a Failure

Joel Chandler Harris

"I see your ma's got comp'ny," said Uncle Remus, as the little boy entered the old man's door with a huge piece of mince-pie in his hand.

"Well, I saw the pie lying there, Uncle Remus, and I just thought I'd fetch it out to you."

"My, my, honey," replied the old man, looking over the child with admiration. "My, my, honey. It ain't Thanksgiving time, en dey ain't got no bizness layin' a mince meat pie roun' loose. Dish here pie," Uncle Remus continued, holding it up and measuring it with an experienced eye, "will gimme strenk fer ter pursue on after Brer Fox en Brer Rabbit en the other beastesses."

Here the old man paused, and proceeded to demolish the pie— a feat accomplished in a very short time. Then he wiped the crumbs from his beard and began:

Brer Fox feel so bad, en he git so mad about Brer Rabbit, dat he dunno what ter do, and he look mighty downhearted. By 'n by, one day wiles he wuz goin' along the road, ole Brer Wolf come up with 'im. When dey got done howdyin' and askin' after one nudder's fambly, Brer Wolf, he allowed, he did, dat der wuz somethin' wrong wid Brer Fox, en Brer Fox, he allowed der wern't, en he went on en laff en make great ter-do. But Brer Wolf, he got mighty long head, en he sorter broach 'bout Brer Rabbit's carryin's on, 'cause the way dat Brer Rabbit deceive Brer Fox done got ter be the talk of the naberhood. Den Brer Fox en Brer Wolf dey sorter talked on, dey did, 'til by 'n by Brer Wolf he up'n say dat he done got a plan fixed ter trap Brer Rabbit. Den Brer Fox say how. Den Brer Wolf up'n tell him dat the way ter git Brer Rabbit wuz ter git' im in Brer Fox's house.

"How you goin' git 'im dar?" sez Brer Fox.

"Fool 'im," sez Brer Wolf.

"Who goin' to do the foolin'?" sez Brer Fox.

"I'll do the foolin'," sez Brer Wolf, "if you'll do de gamin'."

"How you goin' do it?" sez Brer Fox.

"You run 'long home, en git on the bed, en make like you dead, en don't you say nuthin' 'til Brer Rabbit come in and put his hands onter you," sez Brer Wolf, "en ef we don't git 'im fer supper, Joe's dead en Sal's a widder."

"Dis look like a mighty nice game," en Brer Fox agreed. So den he amble off home, en Brer Wolf, he march off ter Brer Rabbit's house. When he got dar, it look like nobody at home, but Brer Wolf he knock on the do'— blam! Blam! Nobody come. Den he knock again—blim! Blim!

Mr. Wolf Makes a Failure   43

"Who dar?" sez Brer Rabbit.

"Friend," sez Brer Wolf.

"Too many friends spiles the dinner," sez Brer Rabbit; "which un's dis?"

"I fetch bad news, Brer Rabbit," sez Brer Wolf.

"Bad news is soon tole," sez Brer Rabbit.

By dis time Brer Rabbit done come ter the do'.

"Brer Fox died dis mawnin'," sez Wolf.

"Whar yo' mournin' clothes, Brer Wolf?" sez Brer Rabbit.

"Goin' after them now," sez Brer Wolf. "I jus' call by fer ter bring the news. I went down ter Brer Fox house little bit ago, en dar I foun' 'im stiff."

Den Brer Wolf lope off. Brer Rabbit sot down en scratch his head, he did, en by 'n by he say ter hisself dat he b'leeve he sorter drop roun' by Brer Fox's house. No sooner said 'n done. Up he jump, en out he went. When Brer Rabbit got close ter Brer Fox's house, all look lonesome. Den he went up nigher. Nobody stirrin'.

Den he look in, en dar lay Brer Fox stretch out on the bed jus' ez big ez life. Den Brer Rabbit make like he talkin' to hisself.

"Nobody around fer ter look after Brer Fox—not even Brer Turkey Buzzard ain't come ter the funer'l."

"I hope Brer Fox ain't dead, but I speck he is," sez Brer Rabbit.

"Even down ter Brer Wolf done left 'im. It's the busy season wid me, but I'll set up wid 'im. He seem like he dead, yit he mayn't be," sez Brer Rabbit.

"When a man go ter see dead fokes, dead fokes always raises up a leg en hollers, *wahoo!*"

Brer Fox he stay still. Den Brer Rabbit he talk little louder: "Mighty funny. Brer Fox look like he dead, yit he don't do like he dead. Dead fokes raise a leg en hollers *wahoo!* when a man come ter see um," sez Brer Rabbit.

Sho' nuff, Brer Fox lift up his foot en holler *wahoo!* en Brer Rabbit he tear out the house like the dogs wuz after 'im.

The Birds, the Beasts, and the Bat

The birds and beasts once went to war. The bat—which could not be said to be bird or beast—at first kept out of the way of both, but when he thought the beasts would win the day, he was found in their ranks, and to prove his right to be there, he said, "Can you find a bird that has two rows of teeth in his head, as I have?" At last the birds had the best of the fight, so then the bat was seen to join their ranks. "Look," said he, "I have wings, so what else can I be but a bird?"

"To fly with all winds" was thought base in the bat by both sides of the fight, and he could not get bird or beast to own him, and to this day he hides and skulks in caves and stems of trees, and does not come out until dark when all the birds of the air have gone to roost, and the beasts of the field are wrapt in sleep.

One must not blow hot and cold.

Aesop's Fables

The Field of Corn

An old man had a field, and when he fell ill, he sent for his three sons that he might take leave of them and give them his last charge. "My sons," said he, "there is one thing which, with my last breath, I charge you to do, and that is, to seek out a rich gift I have left you, and which you may find in my field—" Here the poor old man's voice grew faint, and his head sank down on his breast in death. The sons were in too much grief for their loss to put in force that which the old man had bade them do, till want drove them to seek for what they thought must be a hoard of gold in the field; so they made a search from end to end of it, till there was not a clod they did not turn in the hunt. At last they gave it up. "It is strange that the old man should have set us on this long search for a thing that is not here," said Jack.

"Come," said Dick, "since we have gone through so much toil on the field, we may as well sow it with corn, and so make the most of it." At this bright thought they set to work to sow the grain, and in due time a crop sprang up, five times as large as those crops which grew in the old man's time. The thought now struck the youths that this was the wealth the old man meant and that it was his wish that they should earn their bread by the sweat of their brow.

Seek till you find, and you will not lose by the toil.

The Sick Stag

A sick stag lay in a nook of his ground. His friends came in flocks to ask how he felt, and each one took a share of the food which had been left for his use, so that he died, not from his lack of health, but from the lack of the means to live.

Bad friends bring more harm than good.

The Rose and the Clay

A man in the East by chance took up a piece of clay which lay in his path and was struck to find it smelled so sweet. "It is but a poor piece of clay," said he, "a mean clod of earth, yet how sweet is it! How fresh! But whence has it this scent?" The clay said, "I have dwelt with the rose."

Make friends with the good if you wish to be like them.

Aesop's Fables
The Maid and Her Milk Pail

One day, as a young maid went down the road with her pail of milk on her head, she was heard to say, "This pail of milk will fetch me so much, which sum I will lay out in eggs; these eggs will bring a score of chicks, and they will be fit to sell just at the time when fowls bear a good price: so that on May-day I shall have a new gown. Let me see . . . yes, green will suit me best, and green it shall be. In this dress I will go to the fair, and all who are there will pay their court to me; but with a proud look I shall turn from them."

Wrapt in this dream of joy, she gave a toss of the head to suit the words, when down came the pail of milk and with it the eggs, the chicks, the green gown, and all the bright thoughts of what she should do at the fair.

Count not your chicks till they are out of the shell. Each "may be" hath a "may not be".

His First Bronc

Will James

Will James won the Newbery Medal in 1927 for his book Smoky, the Cowhorse. *An orphan adopted by a Canadian trapper, James spent most of his life as a cowboy. He later wrote about his experiences and drew his own illustrations.*

Billy was a born cowboy; the only kind that ever makes the real cowboy. One day Lem told him he could have a certain black horse if he could break him. It was a little black horse, pretty as a picture. Billy went wild at the sight of him, and ran into the corral to get as close a view of the horse as he could.

"I've always wanted to break in a horse. That'll be lots of fun."

The next morning Lem found Billy in the corral with the new horse.

"Well, I see you're busy right early, Billy."

"He's some horse, ain't he?" he said.

"He sure is," agreed Lem. "And your first bronc, too."

An hour or so later Billy had his saddle on the black horse, and cinched to stay. By this time quite a crowd had gathered around. The foreman, the cowboys, all the ranch hands were watching. All was set but taking the hobbles off the horse's front feet and climbing on. Some of the men offered to do that for Billy but that young cowboy refused. He wanted to do it all himself; it was his bronc.

Billy gathered his hackamore rope and a hunk of mane to go with it, grabbed the saddle horn with his right hand and, sticking his foot in the stirrup, eased himself into the saddle. He squirmed around until he was well set, like an old bronc fighter, saw that the length of reins between his hands and the pony's head was just right, then he reached over and pulled off the blindfold.

Billy's lips were closed tight; he was ready for whatever happened. The pony blinked at seeing daylight again, looked back at the boy sitting on him, snorted, and trotted off.

A laugh went up from all around. Billy turned a blank face toward his father and hollered.

"Hey, Dad, he won't buck!"

Another laugh was heard and when it quieted down Lem spoke up.

"Never mind, son," he said trying to keep a straight face, "he might buck yet."

The words were no more than out of his mouth, when the little black lit into bucking. Billy was loosened the first jump for he'd been paying more attention to what his dad was saying than to what he was sitting on. The little pony crowhopped around the corral and bucked just enough to keep the kid from getting back in the saddle. Billy was hanging on to all he could find, but pretty soon the little old pony happened to make the right kind of a jump

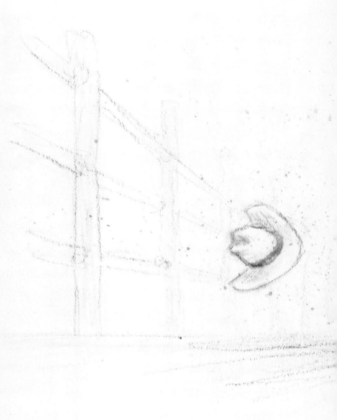

for the kid and he straightened up again.

Billy rode pretty fair the next few jumps and managed to keep his seat pretty well under him, but he wasn't satisfied with just sitting there; he grabbed his hat and began fanning. All went fine for a few more jumps and then trouble broke loose. Billy dropped his hat and made a wild grab for the saddle horn.

But the hold on the saddle horn didn't help him any; he kept going, up and up he went, a little

higher every jump, and pretty soon he started coming down. When he did that he was by his lonesome. The horse had gone in another direction.

"Where is he?" said Billy, trying to get some of the earth out of his eyes.

"Right here, Son," said his father, who'd caught the horse and brought him up.

He handed the kid the hackamore reins and touched him on the hand.

"And listen here, young feller, if I catch you grabbing the horn with that paw of yours again, I'll tie it and the other right back where you can't use 'em."

Those few words hit the kid pretty hard. There was a frown on his face and his lips were quivering at the same time. He was both ashamed and peeved.

His father held the horse while Billy climbed on again.

"Are you ready, cowboy?" Lem looked up at his son and smiled.

After some efforts the kid smiled back and answered.

"Yes, Dad, let him go."

The pony lit into bucking the minute he was loose this time and seemed to mean business from the start. Time and again Billy's hand reached down as if to grab the saddle horn, but he kept away from it.

The little horse was bucking pretty good, and for a kid Billy was doing mighty fine, but the horse still proved too much for him. Billy kept getting further and further away from the saddle till finally he slid along the pony's shoulder and to the ground once again.

The kid was up before his dad could get to him and began looking for his horse right away.

"I don't think you'd better ride him any more today, Sonny," Lem said as he brushed some of the dust off the kid's clothes. "Maybe tomorrow you can ride him easy."

But Billy turned and saw the horse challenging him, it seemed, and he crossed the corral, caught the black, blindfolded him and climbed on again.

Then Lem walked up to Billy and said so nobody else could hear,

"You go after him this time, Billy, and just make this pony think you're the wolf of the world. Paw him the same as you did that last calf you rode."

"Y-e-e-ep!" Billy hollered as he jerked the blind off the pony's eyes. "I'm a wolf!"

Billy was a wolf; he'd turned challenger and was pawing the black from ears to rump. Daylight showed plenty between him and the saddle but somehow he managed to stick on and stay right side up. The horse, surprised at the change of events, finally let up on his bucking; he was getting scared and had found a sudden hankering to start running.

After that it was easy for Billy; he rode him around the corral a couple of times and then, all smiles and proud as a peacock, he climbed off.

Billy had ridden his first bronc.

A MAN'S MAN

Andy Thomson

The door creaked uncertainly, hesitating a little as though trying to decide whether or not to open.

"Son?" Ma's voice asked.

Lickety-split, I shut my eyes before she got her head inside.

"Are you awake, Jimmy?"

I could feel the soft glow from the lamp on my face, and I tried powerful hard not to let my nose twitch. She was looking me over, tempted to wake me up for prayers, but she knew better. Ma didn't disobey Pa, and he said it was foolishness to wake me up for prayers, especially with me having been sick so much through the last part of winter. At last the glow went back some, and I knew she'd set the lamp down on the rickety stand by my bed. After a minute I peeped one eye open. She was kneeling by the bed, real quiet, her face puckered together so hard

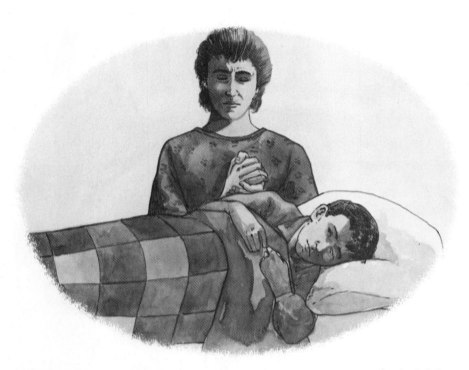

you'd a thought she was mad at something. But she generally looked that way when she was getting up a full head of steam in her prayers.

Lately Ma'd been spendin' plenty of time with her knees to the floor. I expected it was because I'd been sick so much. Crops had been bad the year before, and two of the horses had taken sick over the winter and died just before plowing time. Having me sick was just one more worry for Ma and Pa. They'd both been quieter lately—Pa drawing on the pipe more and Ma staying in my room late sometimes, praying by my bed.

I can't say I minded Ma praying, except when Pa was around. He said she'd mollycoddle me with religion. Now that I was gettin' onto eleven he wanted me to be all boy he said, ready to be a real man's man. I didn't get what he meant by that, but I knew that last summer he'd told Ma I didn't have to pray with her anymore if I thought it was a nuisance, and if I didn't want to go to Sunday school, that was okay, too.

I hadn't yet worked up to missing church. It seemed awful wicked not to go, even though Pa never did. But sometimes on a Sunday morning when I was sittin' at the table knottin' my tie,

I could sense him looking at me, sort of hard, disapproving. Ma never let on like she noticed it, and it made her happy to have me with her in church. So I kept going.

I could feel it through the bed when she stood up again from praying, and then her hand touched my face. I wasn't expecting that, I tell you, and I almost jumped outta' my skin. My eyes popped open, and there we were, lookin' at each other—her knowin' that I hadn't been asleep at all.

But she only said, "Good night, Jimmy. Do you feel all right?"

"Good enough to sleep, Ma," I told her.

She didn't say anything about me not praying, just bent down and kissed me, and I could tell from the dampness on her face and shoulder that she'd been sweating powerful hard, plowing at her prayers like Pa plowed through the stubborn clods of dirt outside when it was spring.

She went out the door, pulling on the leather strap to close it, but it fell open a bit like it usually did when it isn't slammed just right. I heard her steps across the sitting room, and then Pa's voice spoke. He must have just come in I figured, from visiting Jeb Taylor.

"Jimmy sleepin'?" he asked.

"Almost. Can I get you some tea? How's Jeb's boy?"

"Bad, honey. Tea would set nice." I heard the rocking chair creak as he lowered himself into it. In another minute I smelled his pipe going, and I knew he was worrying himself over something. Jeb had a small farm up the road three miles. His boy, Spike, had took sick a week ago and wasn't up yet. Spike and I had been buddies since we could walk, him being the only boy around that was my age. We generally had some high times together in the summers, fishing and eating wild strawberries and finding snake holes.

"I told that mule-headed Jeb to get Spike down t' the doctor's in town," Pa said quietly. There was a clink of cup and saucer as he took his tea from Ma. Abruptly, he changed the subject. "These electric lights are powerful nice out here, ain't they? All we need is one or two good years and we'll fix up the rest of the house with 'em." Then he was silent again.

"Jimmy seems a good sight better," Ma began at last. "I let him walk a bit outside this afternoon."

Pa's voice sunk low, and Ma's voice did too, so I didn't hear nothing again until it was morning and the sun was coming in my window. There was Pa in the doorway, looking me over with the kind of face he has at Christmas and on Ma's birthday.

"Come on, old sport, get outta' the sack!" he called. "I got me some lines strung and hooks sharpened. You comin' or not?"

"Here I come." I bounced out of bed.

"You sure didn't look so chipper yesterday when I mentioned fence-fixing," he added, cocking one eyebrow like he was suspicious. "But we can do that tomorrow. Get your clothes on."

I thrust my feet into my denims and buttoned up a shirt. Ma was frying up pancakes on the wood stove. It seemed like we'd been eatin' pancakes and salt pork forever. But I acted eager and washed up quick in the new sink. It wasn't really new—two years old—but we'd gotten it when Pa had installed indoor plumbing, and he and Ma were so proud of it we kept calling it the "new" sink.

"Don't the boy look good?" Pa asked Ma.

"He does, honey. But are you sure he'll be all right out fishing all day?"

"Sure! Can't let him sit inside like an old woman, right, son?" He winked at me as I sat down

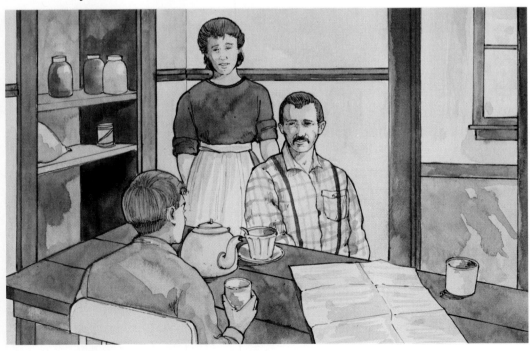

and he poured me a little coffee with milk and sugar when Ma wasn't looking. We drank up. "You're all man, son." Then he laughed, wiped his mustache, and winked at me again.

"Jack! Have you been slipping that boy coffee?" Ma asked. "What would it do to his digestion if—" Then she stopped. "Well, I s'pose it's all right this once, with you going fishing and all." He nodded, and I sort of figgered they were trying to give me a holiday after being in bed three days again. If Pa had really been wanting a mess of fish, we'd have been up two hours earlier.

"I've got some milk to spare," Ma said as we ate. "I thought I'd walk up to Jeb's and leave it for Spike. I reckon they can use it."

Pa nodded. I felt him glance at me.

We caught a string of catfish out on the lake, but it took us all morning, and mostly we just lolled on the bank and talked. "We could go up t' the stream one day and try for the granddaddy bass up there," I said.

"Yup. One fine day we ought to do that, Jimmy, before some out-of-towner-fishing-tycoon with a rod and reel made of pure gold comes and takes him." He grinned at me.

"We could go day after tomorrow," I said.

He frowned a little. "No, son. That's Sunday and you go to church with your Ma, remember?"

"Well, usually, but you said—"

"What'd I say?" He looked a little scared.

"That I didn't have to go if I didn't want to. I thought I'd stay home with you."

He sat up straight. "Did I say that? And you listened to me? I'm surprised at you, Jimmy." I knew he was trying to make it into a joke, but I couldn't figure out why. Pa had always been saying that church was for women and kids. He leaned back and smiled again. "Now listen here, boy. It

ain't what I said last summer that you got to listen to. It's what I say now. You go on to church with your Ma. That big ol' bass'll wait a day for us."

We were quiet a while, with nothing moving except the lines a little bit when no-account minnows nibbled on 'em and moved on. "Church is a mighty fine thing," he said at last. "I reckon I could stand a dose of it, once I pull all my traps from the winter and clean 'em."

He must have seen how astonished it made me when he said that, because he changed the subject and talked about how bad the trapping had been that past winter.

I tired out in the late afternoon. I tried not to look like I wanted to go home, but I honestly did, and for once Pa read my mind.

"Well," he yawned. He stretched himself. "I reckon we better leave some for next time, Jimmy. Come along, I'll tell you about the war a little bit to pass the time."

He carried all the tackle and the catch, and I just lugged along my pole and line. Even so, it got a sight heavy. I could feel Pa watching me.

At last he spoke. "I marched through France with a sixty-pound pack on," he boasted, throwing out his chest. "Now look here, you're past ten years old now, ain't you? You must be nigh onto sixty pounds. See here if I can't carry you one piddly mile back home." So I scrambled onto his back. "Now you know how the pack feels," he laughed. "Say, did I ever tell you about that time I seen the Junkers 88 come out over that little town in France? The Germans wasn't expecting it to be loaded up with GIs. Lemme tell you how we served 'em, son."

He talked on and on, seemed most like hours, and then I opened my eyes, and I was in my bed with the shakes again.

"It's all right, Sonny. Your Pappy's here," he was saying. "You're just having a little relapse, as the doc says. There, there." He pulled the comforter close to me while I shivered it out. But he was sweating himself, and I saw in his eyes that he was afraid.

"Where's Ma?" I asked. I felt scared.

"She's still at Jeb's, Jimmy. She'll be back soon. I'll take keer of ya, boy."

"I thought I was better, Pa. I was up yesterday afternoon. Why ain't I gettin' better?"

"Well now, boy, you were powerful sick. It takes a while. Once I was up and down for six months trying to shake pneumonia. I shouldn't have took you out with me. But honest, seemed like settin' in the sun would have done you some good."

Then he held the comforter down while I shook. "I'm here, boy." And I felt how scared he was. He was more scared than I was. The door slammed. "In here, Ma," Pa said, looking at the door.

Ma come in and next thing I knew she was holding me and had already sent Pa out to make her special tea for driving out ague. But she was white—whiter than I ever seen her, even more white than she'd turned that time she found a snake all curled up on the porch.

"Am I gonna' be all right, Ma?" I asked.

"I've kept you safe in the Lord's hands for ten years now, Jimmy," she said. "I reckon you're as all right today as you ever was." Some of her color came back.

Pa came in with the tea and gave it to me. Pretty soon it had me all in a sweat, powerful hot. "There now," Ma said. "Pa'll go brew a little more for you. I'll run and get your nightclothes off the line and put you to bed awhile."

She and Pa went out, and she closed the door, but not hard enough. Pa was too preoccupied to notice it was open. I tried to fall asleep, but then I heard her say, "Oh Jack!" real soft and scared. I'd never heard Ma use such a voice.

"What is it?" he asked.

"Spike—he died this morning up at Jeb's."

I felt the shock so hard that I went numb. For a minute I just lay there, and then somehow I felt scared. I caught my breath with a sob, but they didn't hear me. They was talking low and fast, and Pa was cussing himself for taking me fishing. Then Ma quieted him down real gentle and set him to making tea, and they both agreed they'd put me on the couch. Pa said when he finished the tea he'd get down to Willis's and borrow the pickup for to take me into town tomorrow. And suddenly I realized what they been so scared of all along. I'd been getting sick a long time and never really getting completely better. And now Spike had died.

As soon as Ma came in, she could tell how scared I was. "Ma—" I began.

"Boy, don't fret yourself over a touch of fever and ague," she said gently.

"I heard you tell Pa—" and then I burst out crying. I wasn't even ashamed of myself for it. I reckon there's times a boy can cry and not be any sissy.

"Spike was a good boy," she said. "Into green apples a sight too much, but he knew the Lord, and Jeb said he was real peaceful last night, and his Mama had been reading his verses to him regular so that Spike understood the Lord enough to trust Him." She was rocking me back and forth. "You know Spike woulda' been a man's man, Jimmy. He was man enough to trust the Lord, and he died peaceful, knowing that Jesus was coming for him. Son, when you know the Lord real good, you ain't afraid any more."

Then she didn't say no more, only cried a little, and I reckoned she didn't have to say much more. I knew she was right. It was Pa that set up late nights worrying and smoking pipe after pipe. It was him that blamed himself and carried on and didn't know much what to do when things were bad.

"I'm sorry, Ma," I began. "If Pa had—"

"Now, son, don't you go blamin' your Pa for anything." She looked down at me. "He loves you, Jimmy. He's slipped away from the Lord, and he knows it. We got to give him time and let the Lord work on him some. But now you know better, I reckon. You do know the Lord, don't you Jimmy? Were you sincere last summer when you repented in here on your knees?"

"Yeah, I was, Ma. I know I'm saved." She didn't say anything more about it, only held me tight a minute.

"Have I got what Spike had, Ma?" I asked at last.

"I don't know, Jimmy. His Ma told me he had a rare sickness, and I don't rightly understand it all. Pa'll get you to Doc's tomorrow. Doc'll know." She smoothed down my hair and kissed me.

"Come on then," she said at last. "Can you manage your way to the sofa in the front? I got your night clothes here."

She put me out on the sofa so that she or Pa could set up with me. Crying like I'd done had wore me out, and I slept after she'd given me a second dose of that hundred percent all-fire tea of hers. That night when she came to pray with me, I sat up, and she let me pray laying down while she knelt alongside. Pa, he just set there by the stove instead of going out like he normally would have.

Ma went to bed for a spell, and I woke up a couple times during the night to watch Pa smoke his pipe or sit with his chair tipped back. Come morning I was well enough to climb into Willis's

old pickup, and we went down the mountain into town—Pa and me. We couldn't all three fit in the pickup, one of the seats being shot in the springs. Ma stayed home, and the last thing I saw as the front door was closing was her getting down on her knees again.

Doc looked me over good while Pa stood there a fiddlin' with his hat. At last the doc filled up a needle.

"What's that for, Doc?" Pa asked.

"That's for all the pork and bread this boy's been making do with, Jack," he said. "No ten-year-old can live on that alone."

"Why, it served me all right when I was growing up," Pa answered, confused.

"Sure it did, and every spring you went down with sickness, didn't you?" he asked.

"Reckon so. Lots of kids did back then."

"Well, times have changed and things have improved. But I take it you've had a bad year, eh?"

"None too good."

"The boy's got spring sickness, all right." He thumped my arm and slipped the needle in. It hurt like fury—worse than usual.

"You needed it badly," Doc said when he saw that it was stinging. "It doesn't normally hurt much." Finishing the shot, he pulled it out and pressed a ball of cotton against my arm. He glanced at Pa. "The boy is weak, sure enough. You've got to get him some vegetables, Jack, before the garden comes in. He's gone most of the winter without any greens. That's why he's coming down with everything. That's spring sickness. Another name for it is malnutrition. His body's all worn out. Along comes chills and fever, and bang! He can't get better."

"I'll take care of him, Doc. I'll get us some of that canned stuff." Pa fished in his back pocket for his billfold. "What do I owe ya?" But Doc waved it away. "Two dollars. Spend it on some fruit and vegetables and a bottle of these pills that the druggist carries. They'll spruce him up some. He'll be better by late spring, I'm sure."

I looked up at the doc. "Did Spike have spring sickness?" I asked.

Doc looked down at me as I buttoned up my shirt. He patted my head. "No, Jim. Spike had a disease called leukemia. His Ma and Pa knew about it for some months." He looked up at Pa. "They didn't want anything to be said, on account of Spike himself. They broke it to him gently, when he was ready. From what I hear, he was brave all the way through."

"He was," Pa said soberly. "His Ma and Pa have a strong faith."

Doc nodded. "Yes, we've talked quite often."

On the way back home Pa didn't say much at all. He picked up the pills and some canned tomatoes and asparagus. As we rumbled along, I said, "You was right yesterday, Pa, about church and all. Y' think you might come sometime?"

"I reckon, Jimmy hon," was all he said. But when we got home and he saw Ma, he just handed her the grocery sack and then sat at the table and cried with his face in his hands. At first she thought it was bad news, but at last when he told her what the Doc said, she just put me to bed again and went out to talk with Pa. After a while he left the house to work the farm a little and think some on his own. He had a powerful lot to think about, I reckon.

Ma came in and gave me a vitamin pill. She sat down and read some verses to me on the resurrection, and we talked some about Spike. He'd always seemed so ordinary to me, it was hard to imagine him being brave like the doc had said. I knew I wasn't as sick as he had been, but I prayed some serious prayers on my own as I lay there lookin' out the window while Ma read. I'd always thought that being brave came with being a man, but I saw that day that women like Ma or kids like Spike could be a lot braver than big tough men like Pa or book-learned men like the doc.

"Don't you find fault with your Pa, Jimmy," Ma warned me again. And I didn't. Pa was the best man in the Smokies, I reckoned. But it was really Ma who had taught me that to be a real man—a man's man—I had to be God's man first.

A Just Judge

Leo Tolstoy

An Algerian king named Bauakas wanted to find out whether or not it was true, as he had been told, that in one of his cities there lived a just judge who could instantly discern the truth and from whom no rogue was ever able to conceal himself. Bauakas exchanged clothes with a merchant and went on horseback to the city where the judge lived.

At the entrance to the city a cripple approached the king and begged alms of him. Bauakas gave him money and was about to continue on his way, but the cripple clung to his clothing.

"What do you wish?" asked the king. "Haven't I given you money?"

"You gave me alms," said the cripple; "now grant me one favor.

Let me ride with you as far as the city square; otherwise the horses and camels may trample me."

Bauakas set the cripple behind him on the horse and took him as far as the city square. There he halted his horse, but the cripple refused to dismount.

"We have arrived at the square; why don't you get off?" asked Bauakas.

"Why should I?" the beggar replied. "This horse belongs to me. If you are unwilling to return it, we shall have to go to court."

Hearing their quarrel, people gathered around them shouting,

"Go to the judge! He will decide between you!"

Bauakas and the cripple went to the judge. There were others in court, and the judge called upon each one in turn. Before he came to Bauakas and the cripple, he heard a scholar and a peasant. They had come to court over a woman: the peasant said she was his wife, and the scholar said she was his. The judge heard them both, remained silent for a moment, and then said,

"Leave the woman here with me, and come back tomorrow."

When they had gone, a butcher and an oil merchant came before the judge. The butcher was covered with blood and the oil merchant with oil. In his hand the

butcher held some money, and the oil merchant held onto the butcher's hand.

"I was buying oil from this man," the butcher said, "and when I took out my purse to pay him, he seized me by the hand and tried to take all my money away from me. That is why we have come to you—I holding onto my purse, and he holding onto my hand. But the money is mine, and he is a thief."

Then the oil merchant spoke. "That is not true," he said. "The butcher came to me to buy oil, and after I had poured him a full jug, he asked me to change a gold piece for him. When I took out my money and placed it upon a

bench, he seized it and tried to run off. I caught him by the hand, as you see, and brought him here to you."

The judge remained silent for a moment, then said, "Leave the money here with me, and come back tomorrow."

When his turn came, Bauakas told what had happened. The judge listened to him and then asked the beggar to speak.

"All that he said is untrue," said the beggar. "He was sitting on the ground, and as I rode through the city, he asked me to let him ride with me. I set him behind me on my horse and took him where he wanted to go. But when we got there, he refused to get off and said that the horse was his, which is not true."

The judge thought for a moment, then said, "Leave the horse here with me, and come back tomorrow."

The following day many people gathered in court to hear the judge's decisions.

First came the scholar and the peasant.

"Take your wife," the judge said to the scholar, "and the peasant shall be given fifty strokes of the lash."

The scholar took his wife, and the peasant was punished.

Then the judge called the butcher.

"The money is yours," he said to him. And pointing to the oil merchant he said, "Give him fifty strokes of the lash."

He next called Bauakas and the cripple.

"Would you recognize your horse among twenty others?" he asked Bauakas.

"I would," he replied.

"Come with me," the judge said to Bauakas.

They went to the stable. Bauakas instantly pointed out this horse among the twenty others. Then the judge called the cripple to the stable and told him to point out the horse. The cripple recognized the horse and pointed to it. The judge then returned to his seat.

"Take the horse; it is yours," he said to Bauakas. "Give the beggar fifty strokes of the lash."

When the judge left the court and went home, Bauakas followed him.

"What do you want?" asked the judge. "Are you not satisfied with my decision?"

"I am satisfied," said Bauakas. "But I should like to learn how you knew that the woman was the wife of the scholar, that the money belonged to the butcher, and that the horse was mine and not the beggar's."

"This is how I knew about the woman: in the morning I sent for her and said: 'Please fill my inkwell.' She took the inkwell, washed it quickly and deftly, and filled it with ink; therefore it was work she was accustomed to. If she had been the wife of the peasant, she would not have known how to do it. This showed me that the scholar was telling the truth.

"And this is how I knew about the money: I put it into a cup full of water, and in the morning I looked to see if any oil had risen to the surface. If the money had belonged to the oil merchant it would have been soiled by his oily hands. There was no oil on the water; therefore the butcher was telling the truth.

"It was more difficult to find out about the horse. The cripple recognized it among twenty others, even as you did. However, I did not take you both to the stable to see which of you knew the horse, but to see which of you the horse knew. When you approached it, it turned its head and stretched its neck toward you; but when the cripple touched it, it laid back its ears and lifted one hoof. Therefore I knew that you were the horse's real master."

Then Bauakas said to the judge, "I am not a merchant, but King Bauakas. I came here in order to see if what is said of you is true. I see now that you are a wise judge. Ask whatever you wish of me, and you shall have it as a reward."

"I need no reward," replied the judge. "I am content that my king has praised me."

Three Rolls and a Pretzel

Leo Tolstoy

Feeling hungry one day, a peasant bought himself a large roll and ate it. But he was still hungry, so he bought another roll and ate it. Still hungry, he bought a third roll and ate it. When the three rolls failed to satisfy his hunger, he bought some pretzels. After eating one pretzel he no longer felt hungry.

Suddenly he clapped his hand to his head and cried, "What a fool I am! Why did I waste all those rolls? I ought to have eaten a pretzel in the first place!"

The King and the Shirt

Leo Tolstoy

A king once fell ill.

"I will give half my kingdom to the man who can cure me," he said.

All his wise men gathered to decide how the king could be cured. But no one knew. Only one of the wise men said what he thought would cure the king.

"If you can find a happy man, take his shirt, put it on the king—and the king will be cured."

The king sent his emissaries to search for a happy man. They traveled far and wide throughout his kingdom, but they could not find a happy man. There was no one who was completely satisfied: if a man was rich, he was ailing; if he was healthy, he was poor; if he was rich and healthy, he had a bad wife; or if he had children, they were bad—everyone had something to complain of.

Finally, late one night, the king's son was passing by a poor little hut and he heard someone say,

"Now, God be praised, I have finished my work, I have eaten my fill, and I can lie down and sleep! What more could I want?"

The king's son rejoiced and gave orders that the man's shirt be taken and carried to the king and that the man be given as much money as he wanted.

The emissaries went in to take off the man's shirt, but the happy man was so poor that he had no shirt.

70

The Wonderful Words

Mary O'Neill

Never let a thought shrivel and die
For want of a way to say it,
For English is a wonderful game
And all of you can play it.
All that you do is match the words
To the brightest thoughts in your head
So that they come out clear and true
And handsomely groomed and fed—
For many of the loveliest things
Have never yet been said.
Words are the food and dress of thought,
They give it its body and swing,
And everyone's longing today to hear
Some fresh and beautiful thing.
But only words can free a thought
From its prison behind your eyes.
Maybe your mind is holding now
A marvelous new surprise!

HANS CLODHOPPER

Hans Christian Andersen, drama-tized by Doris Fisher Harris

CAST

FATHER: Ambitious and pushy

FRANZ: Conceited

LUDWIG: Vain

HANS: Quiet, sincere, and clumsy

SUITOR I: A proud hunter

SUITOR II: An arrogant wrestler

SUITOR III: A conceited sword fighter

PRINCESS: Witty

GIRLS: Three giggling girls

SCENE I

Narrator: The scene opens with three boys seated in a circle. Ludwig is polishing his shoes, Franz is polishing his sword, and Hans is staring vacantly into space. The door opens and their father bursts into the room.

Father: *(Excited)* My sons, your fortune is made!

Franz: We could use a fortune.

Ludwig: We could use a penny.

Hans: Have you noticed it is a beautiful day?

Father: Oh, be quiet! Who cares about the weather?

Franz: He does. The simpleton of the family.

Ludwig: Look at him. He sits and looks at the sky.

Father: Come here, my clever boys. *(Franz and Ludwig move to him.)* The messenger said the King's daughter is to be married.

Franz: So!

Ludwig: What!

Father: I have heard that she is so beautiful that every man who meets her loses his voice. She has grown tired of this and has vowed to marry the man who has the most to say for himself.

Franz: I shall win her.

Ludwig: I shall win her and her money.

Franz: I can say the Latin dictionary by heart.

Ludwig: I can say all the laws of the country by heart.

Franz: I can say all the newspapers front and back for the last three years.

Hans: I can decorate beautiful horse harnesses.

Ludwig: Be still, Hans!

Father: *(To Franz and Ludwig)* Very well, very well. You shall go today.

Franz: I shall take our coal black horse.

Ludwig: I shall take the white.

Father: Hans, go saddle the horses for your brothers.

Hans: *(Shuffles off, still staring at the sky)* Yes, Father.

Father: Now my clever sons, go upstairs and pack. But first put this oil on your mouth so that you can talk better. *(Takes small bottle from pocket and boys oil mouths. They exit, talking, and Father has an arm around each boy.)*

SCENE II

(Father enters and Hans follows.)

Hans: Father.

Father: Now, I must be sure they have what they need.

Hans: Father.

Father: What is it, Hans?

Hans: Father, I want to go to the court and talk to the Princess too.

Father: You? You are silly and ignorant. You do not have the brains to win the Princess.

Hans: May I have a horse?

Father: No!

Hans: May I have fine clothes like my brothers?

Father: No!

Hans: If I mayn't have a horse, I'll take the billy goat. He is my own, and I will ride him to the castle. *(Exits with Father following him)* May I?

Father: Very well, but you will make a fool of yourself.

SCENE III

(The three boys are seated, resting on a hillside just outside the castle.)

Ludwig: See what I have found for the Princess. *(Opens his bag)* Here is a wild rose. I will tell her it looks like her. Girls like that.

Franz: That is nothing. See what I found. *(Opens his bag)* Girls like diamonds better than flowers.

Hans: See what I found on the way. *(Opens bag)*

Ludwig: Ugh. It's a dead bird.

Hans: I found it. It was beautiful. Perhaps I will have time to bury it.

Ludwig: You are silly!

Franz: What else is in your bag?

Hans: *(Pulls an old wooden shoe out of his bag)*

Franz: Clodhopper! It is only an old broken wooden shoe. Are these your gifts to the Princess?

Hans: *(Simply)* She may have whatever I have.

Ludwig: What are you doing?

Hans: *(Gets on his knees and scoops up sand)* Did you ever see such fine sand? It is soft and beautiful. I will put some in my pocket.

Franz: What kind of gifts are these to bring to a princess? *(They exit.)*

Hans: *(Calling after them)* I will bring her all I can. This is all I have! *(Trudges off after them)*

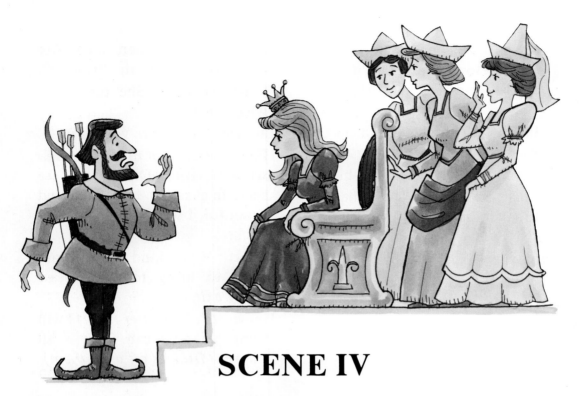

SCENE IV

Narrator: When the boys enter the castle, they find three suitors ahead of them. The Princess is seated with three maids in waiting behind her. As the brothers and the other suitors come before the Princess, the girls giggle.

Suitor I: *(Gets up and nervously goes to stand in front of the Princess)* O beautiful Princess, I am the most famous hunter of the land, *(Voice leaves him)* and I come to claim your hand *(Mouths it)* in marriage *(Realizes that he cannot speak . . . tries to. . . .)*

Princess: He will never do, will he, girls?

Girl I: No indeed.

Girl II: How silly he looks.

Girl III: Look at his red face.

Princess: Away with you. *(Suitor I exits angrily.)*

Suitor II: *(Rushes in after him)* Your majesty I am the best wrestler. . . . *(Voice leaves him)*

Suitor III: *(Rushing in next and almost colliding with Suitor II)* I am the greatest swordsman! I-I—*(Voice leaves him)*

Princess: *(Laughs as men wildly gesture and try to express themselves)* Away with all of you. *(They exit, trying to talk.)*

Girl I: Did you see his face?

Girl II: Did you see his feet?

Girl III: Did you see his ears? *(Franz and Ludwig come stumbling in, each eager to be first.)*

Franz: Your Majesty, I can say the Latin dictionary by heart— *(Voice leaves him)*

Ludwig: I can say the law books— *(Voice leaves him)*

Princess: *(Angry)* Get out! *(Watches them leave)* Did any of those stuck-up fools think I would marry him? *(Notices Hans)* One more. Very well. But I am hungry and I want my lunch.

Hans: It is lunch time. I'm hungry too.

Princess: Do you expect me to feed you?

Hans: No. I have a bird to be roasted. *(Pulls bird from bag)*

Princess: Do you have something to roast it in?

Hans: Yes, here is my cooking pot. *(Pulls out shoe)*

Princess: You are a man of good sense. Where shall we get something to catch the dripping oil?

Hans: Here, I have sand in my pocket. *(He puts it in bottom of shoe)* Will you lunch with me?

Princess: *(Comes and takes his arm)* I like you. You have an answer for every problem. And you don't boast. I will have you for a husband. *(Takes him by the hand and leads him up to the throne. He smiles and sits down. She places a crown upon his head and a robe around him and goes to doorway and calls.)* Come and see the rare and wise man who will be king of the realm.

(Others come on where they have exited. The suitors are angry, and the brothers are amazed.)

Princess: *(Stands beside him and takes his hand)* And now, king of my heart, let's have lunch.

Literature Lesson:
Fables and Folktales

Storytelling has always been a good way to explain an idea. Many stories that are part of our literary heritage have been told and retold to help pass on to new generations the values and ideas that are important to a country. Fables and folktales are two kinds of stories that teach.

• Fables

You have probably been reading fables in one form or another since kindergarten or first grade. Aesop, a Greek slave, was probably the greatest fable writer of all time. Some of his works are included in this unit. Aesop's fables, like most others, are very short stories and come to the point quickly. No detailed setting is needed for the telling of a good fable. The characters, most often animals, are usually just named. Very little other information is

given about them. The point is always a moral lesson, which is written at the end of the fable.

Some of the moral lessons of Aesop's fables have become very famous, like the one you read in "The Maid and Her Milk Pail." That moral has become the well-known saying, "Don't count your chickens before they hatch." The fable "The Wind and the Sun" teaches that gentleness can accomplish what force cannot. "The Boy Who Cried Wolf" teaches that liars are not believed even when they tell the truth, and the famous story about the hare and the tortoise demonstrates that "slow and steady win the race."

Perhaps you will be able to think of other fables you have read. It is very likely that they will be traced to the Greek slave who wrote them down hundreds and hundreds of years ago.

• Folk Tales

The Uncle Remus stories, like "Mr. Wolf Makes a Failure," are examples of folktales. Most experts believe that the slaves of the southern colonies brought the Brer Rabbit tales with them from Africa and over the years made them fit the language and customs of the South. These stories were told and retold by the slaves until Joel Chandler Harris finally wrote them down. Mr. Harris worked hard to keep the dialect of the American Negroes when he wrote.

"Hans Clodhopper" is another example of a folktale. It was passed on orally from person to person until someone finally wrote it down. Some other folktales that you probably know are "Cinderella" and "Little Red Riding Hood," which came to us from France. "Hansel and Gretel," "The Bremen Town Musicians," and "Snow White" are German tales. The Grimm Brothers, who collected the German tales, are two of the major collectors of folktales. You can find books of their folktales in most libraries. You probably read some of the English tales to your little brothers and sisters. "The Story of the Three Little Pigs" and "Jack and the Beanstalk" are part of a long list of favorite tales written down for English children by Joseph Jacobs.

Folktales are often similar to each other; in many of them there are either three sisters or three brothers (as in "Hans Clodhopper"), and the youngest one almost always wins out in the end.

You can always tell which characters are good and which are bad in a folktale, and you can be sure the bad characters will be punished in the end. Although the lesson isn't given as obviously as it is in a fable, you can usually figure out what the lesson of the story is meant to be.

Pinocchio
and the
Gold Coins

C. Collodi

For over a hundred years the novel Pinocchio *has been a favorite with children. The original story was written in Italian and then translated into other languages as its popularity increased. The puppet Pinocchio has many adventures and suffers many misfortunes when he tries to live without working or studying. Convinced that it is easy to become rich and enjoy life, he joins a marionette circus and is almost used as firewood by the circus's fire-eater. The man spares Pinocchio, however, gives him five gold pieces, and sends him on his way home. But once again Pinocchio strays from what he knows is the path of duty. . . .*

. . . Pinocchio had not gone half a mile when he met a Fox lame in one paw, and a Cat blind in both eyes. The Fox, who limped, leaned heavily on the Cat; and the Cat, who was blind, was guided by the Fox.

"Good morning, Pinocchio," said the Fox, saluting him politely.

"How do you know my name?" asked the marionette.

"I know your papa very well."

"When did you see him?"

"I saw him yesterday at the door of his house."

"What was he doing?"

"He was in his shirt sleeves and he trembled with the cold."

"Poor Papa! But he will tremble no more after today."

"Why?"

"Because I have become a great, rich man."

"You a great, rich man!" said the Fox, and he laughed aloud. The Cat also laughed, but in order not to be seen laughing he stroked his mustache with his two front paws.

"What are you laughing about?" said Pinocchio, taken aback. "I hate to make your mouths water, but I have here, as you shall see, five beautiful pieces of gold."

And he pulled out of his pocket the money that Fire Eater had given him. At the sound of the money the Fox involuntarily stretched his leg that was paralyzed, and the Cat opened wide his eyes that looked like two green lamps; but it was all done so quickly that Pinocchio did not see anything.

"And now," said the Fox, "what do you intend to do with all that money?"

"First of all," replied the marionette, "I shall buy a coat for my papa, all covered with gold and silver and with buttons of brilliants. Then I shall buy a new A B C card for myself."

"For yourself?"

"Yes, indeed, because I wish to go to school and begin to study."

"Look at me!" said the Fox; "because of my passion for studying, I have lost a leg."

Pinocchio and the Gold Coins 81

"Look at me!" cried the Cat, "because of my love for studying, I have lost both eyes."

In the meantime a Blackbird flew near them and said, "Pinocchio, do not listen to the counsel of bad companions. If you do, you will be sorry."

Just as soon as the Blackbird had said that, the Cat sprang and caught him by the back. Before the Blackbird had time to say "Oh!" the Cat ate him up, feathers and all. Then the Cat cleaned his mouth and closed his eyes and became as blind as he was at first.

"Poor Blackbird!" said Pinocchio. "Why did you treat him so badly?"

"I did it to teach him a lesson. Another time he will know that he ought not to meddle with other people's business."

They walked along a short distance when the Fox, stopping suddenly, said to the marionette, "Should you like to double your money?"

"What do you mean?"

"Should you like to make of those miserable five pieces, ten? A hundred? A thousand?"

"Why, of course! And how can you do it?"

"It is very easy. Instead of going home, come with us."

"And where do you want to take me?"

"To the Country of the Owl."

Pinocchio thought a little and then said resolutely: "No, I will not go. My father expects me home. Who knows but that the poor old man, when I did not return yesterday, was worried and wept for me? I have been a bad boy, and the Talking Cricket was right when he said, 'Disobedient boys never get along well in this world.' "

"So," said the Fox, "you want to go home? Go home, but it will be the worse for you."

"Yes, it will be the worse for you," said the Cat.

"Think well, Pinocchio, for you have thrown away a fortune."

"A fortune," said the Cat.

"Your five pieces might be two thousand by tomorrow."

"Two thousand," repeated the Cat.

"But how is it possible that they can become so many?" asked Pinocchio, whose mouth was wide-open with astonishment.

"I will explain to you," said the Fox. "You must know that in the Country of the Owl there is a magic field called 'The Field of Wonders.' You make a little hole in the ground and you put inside, for example, one piece of gold. Then you cover over the hole with a little earth, water it with a few drops of water from a fountain, put on a little salt, and go to bed and sleep quietly. In the mean-time, during the night, the gold piece begins to grow and blossom; and the next morning, returning to the field, guess what you find? Why, you find a tree loaded with gold pieces!"

"If I bury five pieces," said Pinocchio, all excited, "how many shall I find next morning?"

"It is easy to count," replied the Fox. "You can do it on your fingers. Every gold piece will make five hundred; and therefore, multiplying each by five, you will have two thousand five hundred."

"Oh, how beautiful!" cried Pinocchio, dancing with joy. "When I have all those gold pieces I will give you five hundred of them and I will take the other two thousand to my papa."

"A present to us!" cried the Fox, disdainfully as if he were offended. "No, indeed!"

"No, indeed!" said the Cat.

"We," said the Fox, "work only to enrich others."

"Only others," said the Cat.

"What good people!" thought Pinocchio; and forgetting all about his papa, the new coat, and the A B C card, he said to the Fox and the Cat, "Come on, then; I will go with you."

They walked and walked and walked until they arrived at the Red Lobster Inn, tired to death.

"Let us stop here a little," said the Fox, "just long enough to get something to eat and rest our-selves. At midnight we can start again and tomorrow we shall arrive at the Field of Wonders."

They entered the inn and seated themselves at the table, but none of them was hungry. The poor Cat felt very much indis-posed and of course could eat only thirty-five mullets with tomato

sauce and four portions of tripe; and because the tripe did not taste just right, he called at least three times for butter and cheese to put on it.

The Fox would willingly have ordered something, but as the doctor had told him to diet, he had to be contented with a nice fresh rabbit dressed with the giblets of chicken. After the rabbit, he ordered, as a finish to his meal, some partridges, some pheasants, and some bird-of-paradise eggs; and then he did not wish any more. He had such a distaste for food, he said, that he could not eat another mouthful.

Pinocchio ate the least of all. He asked for a piece of meat and some bread, but he left everything on his plate. He could think of nothing but the Field of Wonders.

When they had supped, the Fox said to the host: "Give me two good rooms, one for Mr. Pinocchio and another for me and my companion. Before we go we will ring the bell. Remember, however, to wake us at midnight so that we can go on with our journey."

"All right, sir," replied the host; and he winked his eye at the Fox and the Cat, as if to say, "We understand each other."

Pinocchio had scarcely jumped into bed when he fell asleep and began to dream. He seemed to be in a field full of arbors, and each arbor was overgrown with vines covered with large bunches of grapes. Instead of grapes, however, they were all gold pieces, that made a noise when the wind blew—zin-zin-zin. It was just as if they said, "Here we are! Let who will come, do so, and take us." When Pinocchio was on the point of reaching for them, he heard a loud knocking at the door of his room. It was the landlord who came to tell him that the clock had struck midnight.

"And are my companions ready?" asked the marionette.

"Better than that! They left two hours ago."

"Why were they in such a hurry?"

"Because the Cat received word that his father was very sick with frosted feet and that he was in danger of losing his life."

"And they paid for the supper?"

"What do you think those people are? They are too highly educated to insult a gentleman as good as you are."

"Oh, yes! That affront would have displeased me very much," said Pinocchio, hastily. Then he asked the landlord, "Did they say where I should meet them?"

"At the Field of Wonders, this morning at daybreak."

Pinocchio paid a gold piece for his supper and that of his companions, and then departed. He groped his way along, because outside the inn it was so dark that he could not see anything. It was very quiet and not even a leaf stirred. Some birds flying along the road struck Pinocchio on the nose with their wings. He jumped back and cried out with fear,

"Who goes there?" The echo of the surrounding hills took up his words and repeated, "Who goes there?" "Who goes there?" "Who goes there?"

As he walked on, he saw on the trunk of a tree a little creature that shone with a pale opaque light, just like a candle behind a globe of transparent porcelain.

"Who are you?" asked Pinocchio.

"I am the Talking Cricket," it replied, with a little voice that seemed to come from another world.

"What do you want with me?"

"I wish to warn you. Go back, with your four gold pieces that you have left, to your papa, who cries and thinks he shall never see you again."

"Tomorrow my papa will be a very rich man because these four pieces will become two thousand."

"Do not trust those who promise to make you rich in one night, my boy. Usually they are mad or deceitful. Listen to me and go back."

"I want to go on."

"The hour is late."

"I want to go on."

"The night is dark."

"I want to go on."

"The road is dangerous."

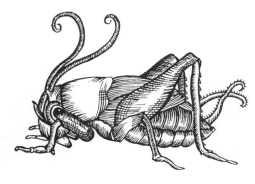

"I want to go on."

"Remember that boys who always do what they want to will sooner or later repent."

"The same old story! Good night, Cricket."

"Good night, and may you escape from the assassins!"

The Talking Cricket had hardly said these words when he suddenly disappeared, just as if some one had blown the light out, and the road was darker than ever.

"Truly," said the marionette to himself, starting again on his way, "how unfortunate we poor boys are! Everybody scolds us, everybody warns us, and everybody gives us advice."

. . . But Pinocchio was not able to finish his reasoning, because at that moment he thought he heard a rustling in the leaves behind him. He turned to look and saw in the dark two coal sacks covering two figures which ran toward him on the tips of their toes like ghosts.

"Here they are, truly!" said Pinocchio to himself. Not knowing what to do with the four gold pieces, he put them into his mouth and under his tongue. Then he tried to run away. But he had hardly started when his arms were seized and he heard two hollow voices say to him, "Your money or your life!"

Not being able to reply on account of the money in his mouth, Pinocchio made many bows and gestures in order to make his captors understand that he was a poor marionette and that he did not have a cent in his pockets. "Come on and stop fooling! Out with it!" the brigands cried. And the marionette made signs with his hands and head, which meant, "I have none!". . .

"Ah! do you make-believe you are deaf? Wait a little and we will show you how we shall make you give up the gold."

Then they began to handle the marionette very roughly, but Pinocchio managed to liberate himself from their hands. Jumping a hedge that bordered the road, he began to run across the fields with the assassins after him, like two dogs after a rabbit.

After a run of fifteen miles Pinocchio could go no farther.

Fearing that he was lost, he climbed to the top of a large pine tree and sat on one of the branches. The assassins also tried to climb; but when they got halfway up they slipped and fell to the ground, rubbing the skin off their legs and hands as they dropped.

However, they did not consider themselves conquered. On the contrary, they collected a bundle of sticks, and, placing them around the tree, set fire to them. In less time than it takes to tell it, the pine tree took fire and blazed like a candle blown by the wind. Pinocchio, seeing that the flames mounted higher and higher, and not wishing to be roasted, jumped down from the top of the tree. Away he ran, just as before, with the assassins always behind and never getting tired. . . .

When he arrived at a certain point, he thought he heard some one. Indeed, he saw on the road— whom do you suppose?—the Fox and the Cat, that is, the two companions with whom he had supped at the inn called the Red Lobster.

"Here is our dear friend Pinocchio!" cried the Fox, hugging and kissing him. "How did you ever get here?"

"It is a long story," said the marionette, "and I will tell you when I have time. I met some assassins on the road."

"Assassins? Oh, my poor friend! and what did they want?"

"They wished to rob me of my money."

"Infamous!" cried the Fox.

"Most infamous!" said the Cat.

"But I started to run," continued the marionette, "and they ran after me. . . ."

"And your money, where is that?"

"I have it all, less the piece I spent at the inn called the Red Lobster."

"And to think that instead of four pieces they might become two thousand by tomorrow! Why did you not follow my advice? Why do you not sow them in the Field of Wonders?"

"Today it is impossible. I will go another time."

"Another time will be too late," said the Fox.

"Why?"

"Because that field has been bought by a rich man, and after tomorrow no one will be permitted to sow there any more."

"How far is the Field of Wonders from here?"

"Hardly two miles. Will you come with us? In half an hour we shall be there. You can sow the money quickly, and after a few moments you can return home with your pockets full. Will you come with us?"

Pinocchio hesitated a little because he thought of the advice of the Talking Cricket; but, after the fashion of foolish, heartless boys, he finally yielded. With a shake of his head he said to the Fox and the Cat, "Come on, I will go with you." And they started.

After having walked half a day they arrived at a city called Stupid-catchers. As soon as they entered the city Pinocchio saw that all the streets were full of sick dogs that gaped for food; clipped sheep that shook from the cold; featherless chickens that begged for alms; big butterflies that could not fly any more because they had sold their beautiful wings for a few pennies and were ashamed to be seen; and pheasants that limped, bewailing their brilliant gold and silver feathers now lost to them forever.

In the midst of the crowd of beggars and unfortunates they passed from time to time several fine carriages filled with people, each of whom turned out to be a Fox or a thieving Magpie or a Bird of prey.

Pinocchio and the Gold Coins 89

"Where is the Field of Wonders?" asked Pinocchio.

"Only a few steps farther."

And so it proved. They walked through the city, and outside the walls they stopped in a field which looked much like other fields. No one was in sight.

"Here we are at last," said the Fox. "Now you must stoop down and dig a hole and put the money inside."

Pinocchio obeyed, dug a hole, put in the money, and then covered it over with earth.

"Now then," said the Fox, "go to that well and take a little water and sprinkle the ground where you have sown."

Pinocchio went to the well. Because he had nothing in which to carry water, he took his hat and, filling it, came back and sprinkled the spot where he had sown the money. Then he asked, "Is there anything else?"

"Nothing else," replied the Fox. "Now we shall go away. You may return here in about twenty minutes and you will find a large

vine with its branches covered with money."

The poor marionette, nearly crazy with joy, thanked the Fox and the Cat a thousand times and promised them a beautiful present.

"We wish nothing," they replied. "To us it is enough to have taught others the way to get rich without doing anything; and we are as contented as we can be."

Thus saying, they bowed to Pinocchio and, wishing him a good harvest, went away.

The marionette, returning to the city, began to count the minutes one by one. When he thought it was time to go back he took the road that led to the Field of Wonders. And while he walked along his heart beat like a big hall clock—tic-toc-tic-toc. Meanwhile he was thinking to himself: "And if, instead of two thousand, I should find five thousand? Oh, what a rich man I should be! I would have a palace and a thousand wooden horses and carriages to amuse me; I would have a cellar filled with good things, a library filled with candy, Dutch cake, almond cake, and cinnamon stick."

Thus imagining, he arrived at the field. He stopped to look for the large vine with many

branches, but he saw nothing. He took a few steps more. Nothing. He entered the field and went right to the hole where he had planted his money. There was nothing there. Then he became thoughtful and began to wonder what he should do next.

Just then he heard a whistling in his ears as if some one were laughing. Looking up, he saw on a tree a big Parrot who was preening his feathers.

"Why do you laugh?" asked Pinocchio in an angry voice.

"I laugh because in cleaning my feathers I tickled myself under my wings."

The marionette did not reply. He went to the well and sprinkled again the place where he had buried his money. When he had done this he heard a laugh more impertinent than the first one. It sounded very loud in the solitude of the field.

"Well," said Pinocchio, wrathfully, "tell me, if you can, ignorant Parrot, why you laugh now."

"I laugh at those silly heads who believe everything that is told them."

"Do you refer to me?"

"Yes, I speak of you, poor Pinocchio. You are foolish enough to think that money, if sowed properly, will grow like grain and plants. I thought so once, and in consequence I have today very few feathers. Now that it is too late to mend matters, I have made up my mind that in order to get together a few pennies it is necessary to work with your hands or invent something with your head."

"I do not understand," said the marionette, who already began to tremble with fear.

"I will explain better," said the Parrot. "Know, then, that while you were in the city the Fox and the Cat returned here. They took the money and then fled like the wind. And now they cannot be caught."

Pinocchio remained with his mouth wide open. Unwilling to believe the words of the Parrot, he began with his hands and nails to dig out the dirt where he had planted his money. And he dug and dug and dug until he had made a hole large enough for a haystack; but the money was not there.

After this sad adventure, a cruel judge throws Pinocchio in jail for being such a fool. Months later, the puppet tries to return home when he is released. He becomes more and more concerned about being good, yet his selfishness and greed often get him in trouble. In his many adventures he is forced to act as a watchdog, is almost put in jail again, is turned into a donkey, and is swallowed by the great dogfish. At long last Pinocchio repents and comes to genuinely love his father, Gepetto, and is turned into a real boy.

Puppets That Teach

Joanne Hall

Puppets for the Lord! For a long time, that has been the theme of Mrs. Doris Moose of Greenville, South Carolina. This lady puppeteer is a wife and mother, but she also has found the time to perform hundreds of puppet plays that teach Bible principles. She has done her plays in children's church programs, camps, and Bible School programs, not only for her own church, but also for many other churches and Christian organizations.

Mrs. Moose's main desires have been first to reach children for the Lord Jesus Christ, and then to teach children how to put Bible truths into practice in their lives. The work all began for Mrs. Moose when she was a high school student, teaching in her church's children's departments. She needed visual aids—something for her young audience to *see* while she was teaching—but she could not find any. So she made her own. The puppet ministry was a natural result of her desire to use visual aids in teaching children.

Mrs. Moose writes all her own scripts, including dialogue and stage directions. She has written at least seventy plays, some of which are published so that other puppeteers can use them. One of her favorite settings for her stories

is the 31-foot-by-9-foot castle shown on this page. Over the years she has built nine sets, including the castle. Although she does most of the building of the sets herself, she recruits help from some church workers for the heavy jobs. Mrs. Moose says that many of the materials she used in the sets were free, such as large cardboard boxes and scraps of material. Paint is the main expense. Building the sets does take time; one display took seventy-two hours.

The different settings are used in many ways; for example, the castle scene can be used as the setting for a variety of battles. In one play bees attack the king of the castle, and the king loses his temper. He loses control of his own kingdom as a result. Other battles occur: battles with lying, stealing, and irresponsibility. Mrs. Moose writes scripts to teach lessons from the Bible on Christian conduct.

Mrs. Moose's husband as well as her sixteen-year-old son, Brian, have always been her puppeteers. Brian began helping when he was eight years old and is now very skilled. Mrs. Moose's mother has played a big part in the ministry over the years, too, by making costumes for the puppets. Many of the puppets themselves are also homemade.

Mrs. Moose's puppet ministry grew out of her desire to serve the Lord by having something that would catch the attention of children. Now her work has been seen by thousands of children, and through her workshops, millions will be reached in other parts of the country. Mrs. Moose says, "It's all fantasy, but fun for the children. If it catches their eyes, they might listen; and if they listen, they might learn."

How to Make a Puppet

Darell Koons

Puppetry is as old as drama. The Greeks and the Romans used puppets for entertainment, and puppet shows continued throughout the Middle Ages as a form of entertainment for adults as well as children. Today we think of puppets as being mostly for children, but in some countries like Japan, puppetry has become a fine art. The Japanese have puppet shows that last for hours, and their puppet shows are as serious and suspenseful as any American or European operas would be. Japanese puppets may seem much simpler than puppets made in other countries. Yet one master puppeteer in Japan, using a woman puppet to act out a death scene, has brought audiences of adult men and women to tears.

Puppets can be made of anything from simple paper bags to fine porcelain. One way to make a puppet is to use papier-mâché, a paste mixed with paper. You can spread the papier-mâché over a framework or skeleton to form your puppet's head. Making the puppet takes a long time because drying time must be allowed between steps. Perhaps it would help to do each of the following steps on a different day.

• Step 1: Getting Started

Before you start, think about the kind of personality you want your puppet to have. What do you want it to look like? Try sketching your puppet on paper. Puppets have their own characteristics, just like people. If you're making a grouchy old woman, how would she look? How would a cheerful, grandmotherly woman look? Or a grandfather? A princess? A clown? As you sketch, remember that you can make changes later, even while you're constructing your puppet.

• Step 2: Gathering the Materials

You'll need the following items to make your puppet:
- wheat paste
- newspaper
- acrylic or tempera paints
- poster board or light cardboard
- masking tape
- yarn or corn silk
- Duco Cement or white glue
- leather or felt
- cloth for the costume
- any other items needed for your particular puppet

You can get wheat paste at wallpaper or interior decorating shops. Mix up enough paste for only one session at a time. Empty out any paste that you don't use during the session, because leftover paste will spoil quickly.

Acrylic paint is waterproof and won't rub off when dry. If you decide to use acrylic paint, wear an old shirt to cover your clothes because acrylic paint won't wash out of fabric. Tempera paint will wash out of most clothing, but it isn't waterproof. If you decide to use tempera paint, make sure that you never let the puppet get wet.

Cornsilk makes soft, shining hair, but if it isn't available, yarn works well too.

Duco Cement works best for gluing the hair on, but you must use it in a well-ventilated area and avoid breathing it for any length of time. You may want to use white glue instead. Never use rubber cement.

• Step 3: Making the Head

To make the form for the puppet's head, wad up one full sheet of newspaper. Crumple the ball of newspaper into the size of an orange. Shape the poster board into a tube around two of your fingers and tape it together. Push the tube into the wad of newspaper, leaving enough of the tube showing to form a neck for the puppet.

Spread newspaper on your working area to protect the surface. Then unfold one sheet of newspaper, laying it out flat. Spread paste over the sheet of newspaper. Then tear large strips of pasted newspaper to shape over the head form. Use smaller and smaller pieces until the head is shaped the way you want it. Build up a ring of papier-mâché on the bottom of the posterboard neck. This ring of papier-mâché is called the "shoulders" of the puppet, even though it really doesn't look like shoulders. It will help support the costume later on.

Some of the simplest puppets have round faces and painted-on features. But you can shape the details of the face right onto the puppet if you want to. Push in the wet papier-mâché to make indentations for the eyes. Build up and shape the cheeks, nose, eyelids, and lips with more pasted paper. Experiment with different shapes. Have fun!

While your puppet's head dries, the "skin" will probably shrink and become rough and bumpy. If you don't want this for your puppet's personality, fill in the rough areas with small pieces of papier-mâché. Then put your puppet in a safe place to dry again.

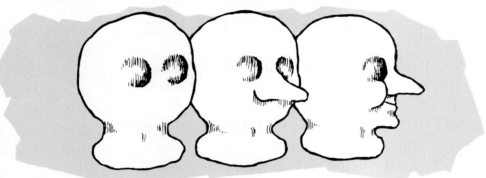

• **Step 4: Painting the Head**

When the puppet's head is bone dry, it's ready to paint. Mix the base color you want to use for the face. (A clown might have a white face, and other puppets would have dark or light skin colors.) Paint the base color over the entire head and neck. When the base color is still wet, blend a little red over the cheeks, but don't paint in the features.

While the puppet is drying, you can mix the colors for its features. When the puppet is completely dry, use a pencil to very lightly sketch its eyes, nose, mouth, and any other features you want.

Look at a classmate's eyes. Notice that the eyelid covers part of the eye. Sketch your puppet's eyes with eyelids too. When you paint, use white paint for the background color of the eye. Make sure that the colored part is neither too bright nor too dark. After you add the black pupil, try putting a dash of white in both pupils to make the eyes seem to sparkle.

Most puppets look better with a slightly open mouth because then they look more like they're talking. Use a dark brown or black in the middle of the mouth. If you want to, you can paint the teeth to show just a little bit, the way a person's teeth show when his mouth is slightly open.

Use red to paint the lips if the puppet is a woman; use a darker flesh tone if the puppet is a man.

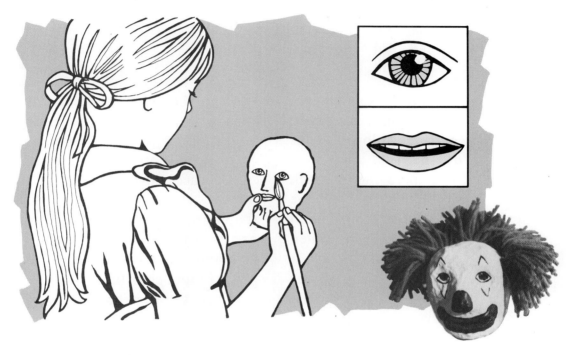

• Step 5: Making the Hair

After the puppet is completely dry, you can glue on the hair. If you use corn silk, you need only to glue it on across the head. If you use yarn, put a line of stitching across the center of the length of yarn. Then glue the yarn on. You can braid or style the hair after the glue is thoroughly dry. If you want short or curly hair, you can glue individual bits of yarn all over the puppet's head.

• Step 6: Making the Costume

When you draw the pattern for your puppet's hands, don't try to draw five fingers. Draw the thumb and then put the other four fingers together to make a mitten shape. Cut the mitten-hands out of leather or doubled thicknesses of felt that have been glued together. You can paint the leather or felt the same base color that you used for the puppet's head.

For the puppet's costume, cut the cloth six to eight inches wide. Make the costume as long as your hand. Put the two pieces of material together, facing each other. Stick the mittens inside the sleeves, pointing toward each other with their thumbs up. Then sew the costume together, turn it inside out, and pull it over your puppet's head like a shirt. The "shoulders" around the puppet's neck should be built up enough to keep the costume on. If you wish, you can make a collar for your puppet out of elastic and cover it with some other material.

Use accessories that fit your puppet's character. You could try shaping eyeglasses from thick wire or adding a belt, beads, a bandanna, or a hat to make your puppet more colorful.

Then get together with your classmates and write a puppet show to put on!

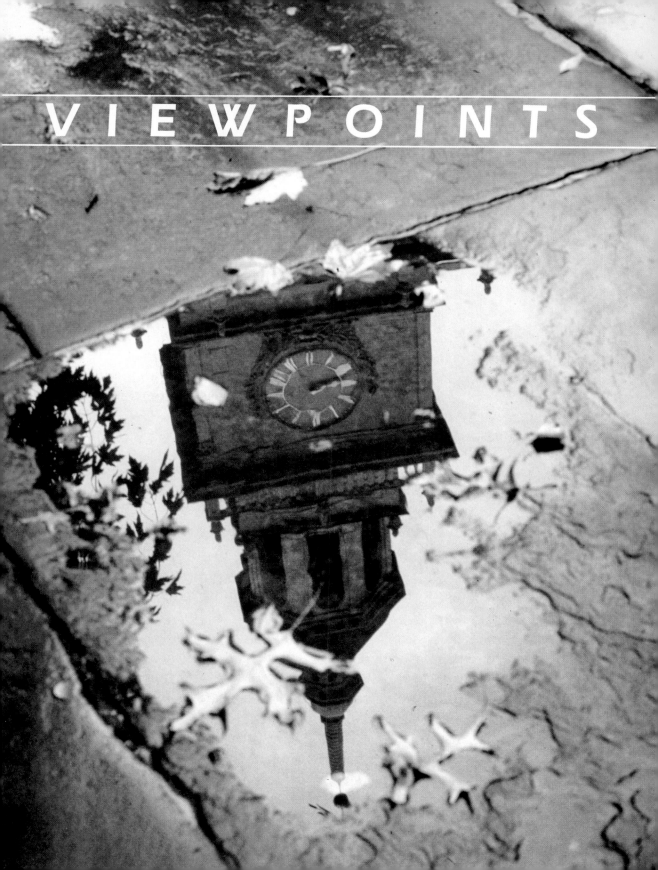

The Prince and the Pauper

Mark Twain, dramatized by
Donna Hess

CAST

Narrator
Edward *Prince of Wales*
Henry VIII *King of England*
Lord St. John *an adviser to the king and prince*
Lord Chancellor *an adviser to the king*
Miles Hendon *English nobleman and Edward's friend*

Tom Canty *a poor boy*
John Canty *Tom's father*
Mrs. Canty *Tom's mother*
Nan and Bet *Tom's sisters*
Grandmother Canty *Tom's grandmother*
Hugo *John Canty's beggar friend*

SCENE 1

The ancient city of London, on a certain autumn day in 1547.

Narrator: Outside Westminster Palace, Tom Canty stood with his face pressed against the bars of the castle gate. He was a small, ill-clad, and poorly-groomed boy. A crowd had gathered to see Edward, Prince of Wales. The Prince was also a small boy, but unlike Tom, he was royally clad and freshly groomed. Just as the prince appeared, one of the guards spied Tom clinging to the gate.

Guard: *(Roughly pushing Tom away)* Mind your manners, you young beggar!

Edward: *(Stepping forward)* How dare you treat my father's subjects so! Open the gate and let him in!

Narrator: The crowd cheered as Tom entered the royal courtyard. The young prince invited the pauper to come with him to his room. Immediately all attendants were dismissed; and Tom, restless and uncomfortable, was alone with the prince.

Edward: What is your name?

Tom: Tom Canty, an' it please you, sir.

Edward: Have you a family?

Tom: I have a father and grandmother who I must admit are not overkind. But my mother is a gentle soul, and I am also blessed with two good-hearted sisters.

Edward: Where do you live?

Tom: Offal Court, out of Pudding Lane.

Edward: Offal Court? Tell me, have you an easy life there?

Tom: I would not call it easy, for broken heads are as common as hunger in the place. But it is pleasant enough. We have our share of fun. The lads have boxing matches and races. And in summer we wade and swim in the canals or play in the sand and make mud pastries. Ah, the lovely mud, there is nothing like it in all the world. We fairly wallow in it, sir.

Edward: Oh, if I could only clothe myself in rags like yours and revel in the mud—just once—with no one to forbid me.

Tom: And if I could clothe me in your splendid robes—just once—and eat a royal dinner!

Edward: Say no more! Take off your rags and put on my royal dress.

Narrator: A few moments later, the Prince of Wales stood clothed in poor Tom's fluttering odds and ends. And Tom—much to his amazement—stood transformed in the stately trappings of royalty.

Edward: 'Tis strange. We look so much alike. Now that we have changed our clothes it is hard to tell who is prince and who is pauper. What's more, now that I am clothed as you, I am able to feel as you did when that soldier shamefully mistreated you. The brute shall pay for his misdeed! Do not stir till I come again!

Narrator: The prince rushed out, leaving poor Tom bewildered, and made his way to the gate. The guard began to scowl when he saw Edward coming.

Edward: *(Shouting angrily)* Unbar the gate!

Narrator: The guard obeyed, but instead of bowing to the prince, he knocked him to the ground.

Guard: Take that, you beggar, for the scolding you got me from His Highness!

Edward: *(Rising in a fit of anger)* You shall hang for laying hands on me!

Guard: Be off, you crazy rubbish!

Narrator: Edward's troubles were just beginning. As the guard pushed him into the crowd, John Canty appeared.

John Canty: *(Furious)* There you are! If I do not break every bone in your body, then I am not John Canty!

Edward: Are you really his father?

John Canty: *His* father? I am *your* father as you will soon have cause to know!

Edward: *(Impatiently)* Do not vex me! Take me to the king. I am the Prince of Wales!

John Canty: You are stark mad! But mad or no, I and your grandmother will soon pound sense into your head!

Narrator: A kind old man stepped forward to stop Canty from harming the prince, but Canty would not be stopped. He took the club that was in his hand and brought it down upon the old man's head. Then he picked up Edward like a sack of potatoes and carried him off.

SCENE 2

King Henry's room in Westminster Palace.

Narrator: The king had become very ill of late, and his illness did not help his temper. When Tom first saw him, he sat in bed propped up by satin pillows and covered with a satin blanket. But these soft coverings did nothing to soften his rage. Though the attendants about the king looked calm, Tom cowered in the corner.

King: I will not rest until that traitor, the Duke of Norfolk, has been put to death! Why do you stand here dawdling—go now and see to it!

Lord Chancellor: Pardon, your Majesty—I do but wait for you to stamp the order for his execution with the royal seal.

King: The seal? Ah, yes—the seal. What did I do with it?

Lord St. John: Sire, if I may be so bold, I remember that you gave the seal to His Highness the Prince of Wales to keep for you.

King: True! Most true! *(Turning to Tom)* Go, Edward, my son, and fetch for me the seal.

Narrator: Poor Tom. When he realized that the king was speaking to him, he turned as pale as death and fell upon his knees as if a shot had brought him there.

Tom: Ah, be merciful!

King: *(Stunned)* What ails you, my prince?

Tom: In truth I am no prince, my lord. I am poor Tom Canty of Offal Court!

King: Edward, do you not know me?

Tom: Oh, sir! I know that you are the king and that I am undone!

King: Come here, my child. Rest your head on your father's heart and be at peace.

Narrator: Tom was assisted to his feet, and he, humble and trembly, approached the Majesty of England.

King: *(To the Lord Chancellor)* We will not trouble the child further. Go to the treasury and fetch the small seal that I take with me when I travel abroad. It will suffice to fulfill the order.

Narrator: The Lord Chancellor went off to seek the seal. Tom knew that all eyes were upon him. They gazed on him reproachfully, puzzled at this sudden change in their prince. At that moment Tom would have exchanged all his princely dreams for one friend.

King: Listen all. This my son is mad. But it is a temporary sickness. Overstudy has done this to him. Away with all his books and teachers until he is made well again! I command you, Lord St. John, to see that the prince's illness is hidden. *(To Tom)* You, my son, must help him in this matter. Though you are ill, you must not deny that you are prince, and you must at least act the part until you are made well.

SCENE 3

Tom's house at Offal Court.

Narrator: The prince found himself in John Canty's house. By the dim light of a waning candle, he could barely make out the features of those in the house. Nan, Bet, and Mrs. Canty huddled in the corner while Grandmother Canty sat at the table eating. John Canty joined his mother, for his struggle with the furious prince had made him very hungry.

Edward: I tell you again—I am the Prince of Wales!

John Canty: *(Stuffing his mouth with food)* Let the show go on! The raving lunatic is entertaining!

Mrs. Canty: Oh, my poor boy!

Edward: *(Kindly)* Do not grieve. Your son is well. Take me to the palace where he is, and you shall see.

Grandmother: *(Mocking him)* On your knees, all pauper scum! We must do reverence to this prince!

Edward: You offend me with your foolish talk!

Narrator: As John Canty jumped up to thrash Edward, Mrs. Canty stepped between her husband and the prince to shield the poor boy from the blows.

Edward: Do not suffer for me, madam. Let this swine do his will on me alone. I tell you, he will pay!

John Canty: *(After a few blows)* Now, to bed, all of you. This entertainment has tired me.

Narrator: The Prince stomped to the corner and sat down to brood while the rest of the household went to their beds of straw. But once they were settled, several sharp knocks were heard at the door.

John Canty: Who is it?

Beggar: *(Running into the room)* Do you know who it was that you hit with your club this afternoon?

John Canty: I neither know nor care!

Beggar: If you will save your neck, you had better care. It was a holy man, and right now he is delivering up the ghost!

John Canty: Mercy! We must up and fly or stay and perish.

Narrator: The family scattered—all except Edward, who waited until everyone was gone. He then looked cautiously about and escaped into the street.

SCENE 4

Edward's bedchamber in Westminster Palace.

Narrator: Tom had slept in Edward's royal bed. But he was used to a bed of straw, so he did not sleep comfortably.

Tom: *(Stirring restlessly.)* Ho, Nan! Bet! Kick off your straw and come and hear the wildest dream I ever— *(Sitting upright)* Oh, sorrow—it is no dream. I am a prince. Yet I am not a prince. What would I not give to be back in Offal Court playing with the other lads. Court life is not all royal robes and dinners. Nobles and lords come to me daily with hard questions that I cannot answer. But though they seem to trust me with weighty matters, they do not trust me to wash and dress myself. 'Tis strange— burdensome—to be a prince.

Narrator: The chamber door opened and a royal messenger entered with several richly clothed lords, nobles, and pages. They surrounded Tom's bed and stood silently, looking down at him. Just as Tom felt he could bear the silence no longer, the royal messenger stepped forward.

Messenger: We regret to bring you such sad news, Your Highness, but your father, the king, is dead!

Narrator: Every one of the attendants bowed his head for several moments. Then at Lord St. John's signal, they knelt before Tom. A mighty shout was raised.

Crowd: Long live the king! Long live Edward, King of England!

Narrator: Tom sat still as a statue, his hands tightly clenching the tassel of his satin robe.

SCENE 5

The city of London.

Narrator: As Edward moved about the streets, he saw a grand procession approaching. Tom was at the head of the parade, seated on a magnificent white horse. As he neared, the crowd began to shout, "Long live King Edward the Sixth!" Edward stopped to listen and realized that his father was dead and that he should now be king. He thought that Tom was trying to steal the crown.

Edward: I tell you *I* am the Prince of Wales! That beggar on my horse is an imposter!

Narrator: Poor Tom neither saw nor heard the prince. And having no one to support his claim, Edward again faced a scornful mob.

Man: Another beggar claims the throne!

Narrator: Those in the crowd began to abuse and make fun of the prince.

Edward: Hands off, you unmannerly curs!

Narrator: But at that moment Miles Hendon, who had been part of the crowd, stepped forward to rescue Edward from the blows. Again the prince was carried off, this time to safety. But when they were free from the crowd, Edward lost his fighting spirit and was sad.

Miles: You are a brave lad to withstand such a pack of unruly kennel rats! But be of good cheer, you are safe now.

Edward: *(Quietly)* I am not afraid; I am grieved at my father's death.

Miles: Your father?

Edward: *(Irritated)* Can you forget so quickly the cries of the crowd? They hail me—or my imposter—as king. That can only mean that Henry the VIII, my father, is dead.

Miles: Then you were not in jest. You actually *believe* that you are Edward, Prince of Wales?

Edward: I not only believe it— I *know* it! Do you think that I would fight a mob of peasants for a flight of fancy?

Narrator: Miles started to speak, but thought better of it. He decided to go along with Edward's "fancy" of playing king—at least for a while, for he believed that rest would cure the boy of such madness. Therefore, he put a tender hand on Edward's shoulder to lead him homeward. But they did not go far before they were overtaken by John Canty.

John Canty: So—you thought you could escape, did you? Well, see now if I do not pound your bones to pudding!

Miles: Not too fast, friend. You are needlessly rough. Who is this lad to you?

John Canty: He is my son!

Edward: That's a lie!

Miles: Boldly said. And I believe you whether your head is sound or cracked, my boy. You will abide with me. It is settled!

John Canty: *(Moving toward Edward)* We will see about that!

Miles: *(Drawing his sword)* If you but touch him, I will spit you like a goose!

Narrator: John Canty cast a threatening look at Edward, then turned and left.

SCENE 6

Miles Hendon's home.

Narrator: Wrapped in Miles's doublet, Edward slept on a bed of straw. Miles was mending Edward's ragged coat when Edward stirred and sat up.

Edward: Sir, you should not sit in the presence of a king.

Miles: *(To himself)* Lo, rest has not healed the poor boy. Well, I had better humor him or he will wish me off to the tower.

Narrator: Miles, though weary, got up and continued his mending while standing.

Edward: I believe you told me that you are called Miles Hendon, and your courage proves you to be of noble birth. How, then, did you come to lodge in this poor dwelling?

Miles: Well, Sire, princes are not the only men betrayed. It is true I am of noble birth. My father was rich, but of a generous nature. My mother was noble and good. Both are now dead. I also had an older brother named Arthur who was much like my father. He, too, is dead. The only one of my family living is my younger brother, Hugh. Unlike the other family members, Hugh has the nature of a reptile. Through slander and deceit he has robbed me of my inheritance. I now make my own livelihood by whatever honest means I find, and I live where I can.

Edward: You have been shamefully treated. When I regain my throne, I promise you that I shall right these wrongs! But I desire to do something for you even now. You have saved me from injury and shame. Name your desire, and if it be within my power, it is yours!

Miles: You are most kind, but there is really nothing—no wait, there is one thing I would request of you, your Highness. I ask that I might have the privilege of *sitting* in the presence of my king.

Edward: Done!

Narrator: Relieved, Miles sat down and continued mending while the prince went back to sleep. When Miles had finished, he decided to go out and buy some food. Moments after he had gone, the door opened slowly and John Canty entered as quietly as a mouse—some would say a rat.

SCENE 7

Den of thieves and beggars.

Narrator: Canty had captured Edward and brought him to his "hide-out." The prince stood scowling, encircled by a crowd of ruffians. Grandmother Canty was among the motley crew.

John Canty: Speak up—where are your mother and sisters? I lost them as well as you when we fled that night. And I mean to have you all back to beg my food for me!

Edward: My mother is dead and my sisters are in the palace.

Narrator: Hugo, one of the beggars, laughed rudely and then came forward as if to thrash the prince.

John Canty: *(To Hugo)* Not now. His mind is gone. But that should not hinder his begging. Take him with you. If he fails to bring us any money, then I shall let you loose to do your will with him.

SCENE 8

A country road.

Narrator: Hugo, who now wore a patch over one eye, was trying to tell Edward the part he must play in the beggar's charade. But Edward turned his back on Hugo and refused to listen.

Hugo: Hear me, boy, you may refuse to listen, but you *will* help me beg.

Edward: I will do no such—

Hugo: Peace! Here comes someone with a kindly face.

Narrator: Quick as lightning Hugo fell to the ground and began to moan as the elderly gentleman approached.

Man: Oh, dear! Oh, poor soul, how you suffer. *(Taking money from his pocket.)* Here, let me help.

Hugo: Oh noble sir, you are a princely gentleman. My brother there will take the money.

Man: *(To Edward)* Here, lad, take this for your ailing brother.

Edward: I am not his brother and he is not ailing! He is a beggar and a thief!

Man: *(To Hugo)* Why you—I'll throttle you!

Narrator: The ailing Hugo jumped up and ran like a man in the best of health. The gentleman followed, waving his walking stick and uttering threats. Edward ran as well—but in the opposite direction.

SCENE 9

An old hermit's cottage in the woods.

Narrator: Edward came upon a small run-down shack. There was but one window. Cautiously he looked inside. In the corner was a bed of straw covered with rags. There was a short bench, a three-legged stool, and an aged man who crouched before the hearth where burned a small fire. Edward decided to knock softly.

Hermit: Enter!

Narrator: Once he was inside, Edward found the small room even less inviting than when he spied it through the window.

Edward: I mean no harm. I am a king in need of rest.

Hermit: A king? Then welcome! A king who casts away his crown and clothes himself in rags is worthy. Come. Lie down and rest.

Edward: I cannot stay long. I must—

Hermit: You will stay. You will find peace here. None shall find you. None shall spoil your refuge. *(Cautiously)* You say you are a king. What king?

Edward: I am Edward, Prince of Wales—now King of England.

Hermit: Of England! Then King Henry is dead?

Edward: *(Sleepily lying down)* He is.

Hermit: *(To himself)* Henry was an evil king. An evil king would have an evil son. *(Turning to Edward who has fallen asleep)* Ah, yes, that is good, rest awhile—rest awhile.

Narrator: The hermit began to pace restlessly about the room, mumbling to himself. When he was sure that Edward slept soundly, he gathered several rags and ropes and moved quietly toward the sleeping prince. Carefully, he bound Edward's feet and hands together. Next he placed another bandage under Edward's chin, brought it up over his head, and tied it fast. All of this was done so carefully that the prince did not even stir. The hermit then took a long knife from the table.

Hermit: Son of Henry the Eighth, have you prayed?

Narrator: The old man's voice awakened Edward. Seeing the knife above him, Edward struggled to free himself from his bonds.

Hermit: It is no use. Your only hope now is to pray the prayer of the dying!

Miles: *(Banging on the door and calling from outside)* Ho, open up! Open up I say!

Narrator: Quickly the hermit covered the boy and went to the door.

Hermit: May I help you, good sir?

Miles: I'm searching for my boy. Where is he? Don't tell me you don't know. I have scourged a beggar to track him here and I will not hesitate to scourge another!

Hermit: There is no need for violence. Your boy indeed was here, but I fed him and sent him on an errand. He set out through the woods only a bit ago.

Miles: Then I'll be gone. But mark you, if I find him not, I will return within the hour.

Hermit: *(Closing the door)* An hour will be too late.

Narrator: The hermit went to Edward, again raising his knife to smite the helpless boy. But as he did so, the door was broken down and Miles rushed in.

Miles: *(Wrenching the knife from the old man)* You murderous old dog! I knew you lied. The boy believes himself a king—and a king does not run errands!

Narrator: The old hermit wrenched himself free and dashed from the cottage while Miles set about to free Edward.

Edward: When is the coronation to take place?

Miles: *(Surprised)* Tomorrow, but—

Edward: Then come, good sir, we have no time to waste. If we fail to get to London before tomorrow, my throne is lost forever.

SCENE 10

City of London on coronation day.

Narrator: All of London gathered to see the crowning of their "prince." Tom was wearing a beautiful robe of gold and rode at the head of the royal procession. Overcome with the splendor, he sat with downcast eyes, embarrassed to look upon so great an audience.

Lord St. John: My liege, it is not the time for dreaming. The people observe your downcast head, and they take it for an omen. Be advised: unveil the sun of royalty—lift up your head and smile on the people.

Narrator: Tom made a feeble attempt to look up and smile as Lord St. John scattered coins to the crowd. Suddenly a pauper woman pushed her way through the mob and past the guards.

Mrs. Canty: *(Clasping Tom's leg)* Oh, my child, my darling! I thought I had lost you forever.

Narrator: Before Tom could speak, Lord St. John pried the woman away and commanded the procession to move on. It was obvious, however, that the

116

woman's presence had greatly affected Tom.

Lord St. John: *(Turning to a guard)* Catch that crazy pauper. She has disturbed the prince and made him once more frown upon the people.

Tom: Please, do not harm her. She is my mother.

Lord St. John: *(Whispering)* He's gone mad again!

Narrator: Now the procession neared the platform prepared for the coronation ceremony. Edward, with Miles at his heels, was trying to get to the front of the crowd. They were blocked, however, and Miles could go no farther. But Edward, who was much smaller, got down on his hands and knees and scrambled through the people's legs. He reached the platform just as they were about to place the crown on the pauper's head.

Edward: I forbid you to set the crown of England on that imposter's head. *I* am the king!

Narrator: In an instant several guards laid hands on Edward.

Tom: Loose him! He *is* in truth the king!

Lord St. John: *(To the guards)* Mind not His Majesty, his malady is upon him again—seize the pauper!

Tom: On peril of your life! Touch him not; he is the king! *(Taking the crown and going to Edward)* O my Lord, let poor Tom Canty be first to swear allegiance to you. Put your crown upon your head and take your kingdom back!

Edward: I am pleased to know that in truth you did not wish to steal the throne.

Lord St. John: *(Uncertainly)* I begin to see a strange resemblance between this pauper and the prince. Enough resemblance to kindle doubt. *(Turning to Edward)* I will ask but one question which will be proof. Where is the great seal? Since my prince—or pauper—was first taken ill, we have not been able to find it. If you are the true Prince of Wales, then you will know the answer to this riddle.

Edward: My good Lord, in the arm piece of the Milanese armor that hangs on the wall of my chamber, you will find the seal.

Lord St. John: *(To a guard)* Fly, and fetch the seal.

Narrator: The crowd made room for the guard and his horse. In only a few moments he returned, holding the seal.

Guard: *(Pointing to Tom)* Now should this imposter be stripped and flung into the tower!

Edward: I will not have it so. Were it not for him, I would not have my crown.

Narrator: Miles had finally gotten close enough to see, but what he saw only confused him. Though Edward stood with the crown upon his head, Tom still wore the royal robes.

Miles: Could it be that my boy whom I took to be lord only of a make-believe kingdom is the Prince of Wales? Or is he being mocked before the rightful heir?

Edward: *(Seeing Miles)* My lord, come up hither.

Miles: *(Miles obeys)* Yes, Your Majesty.

Edward: My people, this nobleman has saved me from both shame and peril, and I rejoice to give him now a true reward. His lands shall be restored to him, and his wicked brother who by slander did rob him of his rights shall be cast into the tower. *(To Tom)* And as long as I am king, every noble and peasant shall do this good lad reverence, for he has reigned well in my stead. Furthermore, his mother and two sisters shall join him at the palace and eat bread at my table as long as they wish!

Tom: My lord, I am not worthy.

Edward: You are no less worthy than I. This masquerade has taught us much. I shall now be a better monarch, for I have learned the value of mercy. And you shall be a better subject, for you have learned to understand the burdens of your king.

Crowd: Long live Edward VI! Long live the king!

THE END

Big Brother

Henry Becker

Well, to start with, my name is Timothy, and I'm in fifth grade at Trinity Christian. I have an older brother just like a lot of boys around here. Well, not *just* like a lot of other boys. My older brother is mentally retarded.

My brother's name is Brad. He's fourteen, but he doesn't go to school anywhere. Mom and Dad work with him at home a lot, and a tutor comes in once a week. He's getting to where he can almost tie his shoes by himself and dress himself with some help. But he moves funny and doesn't talk very well. He can't read at all right now, but Mom and Dad hope he'll be able to someday.

At first when I was growing up I didn't really understand what was wrong with him. Mom would take him out for a walk every afternoon and I played his games with him some, and for a long time I didn't even care that he was retarded. Mom and Dad acted like everybody had a retarded brother in their family—I mean, it was like nothing was different

from normal. And they said, "Brad is the Lord's special blessing to us." I never really understood that, but it didn't make much difference.

But then I started to notice other boys my age. They had big brothers who would play with them and teach them neat stuff and tell them to get lost. And all I had was Brad. Brad just smiles and says really simple things and looks at magazines a lot, especially the *National Geographic,* because he likes the colorful

pictures. I play really simple games with him like Candy Land and bounce the ball. He can't teach me how to hold a bat or how to shoot a basket. I started wanting a big brother like everybody else.

Then this year came. This year two things happened. We moved to this new place, and Mom had another baby, which means that I have a new little sister. Mom couldn't take Brad for his walks in the afternoon. So since I am in the fifth grade now, they figured I was old enough to do it.

That was fine with me. I mean, I like Brad.

The first day everything was okay. I helped Brad with his jacket and everything, and we went for our walk. I had to go slowly so he could hold on to my arm and get his balance. (Mom and Dad figure this walking will help his coordination. You know, help him to be able to move better.) We went a different way from the way Mom would go so we could stop at the pet store. Brad looked in the window at the puppy for what seemed like about an hour. But I didn't mind too much. I always like looking in the pet store. Brad kept saying, "Look at the little puppy, Timothy." The puppy really was great. It kept jumping up at the window and licking the glass in front of Brad's face. It made Brad laugh.

Well, the first walk went pretty well. In fact, I kind of enjoyed it. Brad was a little tired out by the time we got home, but he was happy. He kept talking about the puppy. I told Mom all about it, and she was glad we had a good time. I told Dad about it at supper too.

The second day—that's the day that was really bad. I got home from school and had my snack and did some homework. Then I got Brad ready to go for our walk again. He was excited because we'd had so much fun the day before. I was excited too, because it was fun to see him happy.

But when we got down to the end of the street, there were a bunch of boys there, like about five or six. Most of them were a year or two older, but some of them were my age. I knew some of them. The biggest one, the one leaning against the mailbox, was Mike Richardson. And I knew Gino Borelli too. He's in my class at Trinity.

Mike said, "Hey, Mitchell!" But it wasn't a friendly kind of hey. It was the kind where you know somebody's about to do something rotten. That's why they use your last name, too. They just want to sound tough.

Then Mike said, "Hey, Mitchell, what have you got there? A ree-tard?" And he laughed, and all the other boys laughed, and I got so mad I could feel my ears turning hot. I looked at Brad, and he looked a little confused, and I was afraid he was about to cry. I guess he figured out they were talking about him, but I knew that if he cried it would make things even worse.

Then Mike said, "Ree-tard, ree-tard! Goo-goo." And he stuck his tongue out of the corner of his mouth and crossed his eyes and walked funny, a little bit like my brother walks, and he made all kinds of horrible slobbery noises. And all the other boys just laughed and laughed. Gino Borelli was laughing too.

Brad's eyes were getting bigger and bigger, but he still wasn't saying anything. By then I was so mad that I didn't care if Mike *was* bigger than I was, I jumped on him and started beating him up as hard as I could. I was saying "Nobody's—going—to—talk—about—my—brother—like—that" between punches. And I was crying a little bit, but I don't think they could tell. I'd given Mike a

good punch before all the other boys jumped on me and pulled me off him and gave me a few good punches of their own. They said, "Get out of here, kid." And Gino Borelli, who's the same age as I am, was saying it too.

Well, I finally took Brad's hand and started back for home. He was crying by then and could hardly walk. I didn't say much. I guess I kind of jerked him to try to make him walk faster. I was afraid he'd cry about not getting to see the puppy, but he didn't say anything about that. I guess the fighting really scared him. He kept saying, "Bad boys. They were bad boys, Timothy."

I didn't mean to say anything, but I was mad. So I said, "Why couldn't you be like a regular big brother? You're supposed to take care of me. And I have to take care of you instead."

I was kind of mad at myself then, for saying that. But Brad didn't answer me, and I figured he probably didn't even understand.

Well, there was no way I could keep everything a secret from Mom. I mean, Brad ran to her as soon as we got home and just cried and cried, but she couldn't understand anything he was saying except "bad boys," so she had to ask me. She would have found out anyway, because my clothes were ripped a little and dirty all over. I had a few bruises too.

Well, I told Mom everything, and she didn't say an awful lot. Mostly she just said, "Well, we'll wait and talk about it with Dad." That usually scares me, because it means I've done something bad. But this time I didn't even care much. I just went into my room and closed the door and lay on my bed. Brad was still crying and that was making the baby cry, so Mom had her hands full, but I just didn't feel like going out there to help her. And she never asked me to come. I guess she probably talked to Brad about how those bad boys didn't understand how special Brad was and stuff like that.

Well, when Dad got home I had to tell him the story all over again. Then he and Mom talked to me alone. I don't remember a lot of what they said. They quoted some Bible verses about loving your enemies and turning the other cheek and stuff like that. But the main thing I was thinking

about was what Dad said at first—that was what kept me from remembering everything else they said. He said, "You know, Timothy, you're going to have to go back out there and apologize to those boys."

I got kind of mad, I guess. I said, "Dad, they were making fun of Brad! Why do I have to apologize for beating up Mike when he was making fun of Brad?"

That was when Dad quoted all the verses. But all I could think of was Mike Richardson saying, "Ree-tard! There are *two* ree-tards in the Mitchell family!"

But finally I said I would go. Dad talked to me about all the things I should say, and then he prayed with me. That made me feel a little better, but I still didn't eat much supper that night. I didn't sleep an awful lot either.

The next day I didn't even ask Brad if he wanted to go for a walk. He just stayed in his room and looked at magazines. Every once in a while he would come and say something to Mom about the bad boys and how they didn't love Jesus. Mom was really patient with him and explained about Jesus and stuff.

Mom prayed with me and then I walked down the two blocks to where I knew the big boys would be. There they were, and Mike Richardson was leaning against the mailbox. They watched me coming and laughed. I just went over and over in my mind the things Dad had told me to say. And I prayed. I prayed a lot.

"Hey, Mitchell," Mike yelled at me. "Where's the ree-tard today?"

I ignored what he said, just like Dad had told me to do. As soon as I got close enough I said, "Mike, I'm sorry I lost my temper yesterday, and I'm sorry I hit you."

Well, Dad had said that would startle them so much that I could keep on talking. He was right. I said, "I love Brad, even if he is retarded. We learn patience from him . . . and love . . . and the Lord gave him to us for a reason. I should have explained things to you yesterday, because fighting doesn't solve anything. I disobeyed the Lord yesterday when I hit you." I stopped then and took a deep breath. I was shaking all over, and I prayed that they wouldn't be able to tell. Now this was the place where Dad had said, "Even if they keep on making fun of you, they'll still respect you." So I stuck my hands in my pockets and waited for them to make fun of me.

But it wasn't as much as I expected. Mike just said, "Well, will you look at the preacher man. Why don't you shake your Bible at us a little, huh?" And the other boys laughed, but it was a weak laugh, and I could tell they all felt uncomfortable. In fact, they all started to walk away, like the mailbox corner wasn't interesting anymore. Mike Richardson left too, but he said, "So long, preacher man." And he stuck his hands inside his jacket and went away whistling, like what I had said hadn't made any difference to him.

I had watched Gino Borelli the whole time I was talking. He was the one my Dad had been most concerned about. Dad had said,

"If Gino is hanging around with the wrong crowd, he might start doing wrong things even if he *is* going to a Christian school. Maybe he's not even saved. You need to pray for an opportunity to witness to him." So even though I was still shaking a little, I prayed that Gino would stick around so I could say something to him.

But he didn't. He was about the last one to leave, and he looked at me sort of with surprise, I guess, and maybe even admiration, but he walked away when the other boys did.

When they had all left, I went back home. I had to go to my room for a while until I stopped shaking, but by the time Dad was home I was able to come out and tell him and Mom all about it. They were glad. And Dad said, "Son, it's like I said—they may still pick on you occasionally, but it will be just to test you. I think all of those boys respect you more now. And maybe you'll still have a chance to witness to some of them, especially Gino Borelli."

I prayed for chances to witness to Gino the next few days, but a chance didn't come. He seemed to be avoiding me. In the afternoons I just walked with Brad around the backyard. But by

Monday he was feeling better and when I mentioned the puppy, he jumped up and down and clapped his hands. So we walked down the two blocks and I held my breath, but there was no one at the mailbox. Brad didn't seem to remember—he just kept talking about all the things around him, but especially about the puppy. When we got to the pet store there was a different puppy in the window, a brown one instead of a black one, but he was just as cute. I don't think Brad even noticed the difference. He just jumped up and down and tapped on the glass. Finally we went inside and the store manager was really nice. He pulled the puppy out and let Brad hold it for a few minutes. I wouldn't have thought Brad could be so gentle. He even said soft little things to the puppy—it was neat to see.

Tuesday when we went for our walk again, we turned the corner and saw three boys at the mailbox—Mike Richardson and one of his big friends, and Gino Borelli. I could hardly believe it— and my stomach tied up in knots. I hadn't prayed before I left.

They all three started making fun of Brad, like they had rehearsed it or something. But Brad was the one that surprised me this time. He spoke out so clearly, clear enough for everybody to understand. He said, "You're bad boys. You don't love Jesus. That makes you bad boys. Boys that don't love Jesus won't go to heaven."

That was probably the most I had ever heard Brad say at once. And it stopped the boys cold. They laughed a little, but they left. That sort of surprised me, because they could have made fun of the way Brad talked. But they didn't even turn around.

Then the Lord gave me the courage to call Gino's name. "Hey, Gino," I said. "Come here." And he did come. Almost like he had been hoping I would call. The other boys didn't look back. I prayed a quick prayer.

"Gino," I said, "why don't you come to the pet store with us?"

He didn't say anything. He just smiled and shook his head and went on home. But Dad and Mom had both said it would take time.

The last week or so Gino has started being nicer to me at school. In fact, today I invited him over to my house for next weekend to play Candy Land with Brad and do some other stuff. He kind of laughed when I talked about Candy Land, and said he would if I promised not to tell anybody else about it.

Brad and I walked down to the pet store almost every day last week. I decided to start saving up to buy him a puppy for his next birthday. After all, he did help me out that last day that the bullies showed up. I don't know if I would've known what to say if he hadn't taken over.

Oh, yeah. After Brad helped me that time, I said, "Hey, Brad, thanks for what you did. I was really glad to have you help."

And Brad put his arm around me and smiled. And he said, "That's okay, Timothy. That's what a big brother does."

The Quarrel

Eleanor Farjeon

I quarreled with my brother,
I don't know what about,
One thing led to another
And somehow we fell out.
The start of it was slight,
The end of it was strong,
He said he was right,
I knew he was wrong!

We hated one another.
The afternoon turned black.
Then suddenly my brother
Thumped me on the back,
And said, "Oh, *come* along!
We can't go on all night—
I was in the wrong."
So he was in the right.

The Tal-Omega

Jeri Massi

When Bruce learned of the contest to send the first child through space to the research center on Jupiter 2, he jumped at the chance. Being an orphan, he longed to be a part of something special, to belong. Now, after being declared the winner, he was in the second week of his voyage into space. For a week he had eaten and talked with the Tal-Omega *crew, and he had seen space through the portholes of the ship. For a boy with no family, this week of hard work, horseplay, and high adventure had been like a dream come true. Little did he know that his newfound contentment would soon be threatened.*

"Tal-Omega—Tal-Omega. Seven days out from orbit. 0600 hours. Crew roster is as follows: Captain John Denton, helm. Lieutenant Laurence Richards, navigation. Lieutenant Dwight Finelli, communication and survey. All levels acknowledge."

In the sickbay, Dr. Hanson hit the intercom toggle. "Sickbay acknowledges." He turned to Bruce. "I'm going to anesthetize you, Bruce."

"Yes sir."

"That injury's going to require a little surgery, nothing serious.

If we were on Earth, you wouldn't even need to spend the night in the hospital. I'm going to call in Simmons and Mitchell to prep you while I decontaminate." He reached up to a small hatch in the low metal roof. The spaceship's quarters were cramped, and sickbay was no exception. Bruce occupied the only permanent bed. Dr. Hanson had room to operate with one assistant, but that was all. Of course, with a crew of only fifteen, the sickbay was usually more than enough.

"Until I had to get my arm caught in that hydraulic door," Bruce thought ruefully.

At the moment he felt no pain, but the thought of immediate surgery frightened him. He wished he could be someplace else—no, not really. He had never felt as comfortable with a group of people as he did with the men of the Tal-Omega spaceship. "They've made me feel like part of the crew, not just a passenger on the way to Jupiter 2," he added to himself. For the briefest moment his mind turned to the second moon of Jupiter that would be his home. He would indeed be a newcomer at the school there, for all the students on Jupiter 2 had been born there and had never met a boy from Earth.

Earth. For the first time, memories of green grass and blue sky thrust at him with a sharp pain of homesickness. "Even the greenhouses on Jupiter 2 won't be like Earth," he thought. "Like home."

"Now just breathe easily, son. Simmons and Mitchell will come in to prep you for surgery. I'll be back in a minute to give you an injection." Dr. Hanson strapped a breathing cup over Bruce's face and ruffled the boy's hair.

Bruce tried not to inhale deeply. In a moment he noticed that he wasn't as nervous as he had been the moment before. Then the walls, normally so close and

cramped, looked far away. They blurred, and he relaxed. "And so pretty," Bruce thought happily, as the bank of controls surrounding the cubicle glowed like many Christmas lights. The screen just above his bed showed a computer graphics illustration of his hand with highlights in red for the areas where there was damage. In another moment it, too, blurred before his eyes.

Bruce closed his eyes and yawned. He heard, rather than saw, the doctor leave. The swish of the sickbay door caused him to lift his eyelids sleepily. Two shadowy figures came in. Simmons and Mitchell, Bruce thought vaguely, then closed his eyes again. Of the fifteen crew members, Simmons and Mitchell were his least favorite. They were simple ship-mechs. They could function in any department of the ship, doing semi-skilled work. Both men were tough cookies.

"He's out. Cut that gas," Mitchell said.

Simmons lifted the breathing cup and put it back in its hatch. Then he leaned over Bruce. "Poor kid. He really tore up that arm."

"Quit stalling and set that dial," Mitchell said. His voice sounded far away. As Bruce came in and out of a doze, their voices seemed to get louder and softer, then garbled, and then clearer. He had no sense of time, but at some point while they were setting up, Mitchell was saying, "His life won't be worth a plugged nickel soon enough."

"I'm not hurting any kid—"

"Don't you turn on us now, Simmons!"

"You threatening me?"

"You can lay to it, man. Lay to it. I'll see to it that nobody turns traitor on us."

"I just never thought it would come to roughing up a kid."

"It won't. He'll join us as soon as he sees the flash of a laser. I'll have him eating out of my hand within an hour of the takeover. Won't I, Brucey-boy? Ha-ha."

Bruce struggled to speak but could only manage an inaudible sigh. The voices faded as he drifted deeper into sleep.

Sometime later a voice again intruded into his dreamlike state.

"Bruce, I'm going to put you to sleep now."

"Don't kill me." Frightened, Bruce began to struggle. "I won't tell. Don't put me to sleep."

"It's just an injection, son. It's time to operate."

"No, Mitchell, I won't tell."

Then darkness descended and Bruce knew nothing else.

Bruce opened his eyes. His first thought was for his arm. He turned and looked at it, waggling his fingers. Everything seemed to be working. The delicate laser surgery had fastened his torn skin back together more neatly than old-fashioned sutures ever could have done. He moved the arm and felt a little pain, but it wasn't too bad.

He lay back and tried to relax, wondering why he felt so strange. Something nagged at the back of his memory. "You'd think I was scared to death," he thought wearily. He closed his eyes. Memories of the events just before the operation teased him. He could almost hear the voices fading in and out. Patiently, he forced himself to relax and concentrate. Bits and pieces of the conversation

began to fall into place. His uneasiness grew.

The swish of the door interrupted Bruce's thoughts. He looked up anxiously as Dr. Hanson entered the tiny sickbay. "Hello, son. Feeling better?"

"Yes sir."

Hanson smiled at him and spoke to the computer. "Dr. Hanson requesting personal read-out, vital signs, and recovery analysis for current subject, please. Visual display only." The computer whirred and then flashed the information on the main screen. Hanson frowned at it, and then glanced at the boy.

He didn't like the signs of stress he saw. Carefully, he checked the read-outs from the computer. The boy's adrenal level was high. He checked Bruce closely but could find no reason for the unusual stress.

"I think I'll keep you here for the off-watch, son," he said. "I sleep close by. The computer can tell me if you wake up or need anything."

"Please, sir, I don't want to sleep."

"If you need company, I can stay and go a few rounds of checkers or chess with you," Dr. Hanson said gently.

"No, I—" To his horror Bruce felt tears coming into his eyes. "No, I—" he tried again. And then he burst out crying. He was ashamed of it, but he couldn't stop.

"Steady, boy. You're all right." Dr. Hanson put his strong arms around Bruce. The doctor was a gray-haired man, ramrod straight with keen gray eyes that seemed to see everything. Instinctively, Bruce had liked and trusted him from the beginning of the voyage.

"Something's wrong," Bruce sobbed. "I can't remember what it is."

"You had a bad dream going under the anesthetic, son," the doctor said. "That's all. We call it *angst*. It's common out in space. You'll be all right."

"No, it wasn't a dream. It was more like . . ." The bits of over-heard conversation finally clicked in Bruce's mind. "Mutiny!" he exclaimed.

Suddenly Dr. Hanson's arms tightened and his hand closed over Bruce's mouth. "Be quiet!"

Bruce tensed. "Not Dr. Hanson, too," he groaned inwardly. He couldn't be in on it; he just couldn't!

"Don't use that word unless you mean it," Dr. Hanson said. "And if you mean it, don't say it so loudly."

He slowly took his hand away. "Now, tell me what you know."

There was no escaping the doctor. Bruce wanted to keep silent and bravely demand to see the captain first. But instead he heard himself saying, "Mitchell and Simmons thought I was asleep. They were talking about a takeover. They expected to have me join them as soon as I got scared enough."

Dr. Hanson didn't relax, and his hand was ready to clamp over Bruce's mouth again. "Well? Will you?"

Bruce could feel his lips trembling from fear, but he said, "I'm with the captain."

"Are you, boy?"

"If I get out of here alive, I will go straight to him and tell him." His words made him feel a little braver. A week ago he would not have believed it of himself.

"You're a spunky kid," Dr. Hanson said, his tense attitude relaxing a little. "But don't go to the captain. Mitchell would be on to you in a second. I'll get the captain down here. The crew would expect him to come and see you, your being so young. I'll tell him you're awake and a little pale. When he comes we'll tip him off. Wouldn't it be good to know who's in on it, though?"

"You're not with them, then?" Bruce asked, shakily.

Dr. Hanson suddenly laughed. "No, Bruce. But mutiny. . . ." He lowered his voice. "That word's poison out here. I was ready to break you of the habit of using it if you weren't serious about it. And if you were serious about it, I had to keep you quiet. No place for hysterics when a crew's in the middle of that dirty business."

Dr. Hanson flicked the intercom. "Captain to sickbay, please," he said.

In a couple of minutes Captain Denton walked in, bowing his head a little to avoid bumping it on the low bulkhead. The computer whirred and clicked as it arranged for more air conditioning in the tiny sickbay. The two grown men and the boy on the bed filled up the tiny room. Dr. Hanson murmured the story to Captain Denton.

"Mitchell and Simmons are both on duty," the captain muttered. "They traded shifts with two of the other men."

"Who else is up there?" Dr. Hanson asked.

"Job Hands—"

"I wouldn't trust him with my granny's glasses!"

"You don't think—" Captain Denton cut himself off as the sickbay door swished closed behind him. He and Dr. Hanson tugged at it, then punched the emergency number code on the computer panel.

"It won't let us out!" Dr. Hanson exclaimed.

"This is Captain Denton," the captain said to the computer. "Open the sickbay door."

"Access to sickbay denied," the computer said.

"This is Captain Denton, serial number 321836. Open the door. That's a direct order," Captain Denton said.

"Denied," the computer replied. "No access to sickbay without proper clearance. Your code number is obsolete."

"Somebody's been tampering with the computer," Dr. Hanson

said. "They must have altered the codes. Who—?"

"Anderson!" Captain Denton smacked his fist into the palm of his other hand. "Yesterday he told me that fuel was leaking into the protective covering that houses part of the computer's memory. I gave him five minutes to clean it, and sent Mitchell in with him."

"That's it then," Dr. Hanson said. "Simmons, Mitchell, Hands, and Anderson are in on it."

"And they're all on duty on the bridge," the captain said grimly. "They've planned carefully, all right."

"Well, we can do a little maneuvering on our own. I'm still the ship's doctor!" Dr. Hanson punched up a sequence on the computer and said, "This is Dr. Hanson. Run an emergency check for food poisoning among the crew. Alert to all subjects sleeping or unconscious."

"Why are you worried about food poisoning?" Bruce asked, puzzled.

"I'm not, son. But the computer will give me a chart of the layout of ship's personnel—where everybody is. I have a hunch that the mutineers probably just locked all the loyal men into the crew's cabin during the shift change a half-hour ago. Anybody not on shift was probably in his bunk."

In a moment a schematic map appeared on the computer's viewing screen. It showed red flashes in one of the cabins.

"Right you are," the captain said. "Six men are in their cabin —locked in, no doubt."

"The intercom's jammed," Dr. Hanson said.

"Simmons and Mitchell are going to make sure there's no communication between us and the other prisoners," Denton answered.

Dr. Hanson, suddenly noticing how cramped they all were, sat down next to Bruce. "So here we are," the doctor said.

"Couldn't have put it better myself," the captain agreed.

"What will they do to us?" Bruce asked.

"Maroon us, I reckon," Captain Denton replied. He leaned against the bulkhead and frowned in thought. "We're heading out to the research station on Jupiter 2, and I know there's nothing out there they could want. My guess is that the mutineers are gold hunters."

Dr. Hanson nodded. "And we're only an hour and a half away from Mars."

"Mars?" Bruce asked. "Is there gold on Mars?"

"Some people think so," Captain Denton replied. "Private scout ships have gone out and picked up traces of it. But there's been nothing official—scientific reports are against it."

"They would maroon us on Mars?" Bruce asked. "We can't live on Mars."

"Not on the surface, anyway," Dr. Hanson agreed. "But they'll let us suit up for it."

"Even so, that would give us only an extra day," Captain Denton said. "If they maroon us, we're goners."

Dr. Hanson looked at Bruce a little worriedly and nodded. Captain Denton saw the look.

"Bruce, why did you compete for the Jupiter trip?" he asked.

Bruce shrugged. "I don't have any family on earth," he replied. He hesitated, then said, "So I thought if I grew up on Jupiter

2 and learned how to work in a space research center, I could get a good rank in the Space Force, and then really be a part of something."

"Son, being a part of something means more than being good at it," Dr. Hanson began. But Captain Denton waved him to be quiet.

"Leave the boy alone, Doc," Captain Denton said. He looked at Bruce. "Now you're a part of something, Bruce. You didn't turn coward and run after Mitchell to beg him for anything. You did what was right. And now you're sitting here with the two of us— captured. Are you glad that you're with us?"

"I'd rather be here than with them," Bruce answered.

"Even if it means getting marooned on Mars?"

"It won't mean that. We can think of something."

Captain Denton nodded. "Well, it's our job to get you and the supplies to Jupiter 2. So we've got to get out of here. Any ideas?"

"See if we can short-circuit the wiring that's keeping the door closed," Dr. Hanson suggested. "We can use some of my laser surgical tools to cut into the paneling."

"Possibly." Captain Denton glanced at Bruce. "Anything you have to say to that?"

Bruce's heart jumped a little bit at being included in the planning. "Won't the computer alert somebody?"

"Perhaps. But we might be able to get out before they do anything especially nasty—like cut off the air in here."

"We could try to cut our way through the door itself," Dr. Hanson said.

"Could we have a back-up plan, just in case?" Bruce asked.

Captain Denton looked at him. "Like what?"

Bruce nodded at the trash chute. "Open that for a couple of minutes and let some air get into it. I'm small enough to climb through it. I can crawl up the trash chute and get anything you need."

For a minute both men were silent. Then the doctor whistled through his teeth. Captain Denton looked thoughtful. "If we could get to the loyal men—but we don't have any weapons."

"I've got two laser pistols up in a hatch in the bulkhead," Dr.

Hanson offered. "Not much for eight men." He glanced around.

"On the other hand—" Denton began.

"What?" Dr. Hanson asked. Bruce's heart was beating hard.

"You know—ether, ammonia, and iodine—chemicals in the right combinations—"

"Explosives!" Hanson exclaimed. "I should've thought of that right away."

Dr. Hanson dropped to the floor and crawled under the fold-up bed. Bruce heard him slide back a cupboard door in the wall. "Most of my chemicals are stored down here in rubber compartments," he said with a grunt. "Give me a hand, will you?"

Both of them helped him haul out several tubes of medicines. While the doctor mixed his chemicals, using the bed as a table, Captain Denton outlined his plan.

"You got sleeping gas, Doc?" he asked.

"Good old nitrous oxide," Dr. Hanson replied. "Otherwise known as laughing gas. Enough of it should put them to sleep eventually, before they get too excited about orbiting around Mars. But we ought to blast them with it soon, before we come closer to Mars, because nothing fights sleep in a man like greed."

"How do we channel the gas to the bridge?" the captain asked.

"Put it in the humidifier," the doctor answered. "A room the size of the bridge has its own humidifying tank. That way we can knock them all out."

Captain Denton nodded. "Here, son," he said, buckling a holster around Bruce. "You know how to use a laser pistol?"

"Yes sir."

"Don't hesitate to use it if you have to—if some of the mutineers catch you."

"Okay."

The doctor held up six gauze bundles, three in each hand. "These packets explode on impact—so don't trip." He gently pushed them into the pockets of Bruce's jumpsuit. Finally he handed the pressurized canister of sleeping gas to the boy.

"Climb over to the air-conditioning units and put the sleeping gas in the humidifier," Captain Denton said. "First, empty the water. You might flood some of the crawlspace, but it shouldn't damage anything. Then go to the crew's cabin and try to get in. Cut your way out from there with the laser. We'll do the same here and meet you at the bridge exactly half an hour from now. By then all those boys should be sleeping."

"Wait," Dr. Hanson said. "What if somebody jettisons the trash?"

Bruce stopped. He hadn't thought of that.

Captain Denton looked away. "You're right. They might suspect our plan. They know we've got Bruce." He glanced at Bruce. "We'll try something else. If Simmons and Mitchell are planning to maroon us, they wouldn't have any qualms about jettisoning you out into space."

"But Captain Denton," Bruce exclaimed. "We'll all die anyway if I don't try it!" He stooped down and opened the trash chute door, letting some air out into the stagnant, dirty trash tunnel. He was glad there were no rats or bugs in space. The first puff of air from the chute sent out a filthy smell. Bruce's eyes watered. "Whew!"

Captain Denton put a restraining hand on his shoulder. "Son, this is no game. You could be killed."

Bruce stood up. "I know." He looked down. "But when we were all planning it, I—" How could he explain it to Captain Denton about how much he wanted to try it, even if it failed, even if he got thrust out into space? "You see I never did anything like—I mean, I never really had friends before and I—" Then he hit on the answer. "You'd do it yourself if you could fit!"

Captain Denton nodded. "But I'm the captain."

"We'll all get killed if I don't. It would just be a matter of time," he pleaded.

"The boy's right about that," Dr. Hanson observed.

Captain Denton relented. "All right. Go ahead then." He thrust out his hand. "Remember, you have thirty minutes. Doc and I will cut a way out of here."

Bruce shook hands with him, then with Hanson. "Wait a second," Hanson said. He opened a cabinet and pulled out an aerosol can. "The pain killer I injected into your hand should keep it from hurting, but this might help, too." He sprayed a silky, gummy substance onto Bruce's hand. In an instant the substance hardened into a tough, rubberlike glove. "That'll keep out infection," Hanson said.

Bruce checked his equipment again, then crawled into the tunnel.

The tunnel was narrow, like a thin tube, just wide enough for a small boy to shinny through, squelching his way through a swamp of discarded print-outs,

sour milk, water, and coffee, sodden bits of unused soap, leftover food, and plain old dirt that clung to the walls.

Clutching the canister in one hand, the boy bellied his way through the waves of trash. It billowed around him so that in places he had to keep his hands pressed under him instead of up by his shoulders. Even then his head and back would scrape the roof. There was no turning around in here—no going back. He wondered what would happen if he couldn't force his way out a trash chute.

He pushed himself through a mountain of paper and saw light gleaming ahead. It was the mess trash chute. He got up to it and forced it open with his good hand. Nobody was in the mess hall.

The tunnel was too narrow for him to bring his knees up to climb out. He pulled himself through with his hand and elbow. Don't trip, Dr. Hanson had warned him. If he fell it would be the end of him. Slowly he eased through the opening until his hands could reach the floor. Then he crawled out on both hands and scrambled with his feet until he was out of the tunnel. Standing up, he made his way to the air-conditioning maintenance area.

The plan went without a hitch. Bruce let out the water in the humidifier, deposited the gas canister inside, and activated it.

Noiselessly, he returned to the trash chute and pulled on the door. Nothing happened. He yanked again, then braced both feet against the wall, grabbed the

stubborn handles with both hands, and pulled for all he was worth. He thought his heart would crack from the strain.

The computer's voice interrupted him. "Please wait until trash disposal is completed. Trash chute depressurized during disposal."

He almost fell to the floor, stunned, barely catching himself on his feet. If he had entered the tube a moment earlier, he would be floating out in space now.

"Who jettisoned it?" he wondered. "Was it somebody who knew I was in there?"

Maybe Dr. Hanson really was a mutineer! He still had a laser pistol of his own. Had he used it on the unwitting captain and then jettisoned the trash?

Bruce swallowed and listened to the roar in the chute. Suddenly the noise ceased and the computer said, "Trash disposal complete. Tube sealed."

"Maybe," he thought, "Mitchell had been listening through the intercoms." If so, he'd be on his way to the humidifiers to get the gas out. On the other hand, if Dr. Hanson were a mutineer, he might keep jettisoning the trash to make sure Bruce was out of the way, because he knew that Bruce had a laser pistol.

What could he do? Bruce looked around the room, knowing that escape by any other way was useless.

"Besides," he told himself. "I don't know if Dr. Hanson's in on it, and I gave my word to get to the other men and free them. There's no other way." He pulled open the trash chute door and waited for air to seep into the tunnel.

"At least it's clean this time," he told himself. He gripped the rim of the chute and climbed in.

Soon he was squirming his way to the crew's cabin.

He reached it in no time and banged on the door, panting with relief and fear.

"I must have been wrong about Dr. Hanson," he thought. "Maybe we can still save the ship, and I'll make it to Jupiter 2." But for some reason the thought of Jupiter 2 disturbed him, and he pushed it out of his mind.

There was a scrabbling noise, and then the hatch opened. All he could see were legs, and then one of the men, Finelli, bent down.

"Hey, it's Bruce. Heave to, somebody. Give me a hand." The six men hauled him out and grouped around him, talking all at once.

"Well, wasn't that smart?"

"Good thinking, son. Who'd have thought of it?"

"You can find the captain for us."

Lieutenant Finelli's face went white. "We jettisoned that trash not three minutes ago so one of us could try to squeeze out through the tube! You might have been killed!"

The shock of relief made Bruce's knees sag. Jettisoning the trash had been an accident! "The captain's in sickbay," Bruce said. He pushed his thoughts away and quickly outlined the plan, adding, "The captain gave me thirty minutes to put the gas in place, find you, and get to the bridge."

"That probably leaves us fifteen minutes," Finelli said. "Hand out the explosives. Who's an engineer here? Let's figure out how to blow out the door with that laser pistol. You there, help clean Bruce off."

It took fourteen and a half minutes to cut a way through the door. Just as they emerged, the captain and the doctor were coming up the narrow, tubelike hallway.

"The computer ran a scan for me," Dr. Hanson said. "Everybody's gone nighty-night on the bridge. Let's go tuck them in, shall we?"

After the sleeping mutineers had been confined to the brig, Bruce thought the trip would continue as planned. But after the next watch he was called to Captain Denton's quarters.

"Come in, Bruce."

Bruce stepped into the captain's cabin. It was fairly roomy, considering the size of the ship itself. There was a bed, a desk, and some wall hangings. Captain Denton was at the desk. He turned his small swivel chair to face the boy. "Come here, son."

Bruce stepped closer. Even in his chair, Captain Denton was still taller than Bruce.

Suddenly Bruce swallowed hard. Now he knew that he didn't want to go to Jupiter 2, with its scientists and technicians who would poke him and ask him questions and examine him and feed him carefully and record everything about him. He didn't want to be a new kid again. He wanted to stay with Captain Denton and Dr. Hanson and live aboard the Tal-Omega.

"You've got your uniform back into good shape, I see."

"Yes sir."

Captain Denton's keen eyes held Bruce's attention. "Anybody tell you that we've aborted the mission to Jupiter 2?"

Bruce jumped a little. "No, sir."

"Can't make it now that we're short-handed this way. We've turned around—heading back to Earth for a new crew before going out again. The Space Force will detour a freighter to get supplies to Jupiter 2."

Bruce nodded a little. He felt relieved, but he could sense that Captain Denton had more to tell him.

"I know of a school," the captain continued, "that trains people for space flight. Would you like to join the Space Force? I'll show you the school when we get back to Earth."

"Will they accept me?" Bruce asked, his eyes shining.

"Well, I've sent my report about the mutiny on to Earth. You're big news now—a hero. Sure, the Space Force would take you. And I'll help you all I can."

"What about Jupiter 2?" Bruce asked.

"There are other kids who want to go, Bruce. A replacement will be sent out on the next flight."

"Okay. I—I mean, thank you." Bruce stumbled over the words. Suddenly he thrust out his hand to the captain. "Thank you very much."

Captain Denton smiled and shook his hand with a firm, hard shake. "You're welcome."

Skill Lesson:
Card Catalog

The library is a wonderful place to visit, but you may not be getting the full benefit from it if you don't know how to use one of its main resource tools—the card catalog.

The name of every book in the library will appear on at least two cards in the card catalog: once by its title and once by its author. Nonfiction books are also listed on at least one subject card in addition to their title and author cards. The drawers are labeled to tell which part of the alphabet you can find in each. Any book you want to find in the library will be there.

Suppose after reading "The Tal-Omega," you wanted to read a book that would tell you more about space travel. You don't know a title or author; all you know is the subject you're interested in. So you look up *space travel* in the card catalog under *S.* If your library uses the Dewey Decimal system, you might see a card that looks like this:

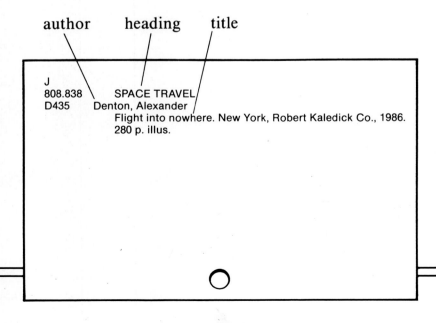

Once you've found the book you want in the card catalog, write down the little numbers and letters in the upper left-hand corner of the card. Those are called the *call numbers.* In a library organized by the Dewey Decimal system, the books are on the shelves in numerical order; so you should be able to find the book you need.

If you read the book by Mr. Denton and liked it, you might want to read some other books by him. Then you would look up the name *Denton* in the card catalog. And if you recommended the book *Flight into Nowhere* to a friend, he would look up the title of the book under the initial letter, *F.*

When a book is listed by subject, the subject heading is in all capital letters. That way you can tell at a glance the difference between subject cards and title or author cards. This is what the title and author cards for *Flight into Nowhere* would look like:

```
J
808.838      Flight into nowhere
D435         Denton, Alexander
             Flight into nowhere. New York, Robert Kaledick Co., 1986.
             280 p. illus.
```

```
J
808.838
D435         Denton, Alexander
             Flight into nowhere. New York, Robert Kaledick Co., 1986.
             280 p. illus.
```

If your library's card catalog system is on a computer, the librarian will show you how to use it. The methods to follow are still the same.

Remember when you use the library that the card catalog is there to help you. If you don't understand something you look up there, you can always ask the librarian to help you. But if you go to the library regularly and practice using the card catalog often, soon you won't need any help—you'll be a professional!

The Surprise

Dick Peck

"That's another one for me!"

Sometimes after dinner on a spring night, the family would sit on the front porch and watch the street. Tonight only Kris and Dad were there. To pass time, they'd each pick a color and see who could first spot ten cars of that color. The first one to reach ten won the game.

"How many is that?" Dad asked.

"Nine," said Kris.

"I knew I shouldn't have picked brown," Dad answered.

"But you did! I gave you your choice and you picked brown. You know white always wins," she grinned contentedly.

It was true. Blue or white would almost always win. Kris had learned never to pick gray or brown.

"You haven't won yet," Dad said. "You need one more car."

"Ten!" she shouted, as a white Ford swept by.

"Aw, that car wasn't white. That was beige," he protested.

"No, Dad. It was just dirty. No use trying to get out of it—you lost."

"Okay, Missy. I'll get some lemonade for us. You keep watching for the wrecker."

Dad went inside while Kris peered down the street, looking for Mom and Bob to come back. She couldn't help feeling just a little bit glad that Bob had to go to a club meeting tonight. That way she could have Dad to herself. She knew Dad loved her, but he and Bob had gotten interested in old cars together and were always talking about them. She just couldn't. No matter how hard she tried to like them, cars bored her. She sighed and glanced up at the eaves of their old white house.

"It's a nice house," Kris thought. "We never had a house all to ourselves before. Now we even have our own yard—a big

150

yard—and an attic." When they moved in, Dad said that there might even be a million dollars stashed in the attic. "Who knows," he had said, "it's an old, old house." But dads were always joking.

"Here's your lemonade, Misskit." Dad interrupted her thoughts, holding open the screen with the toe of his shoe as he juggled two big glasses of ice and the pitcher of lemonade.

Kris had more names than she could remember. Her real name was Mercedes Kirsten, and Mom called her Kris. But Dad always had special names for her— "Mouse" or "Missy" or sometimes "Misskit," a combination of "Missy" and "Kitten." It was embarrassing sometimes. Once he had called her "Misskit" right in front of her friends, and Lanette thought he'd said "biscuit"! It took the longest time to explain to Lanette that Dad *hadn't* called her a biscuit.

When Mom and Bob got home, they both sat on the front porch with Dad and Kris. "The wrecker hasn't come with the car yet, has it, Dad?" Bob asked. "Great! I want to see it pull in."

Dad and Bob started talking gleefully about the old convertible the wrecker would be bringing. Mom joined in occasionally. She liked cars, too—for Dad's sake, anyway. Kris sighed.

"Will the wrecker driver put the car in the front yard?" she wondered. She remembered seeing cars in front yards when her family would go driving in the country on warm summer nights. Dad would keep all the windows down and look for pockets of cool air in the valleys between hills outside the town where they lived. He always told them how his family used to do that when he was little.

But Dad said that his family had had a convertible. Kris had seen a convertible once or twice. She'd never ridden in one, though. "They look wonderful," she thought, "but your hair would get pretty messy with the top down." She wasn't sure she liked that part, but Dad had said it would be fun. "Worth messed-up hair," he'd promised.

Dad said the wrecker would bring two cars tonight if the men could get them here before dark. One would be a convertible, the other one "a parts car," as Dad called it. They'd get the extra parts from it they needed to repair the convertible, he said. But if the men couldn't get both cars here by dark, they'd have to bring the second car on Monday because Dad wouldn't do business on

Sunday. It didn't matter much to Kris, since both cars were old anyway.

"I want to see this convertible before I ride anywhere," Kris thought. Dad's description didn't sound like the beautiful convertibles she had seen. Those were shiny and new-looking. Her grandfather said that he might buy her one someday, but Dad had just smiled.

She watched more cars pass. For the third or fourth time that day, she thought of camp. Last year almost all the girls in her Sunday school class had gone to camp and shared a cabin. They talked about it all the time. Their cabin had taken first place in all the team competitions—the canoe races, softball games, relay races, even the costume party. For a moment her mind wandered longingly to water-balloon fights and Indian raids. But Mom and Dad had decided that this summer they should do things as a family and not spend so much money going their separate ways.

"Hey, I see it coming!" Bob yelled.

Sure enough, a huge blue wrecker was coming down the street, signaling to turn at their corner. Kris couldn't see what was behind it, but whatever it was, it was making a horrible noise. "Probably the car it's towing has a bad wheel bearing," Dad said.

When the wrecker turned and pulled up beside their fence, Kris's heart sank. It was a convertible all right, but the top was rotten and part of it had blown backward from the wind. Even worse, the wheels and the bottom of the fenders were covered with red clay. Where in the *world* had Dad found it?

"Dad," she exclaimed, "what is that thing? Why did you ever buy such an ugly car?"

"It'll be great, Missy. Don't worry. We'll fix it all up and ride in the country. You just wait. You'll love it. Just wait!"

There was no stopping them. Dad and Bob were already out by the fence, pointing to the back yard. "Well, at least my friends won't see it lying in the front yard," she thought. "But honestly, what will the other car look like? Maybe the wrecker won't bring it."

Dad motioned for Kris and Mom to follow as he and Bob went into the back yard. Kris could only hear a whirring sound until she rounded the corner of the house, just in time to see the wrecker drop the car in the corner of the backyard.

"Dad, that's the garden!" she squealed, as the front wheels of the convertible hit the ground in a cloud of dust.

"It'll be all right. We weren't much good at gardening anyway. Besides, we have to keep the car away from the street. You don't want somebody to steal it, do you?"

If that was a joke, Kris didn't laugh. Mom had said it would take a lot of money to fix the old car up, and Kris wanted to go to camp. No matter how nice Dad was, this was too much! Dumping ice from her glass into the yard, Kris headed for the house.

The other car arrived about dark. Dad had the wrecker driver park it in the garden next to the convertible. Kris could just barely see them from her window. She could see Dad in the headlights of the wrecker, handing the driver some money. "Two ugly cars in the garden," she thought. "I think I'd be happy for Dad to grow lima beans again if only those cars were gone!"

In the days that followed, things only got worse. Instead of playing count-the-cars or doing something fun, Dad and Bob were always poking around those cars in the garden. And it seemed certain she would not be going to camp. Mom, Dad, and Bob kept talking about the convertible as though broken-down old cars were the best things in the world.

"Won't be long now, Missy," was all Dad would say. "We'll have ourselves a convertible. In fact, tomorrow after school, you can help. You and Bob can take the seats out of the convertible so we can get them to the upholstery shop. Bob will know how they're fastened down, but he'll need you to help."

When school was out the next day, Kris walked with Lanette to her street, but when she turned down the street toward home she thought about the car-seat task Dad had planned for her. She kicked at a stone on the sidewalk as she walked. "Help your brother," she thought. "Why, that car even smells! It must have gotten moldy from the rain coming in the holes in the top. There can't be anything in it worth saving, much less those grubby old seats."

Worse still, Lanette had teased her. "What are those things in your garden?" she said. "Are you going to have a junkyard?"

As Kris passed the edge of her yard, she heard Bob's voice. "Hey, Kris! What took you so long?"

"I'm coming, I'm coming! Can't you see? If Dad hadn't asked me to help you, there's no way I'd touch that smelly thing."

"Oh, come on! I've almost got the seats loose, and I need you to help lift them out," Bob answered.

With a sigh, Kris pushed open the back door of their house. At least she'd change clothes; if she had to crawl around inside that car she wasn't going to do it in a nice dress.

The convertible had two front seats, "bucket seats," Dad called them. Bob had loosened all the bolts by the time she got outside again. Before long, she found herself sitting on the floor behind the driver's seat—trying to tip it forward enough for Bob to get a hand under the edge to lift it out.

"Push, Kris, push!"

"I'm pushing! It won't tip, Bob."

"It will. Push harder!"

It did. And as it tipped, Kris saw the envelope.

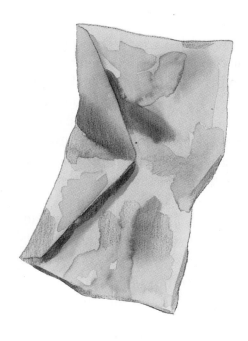

Bob didn't see it. He couldn't. The seat was between him and the floor of the car. He had his hands full just carrying the old seat to their shed near the house.

Kris glanced toward the house and then back to the envelope. "What's in it?" she wondered. She remembered how Dad had said there might be a million dollars hidden in the attic. This car wasn't an attic, but it was just as old and junky as one. The envelope might be a good surprise to Dad. She was tired of being left out of all the family talk. It would be nice to really surprise him with something *she* had found in the car.

Bob reached the shed. There was no time to think. If it were going to be *her* surprise for Dad, she would have to act now. Quickly, she stuffed the envelope through a hole in the carpet where the seat had been. The carpet was thin and smelled musty. She could slide the envelope far enough under so that it made only a little lump. Bob wouldn't notice, would he?

"Aw, Kris, you could have had that other seat out by now," Bob said as he approached. "At least try to be some help." The seat Bob had carried to the shed was heavy and had dug into his hands. He opened and closed his fists, trying to make the red marks go away. He paid no attention to the lump in the old car's carpet. Kris didn't say much as she helped him remove the second seat.

Supper seemed to take forever that night. Even while Kris was helping Mom wash the dishes, she couldn't take her mind off that envelope. "It's probably just letters, but maybe they'll be interesting," Kris thought. Dad always said that he liked interesting old stuff. Maybe she could surprise him after work tomorrow. If only she could get out to the car again for a look.

Wiping her hands on the towel, she glanced into the living room. Dad was reading the newspaper.

She carefully walked down the hall and toward the back of the house. Was Bob in his room? He ought to be studying. His door was half-closed, blocking her view of his desk. "No point asking if he's in there," she thought. "He might come out. Go out now, before Dad wants to have family prayer time."

Quietly opening the back door, she checked to see if Bob might be outside kicking his soccer ball. But there was no one in the back yard. Kris shot across

the lawn between the house and the garden. "Don't squeak. Please don't squeak!" she thought as she gently tugged at the convertible's door.

With a quick look to the house, she worked her hand through the hole in the carpet. The envelope was still there! Tugging at its corner, she tried to wiggle it out through the hole.

"Come on, come on . . . Oh, no!"

The envelope had ripped, and when she pulled her hand back through the hole, Kris was holding a one-hundred dollar bill. "*Money!* There *is* money in the envelope! It's just like Dad said about the attic. The old car had money hidden in the envelope!" But what was the white powder on the money? And there was more powder in the envelope.

"Missy, are you out there?" Dad called. Kris's heart jumped.

What now? What should she do with the money? It would be a good surprise for Dad—but it was almost the amount she needed for camp, too! If she gave it to Dad, maybe he would finish working on those junky cars sooner so that she and Dad could have fun together again. But if she gave it to him and he did spend it on the cars, there would still be no camp. If she could just have Dad to herself and explain all the reasons why she wanted to go to camp. Even her Sunday school teacher had urged her to go.

"Find your brother and let's have our family prayer time before it gets late," Dad said from the house. "You need to finish your studying."

"Later," she thought. "I'll wait and give it to him later." She tucked the envelope in her pocket. "Coming, Dad!" she shouted, as she ran toward the house.

It was difficult for Kris to concentrate during the family Bible study. She liked the Old Testament, particularly Joshua 6, where her family had been reading about God's helping Israel conquer Jericho. But several times her hand felt for the envelope—just to be sure it was still in her pocket. "Still there," she thought, "it's still there." Dad's voice seemed to be far away. What was he saying about something hidden in a tent?

"Kris . . . ," Dad repeated, "are you still with us? I asked what you would do in a situation like Joshua faced."

"I'm sorry, Dad," Kris blushed. She was concentrating now, but she had no idea what the rest of the family was discussing in this passage.

"Would you ask me again?" she said sheepishly.

"We're in chapter seven now. What would you do if you were in a situation like the one Joshua was in?" Dad asked. "Someone Joshua trusted, someone who fought with him at Jericho, had disagreed with God's plan. He had taken things from Jericho and hid them. What happened at the next battle?"

"They lost it, Dad," she said. "And the man who had hid the silver and gold got everybody else into trouble."

Kris thought again about the money. She wanted to tell Dad about it. Should she tell him now? "This isn't the right time," she thought. "How can I just blurt out my whole idea in the middle of our family prayer time?"

"Let's pray and then off with you two to finish your homework." It was hard for Kris to pray. Her mind kept going back to the envelope.

Later it was almost impossible for her to concentrate on her studies. She started back down the stairs to talk to Dad. She heard Mom and Dad talking seriously and knew that this would not be the right time to get her way with Dad about money and camp. Later, as she drifted off to sleep, the thought nagged her. "I'll find a time tomorrow. I really will tell him . . . ," she murmured.

Tomorrow passed and so did the next day. Kris couldn't find what seemed like the right time to tell Dad about the money. But keeping it a secret made her feel funny. Now it was uncomfortable to be around her parents. In fact, when Dad looked at her at dinner and asked why she was so quiet, Kris just wanted to get away—somewhere, anywhere—away from his eyes.

A week passed. As Kris walked home from school, she said to herself, "I've got to talk to him, but how? I'll just ask him to stop work on that car and take a walk with me or something."

Bob called to her from the back yard. "Kris, have you heard?" he shouted.

"Heard what? Anyway, how could I hear anything—I've been in school all day, and then at orchestra rehearsal!" She didn't really mean to answer her brother so harshly, but it seemed that just about everything was going wrong and now he was asking dumb questions.

"Mom said the police were coming over after Dad gets off work," Bob answered. "Dad called Captain Wells. It's something about the cars. What do you think it is?"

Suddenly, it was as if her heart froze. Kris didn't feel like that very often. Once or twice before, maybe, when she had done something very wrong and she knew it.

What had Dad done? He *wouldn't* call the police just to talk to her? Captain Wells was Dad's friend. Sometimes they went shooting together at the gun club. But did Dad know about the money? Why would he call the police if he did? Did he think someone else had taken it? How could she ever explain she had just been keeping it—looking for the right time to tell him?

She could hardly walk to the house. There was no getting around it now. She had to talk to Dad before the police came.

"Bob, if you see Dad, I've got to talk to him," she said.

"What for?" Bob asked.

"I can't tell you. I've just got to talk to him—now. I'm going in; so you tell him if you see him first. Tell him it's important."

It wasn't much later before Dad came into her room.

"Hi, Mouse. Bob said you wanted to see me. What is it?"

It was hard to talk. Her throat hurt and there were tears in her eyes. She didn't want to cry, but she wasn't sure she could do anything about it.

"Dad, it's the money. I didn't mean to keep it—I *really* didn't. You've got to believe me! I wanted to go to camp so badly! I was waiting for the right time so that I could talk you into letting me go. I wouldn't steal the money—I wouldn't . . ."

"Wait, Missy, wait!" Dad interrupted. "What are you saying? I don't know anything about money or camp."

"The money! Didn't you know I have the money? Isn't that why

you called Captain Wells? I found it under the seat of the convertible! And I thought . . . that maybe it would be money for me to go to camp this summer . . . but I wouldn't have kept it. I just couldn't find a good time to tell you."

"Kris." Dad said it gravely, in the serious, calm voice he used whenever she was in trouble. "Where is the money? Show me what you're talking about,"

Kris went to her dresser, opened a drawer, and removed the envelope. It was still folded the way she had put it in her pocket the night she found it.

As Dad opened the envelope, the money fell out. It fell through the part of the end that had ripped when she pulled it out of the convertible, the night she had hidden it from Bob. Some powder fell out, too, with the money.

"Where did you find this?" Dad asked. It worried Kris when Dad didn't use her special names. He didn't call her "Misskit" or "Mouse" if he was upset.

"It was under the seat. When Bob and I took out the seats it was just lying there. And then I hid it. First, I wanted to surprise you. But then . . . when I found the $100 in it I thought that it was God answering my prayers about camp. I'm sorry, Dad. I really am sorry."

She was still standing by the dresser. Dad looked as if he were thinking, but what was he thinking?

"Come over here, Missy," he finally said. "We need to talk. Let's sit down for a minute."

"Do you remember the story of Achan?" he asked. "We talked about him one evening last week."

"Dad, I remember! It was the same night I found the money, but *honestly,* I didn't mean to keep it. I didn't!"

"I know that. I believe you. Achan wanted something for himself that God didn't want him to have. There was nothing evil about what he hid—it was his disobedience and refusal to accept what God wanted for him. Sometimes we want things that look good to us and not what God wants for us. But do you remember that by Achan's hiding those things in his tent, he brought danger to the whole nation. What did we read? When Israel went to fight Ai, the men of Israel were defeated and many were killed. Achan's sin had an effect he hadn't expected," Dad explained.

"Now," he continued, "Did you realize that by hiding this envelope you not only showed God your rebellion about your parents' decision but you also brought danger to yourself? And did you know that you could have endangered the family?"

"No, I didn't!" Kris answered. "I didn't, Dad. You've got to believe me. But why are the police coming? Bob said you called Captain Wells!"

"I did—and I do believe you, Mouse, but let me explain. While I was working on the convertible, I found a letter in the glove compartment. Apparently the man who owned the car before had been in trouble. The letter was from his parole board. Do you know what a parole board is?" Dad asked.

"I think it's something like being on probation, isn't it? Don't they check up on people who have gotten out of jail?"

"That's right," he said. "And this man hadn't been meeting with the parole board when he was supposed to meet with them. And do you know what else?"

"No," Kris answered.

"Well, I found some other things in the car, under the seats, that made me think that either the man who owned the car or his friends may have been using some kind of drugs."

"I missed the envelope you found," Dad continued, "but the powder could have been very, very dangerous. If you had been curious about it and tried to sniff it or taste it, it could have made you sick—or worse. I'm thankful you didn't try it."

"But you put yourself in a dangerous position. And because it's illegal for us to even possess certain drugs, you endangered the family's reputation by not reporting what you had found. That's one reason I called Captain Wells. He's a friend, but we needed for him to know that we weren't hiding drugs in these cars. Think of what that would do to our testimony for the Lord, if someone thought we had put that envelope in the convertible."

"I'm sorry, Dad. I really am sorry."

"I know you are, Mouse, but you made the wrong choice this time. I'm just thankful you weren't hurt. And I appreciate your telling me before Captain Wells arrived."

When the patrol car stopped in the driveway, Kris could see Dad talking with Captain Wells. Dad gave the officer that was with Captain Wells the envelope with the money and what little powder hadn't spilled out. They talked for a while after that, before the men got back in the patrol car and drove away.

Kris looked out her window. Dad was still standing in the driveway. It looked as if he were thinking, or maybe praying. Kris turned and sat down on the edge of her bed.

"Heavenly Father," she prayed. "I didn't even think of it, but I've sinned against you too. I didn't accept my parents' decision about my summer and I tried to get my own way. Please forgive me. I know I've disappointed You, and Dad. My sin did find me out. Forgive me and help me try not to work out my own way to get what I want. Forgive me for deceiving my parents by hiding the money. I pray in Jesus' name, Amen."

Kris didn't go to camp that summer.

Not being allowed to go had been hard, but not as hard as she had thought. The family had gone biking several times, once for almost thirty miles! And Dad had taught her how to play tennis. It had been a good summer. Bob and Dad finished their work on the convertible and then called a junkyard to come tow away the parts car (or what was left of it after they had used so many parts to fix the convertible). The garden was empty now. Kris knew the lima beans would be back next summer. And Dad had said, "Maybe next summer we'll be able to take you and Lanette to camp in the new car." Kris wasn't sure her friend would want to ride in their new car.

Dad had taken the convertible to a paint shop more than a month ago. Summer was almost over now and they still hadn't had a ride in the country—when Dad and Bob had finished with the car, it still looked ugly. They had sprayed gray stuff on it ("primer," they called it), and it looked like an ugly, gray tank.

The breeze through the bedroom window was wonderful—warm, soft air—just enough to move her curtains. Kris closed her eyes and thought about what it would be like to be canoeing at summer camp. She thought about the Indian games her friends would be playing and the campfire she'd heard so much about.

Her mind was far away when she heard the horn in the driveway. In fact, she wasn't sure whether she had really heard a horn until she turned and looked. When she did, she could hardly believe her eyes!

"The convertible!" Kris was outside almost before Dad had turned off the engine.

The car was dark green now, a beautiful deep green. The top was down and she could see the seats. They were covered in a soft, tan leather. The carpet was new and the holes that she remembered were gone. And the tires looked brand new, with shiny wheels.

"What do you think, Misskit?" Dad asked.

"It's *beautiful*!" she said. "Beautiful! I never thought it would look so good. Oh, Dad— can we take Lanette along for the first ride?"

"I think so," he answered. "I'll tell you what," Dad continued. "What if I round up Mom and Bob, while you call Lanette? Then we'll head out into the country and look for a pocket of cool air, down in one of the valleys between the hills. Maybe on the way back we'll stop for an ice cream cone."

"That would be great! It'll just take a minute. Let me call Lanette," she said. She started toward the house and then stopped, turning to him.

"Dad, thanks. Thanks for *everything.*"

"You're welcome, Misskit."

With a smile, and one last glance at the car, she turned again and ran toward the house.

Fees of Indenture

Andy Thomson

"Here, man, throw that bundle down there," Captain Taylor said, turning from the ship's clerk. He thrust his hands into his breeches pockets and spread his elbows out wide.

"Aye, sir," the sailor said, dropping a bundle of straw and rags onto the dock. The rags stirred feebly and then were still again.

The captain eyed the bundle distrustfully. "The little wench is alive?"

The sailor looked down. The rags and straw nearly hid the girl, but he saw that she was breathing. "For a while, Captain."

"We've sold all the hardy folk," the clerk put in. "You'll take a loss on her and those four others aboard with the fever."

"Ah, that's a triple loss on her, then—both parents died aboard. I wish I had never laid eyes on such a miserable wench. Four times I had her whipped. Four times! And now she gets revenge by dying on my hands—No!" he exclaimed suddenly as his eyes caught sight of one of the townsmen. "See that goodman over there? Call him over here." The captain thrust his sturdy pipe stem into his teeth. He had snatched profit from the grip of loss before. Thoughtfully, he stroked the edge of his frock coat between his thumb and forefinger. The clerk brought the goodman with him across the wooden slats of the dock.

"Nay sir, nay. I have enough," the man said. "Not for any price will I take another, nor a sick one at that. I have enough servants."

"See here what a bargain that one yonder might be. She has the price of both parents' indentures on her bill, yet I would release her to you for only half of her own rate," the captain insisted. "That's a tenth of what I could ask."

"And I could pay the burial and church fees? Many thanks, but no," the man replied.

"Oh come, friend, she may yet recover, now that she's on blessed land."

"No, *friend,* " the man said, accenting the last word. "You've taken loss on the wench I see, but I know you. You will still try to stuff a few more coins in your pocket while leaving burial fees to another. Besides," and he nodded back to the bundle. "There might be a buyer for you. The Widow Bradbury."

The captain saw that a gray-haired woman was kneeling by the pallet of straw, examining the feverish girl. The town physician, fresh off the ship from examining the other indentured servants, was standing by her.

"Why, the little girl would make a pleasant companion," the

captain began, wheedling. The physician looked up sternly.

"You still mean to sell her?"

"Of course."

"Think of the mercy of God, sir, and release her. The girl's more dead than alive. Let the Widow take her. She at least will bear the burial costs if it comes to that."

"Doctor, you would beggar me. Volunteer your own goods to the service of the Lord, not mine," the captain replied smoothly. "I have my own tender little ones at home, dependent upon my business ventures abroad, and—"

"Enough of those lies, man."

The woman looked up. "I will buy her," she said, preventing the doctor from arguing any further. "How much do you ask?"

"He wants more than you have, good lady," the doctor interrupted.

"There are my savings, doctor," she said softly.

"What? Make yourself *and* the girl destitute?"

"Half her rate, madam," the captain said quickly. "It's a fair deal, for I'm in a hurry to leave port, and I am not completely heartless."

"Only mostly," the doctor added under his breath.

"I haven't got that much," the Widow said. "Not readily available."

"Ah well, more's the pity. She would have made a fine—"

"She'll only die if you keep her," the woman said. By now she had one arm under the girl's head. "What profit would that be?"

"No despair," he answered quickly, winking to the clerk. "I can take some money from you now in earnest. If the girl lives, then you may pay me when I return in two months. If you haven't the money then, I will take her off your hands and resell her."

She nodded, and the clerk wrote down the transaction.

"I doubt him, madam," the doctor whispered, picking the child up off the straw and rags. "Bear in mind that he lives off broken hearts."

The captain pretended that he hadn't heard it, but he smiled. Soft, sentimental people like the Widow Bradbury were just the people to buy up these little ones. No doubt within two months she would have restored the girl to her full worth, and he would manage to regain his losses.

"Her name is Elizabeth," he said.

It was night when Elizabeth awoke. She had been washed and her hair had been cut close because of the fever and the vermin from the straw. But she didn't feel these comforts, only the heavy warmth of a quilt over her, and she saw that the walls were straight, not bowed. The lamplight flickered, but it did not bob up and down. She was on land. Land.

"The ship—" she began. "My mother—"

"Poor girl. Rest. The ship is gone from port by now," a voice said. It was a woman's voice. "Your parents are in God's hands now and He has brought you into mine."

Her eyes closed and she fell asleep again until the next morning. When broth was put to her lips, she drank it.

"Mother?" she asked, confused.

"Your mother is with God now," the voice said, and instantly Elizabeth remembered having been awake the previous night.

The girl closed her eyes. She was in Philadelphia at last— alone. Scarcely out from Dover Mother had died in the stinking hold of the ship. Father had followed soon after, leaving her with nothing but their indentures to pay. And now, she realized, she had been sold, but she had no memory of the scene on the docks.

Only a few days ago the fever had laid hold on her, yet it had been severe. Even now she was weak, but the last nine weeks had taught her that weakness would not be tolerated. The frail and sickly would die.

"My name is Elizabeth," she began bravely, trying to get up, "and I can spin—"

"Enough of that," the woman said, and gently forced her back to the bed. "I don't hold with slavery. We can save enough to pay the rest of your price, and then you may live with me until you can make your own way in the world." The girl lay back, surprised at being ordered to rest. For the first time she felt the comfort of where she was: the clean bed and orderly room. Under the soft quilt her body relaxed, but her eyes, though tired, keenly watched the Widow Bradbury, who, under the law, was Elizabeth's absolute authority and who could sell her or keep her at will, no matter what she said about letting her go. But the Widow did nothing more dramatic than smooth the covers and the feather pillow.

After a moment Elizabeth moved closer and rested her head on the woman's arm. Unfaltering, she looked into the Widow's eyes.

"Thank you," she whispered. And then the girl fell asleep.

But already the Widow had heard the comments from the clerk and other crewmen about Elizabeth. She foresaw that much time would go by before the girl would thank her again.

The voyage had hardened Elizabeth. Perhaps, the Widow Bradbury thought, she had been hardened even before that by the debtor's prison and the cold, hard streets of London.

She did not cry for her parents. And after that one moment of gratitude in the Widow's arms she did not again speak kindly or softly to the older woman. She seldom spoke at all.

She spun when there was spinning to do, and she wove when

the spinning was done, and she accompanied Mistress Bradbury to town to sell the yarn and cloth they had made.

Unwillingly, she attended Sunday meetings, morning and evening, with her mistress. She did not fidget. No, she sat still and her hard brown eyes glared at every word. She held her head high, kept her jaw tight, and spoke nothing to anybody there.

"Nay, the ship's hold—cruel place that it is—did not break her," the physician said softly one Sunday morning when he and his wife met the Widow in the street where new planking was being laid for a sidewalk. Elizabeth was walking ahead, absorbed in looking at the straight, raw planks of wood. "It bent her sore," he continued. "She may never be straightened, Widow."

Mistress Bradbury looked sober. "She has seen grief, doctor. Though now Satan has bent her to hate God, yet she may be made straight." Her eyes looked vague for a moment. "Once she felt gratitude. She may feel it again."

Elizabeth looked back, sensing that she was being discussed. Now that the morning

service was over she was eager to get back home. There was only catechism at home to be learned, but often the Widow would read to her from the Book of Martyrs. That was something, at least. Hearing that other people had suffered made Elizabeth feel better for some reason. And it proved to her that God would make anybody suffer: His own Son, His own people—and her.

"Come, Elizabeth, walk with me," the Widow called. Elizabeth joined her, and they bade good day to the doctor and his wife. But as they started home, the minister joined them. He was a young, serious man with a quick step under his long black frock. She knew that he was studying her with his large, serious eyes.

"And how is our Elizabeth this Sabbath?" he asked gently.

"Well," she said shortly.

"Mind your manners, my girl," the Widow said.

"And you, sir?" Elizabeth dutifully asked.

"Well, thank you," he replied, smiling at her. He suddenly stooped down so that he could see her eye to eye. She had never seen a minister do such a thing. "Elizabeth, is it really well with you?" he asked. "Is your soul safe with God?"

"I have nothing safe with God," she replied angrily. She turned away and kept walking. The minister stood up, looked for a moment at the Widow, and then turned in at his own door.

"I will not go back to that church any more," she said when they returned to the three-room house where the Widow lived.

"You must come to meeting, Elizabeth," the Widow replied gently.

"I will not, I say. And no one can make me."

"I will, if you force me."

Elizabeth hesitated on that, then insisted, "No, I will not. You are not my mother."

"But you are my ward, and you will obey me, child."

"No, I say. No!"

"I mean that you should obey me," the Widow said. "Give in now, and I won't be angry. It is a normal expectation that you attend the meetings with me, nothing cruel. If your pride rebels again and makes you say no, I will switch you." She glanced meaningfully at a dry switch lying in the kindling box alongside the fireplace.

"No! There, I say it again. I will not go."

"Elizabeth."

Elizabeth knew the switching would come. By now she knew that the Widow would always keep her word, even on whippings. Nevertheless, the girl held her head up.

"Bring me the switch," the Widow said.

The girl took a breath and obeyed. "Aye, that I'll do." Elizabeth brought it to her and held it out.

After it was over, tears of resentment sparkled in the girl's eyes as the Widow handed it back to her. But the girl only said, "You'll need something harder

than that. For I was whipped aboard ship with a leather thong." Lip trembling, she thrust the switch back into the woodbox.

"I thought a lighter punishment given by one who loves you would succeed where cruelty failed," the Widow replied. Elizabeth only stood still with her head down and didn't answer.

"Child, I have been good to you; I have nursed you, prayed for you, and now I've whipped you. Does nothing touch your heart?" she asked.

Elizabeth looked up. "I don't know," she said wearily. "Maybe you should stop trying. You say God loves me, yet He has given me harder punishments than you could ever give me. What hope do I have with Him? If I love Him, He will kill me, and if I hate Him, He will also kill me."

"The company of unrepentant sinners taught you that, child."

"I was born to unrepentant sinners."

"You can be born again."

In that moment she almost gave in, at least to the arms of the Widow, to be comforted. But in the end she resisted and walked away.

"Very well," Elizabeth said. "I will obey my mistress and go to the meetings with her."

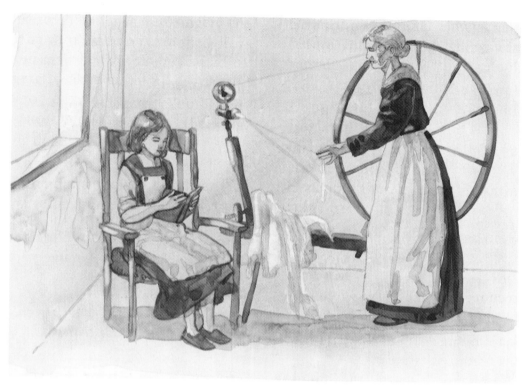

A few more weeks went by. The Widow began to instruct her in reading and ciphering, using a hornbook and a slate. Elizabeth could soon spell out her own name. She began to pick her way through parts of the Widow's great musty-smelling Bible. It was not a book she would have chosen, but parts of it were easier than the Martyrs, and the Widow owned only those two books to choose from.

Often the Widow would bid Elizabeth read aloud while she spun at the wheel, listening. "I have no quarrel against your handiwork, child, but my eyes grow too dim for reading," she would say. "So I will let your eyes read while my hands see the spindle and yarn." It was true. The Widow needed no eyes for her work.

Elizabeth began to realize that she was having an easy time of it. Though by law the Widow owned her, she was as free as though they were mother and daughter instead. Elizabeth began to feel anxious about the remainder of her bill. Would they have enough to pay it?

"Oh, rest yourself about that, dear girl," the Widow assured her. "We have done well with the loom, and I will take some from my savings if all else fails. It is all I have, but surely I can spare enough to complete payment on half of a child's passage."

Yet the physician, who often looked in on the Widow to see how she did, was worried. "Mark me," he said. "Slave traders that hark from Africa and England are not to be trusted. He will think he's given you a bargain, and it will needle him."

"God's hand is on her," the Widow replied. "On her life, at least, if not her soul yet. Let every captain rise against me, so long as God assists me."

Elizabeth was at the spinning wheel when the Widow said this. The girl looked up and cocked an eyebrow, but added nothing.

"Child, would you run to the market for me for dye?" the Widow asked, smoothing some of Elizabeth's hair back into the girl's stiff bonnet. "Master Kettlewell is holding some for me to make his vest."

"Aye, Mistress," Elizabeth said, standing up.

"My trap is outside, girl. I will take you. Kettlewell's shop is on my way," the doctor said. "God give you a good day, Widow."

"And you, doctor. Hurry home, Elizabeth."

The market was close, for the Widow's house each year seemed to be more and more drawn into the city of Philadelphia as it grew around her. In minutes the horse was trotting over cobblestones, and Elizabeth could see the tall masts and riggings from the wharf leaning this way and that over the rooftops like crazily tilting trees. "There you are, Elizabeth." The doctor said, pulling the horses to a stop. "Can you manage your way home alone?"

"Yes."

She gathered up her bulky skirts and leaped out. He laughed at her and watched while she crossed the cobblestones to get to Kettlewell's. Then he stopped. There was Captain Taylor coming down the sidewalk, a month early! The doctor reined in and tied the reins to the brake. Hurriedly, he climbed out.

Elizabeth trotted out of the shop.

"Hi! Go back!" the doctor called, suddenly afraid, but Taylor saw her.

"You there!" He seized her arm. "I know you."

The doctor crossed in three quick strides. "Leave her alone, Captain."

"Well said. Of course." He obeyed. "I was just admiring the

Widow's work, Doctor."

The doctor put one arm around Elizabeth's shoulders. "Aye. The Widow's work. Bear that in mind."

"Oh that, of course," Taylor laughed. "I'm as willing as you for the Widow to keep her, though I admit, I am calling a bit early for my payment."

"What brings you back this soon?" the doctor demanded.

"Sickness aboard ship. Fever spread to the crew. We could not have managed Barbados. I thought I would take advantage of my return to collect the balance due me. If you remember, we did not agree to a term of payment."

"Enough. The Widow has it," the doctor said, waving his words away.

"Money for the parents' passage and the girl's."

"You thief! It was half the girl's passage!" the doctor exclaimed.

"No, friend, that isn't what the Widow signed. She must pay all indentures to keep the child."

"I'll see you hanged for your sleight of hand with widows and the fatherless!"

"On the contrary, I have my contract. A judge will award the girl to me." He lifted Elizabeth's chin, and she pulled away.

"Pretty thing. I can sell her for the full price now."

"Come along, Elizabeth," the doctor said, pulling her away.

"And speaking of hanging, Doctor," Taylor called. "Have a care the Widow does not try to flee with her, else it will be the Widow who is hanged, not me—for kidnaping!"

The doctor lifted Elizabeth into the trap and then jumped in. "Oh, the villainy of the man! He would have spirited you away instantly, had I not been watching. No, no," he added hurriedly, seeing how white she was. "Think nothing of my words. A dozen men there were nearby who know you. He'd not have tried it, I daresay."

"What would it have mattered?" she asked, tears springing to her eyes. "I'm trapped, aren't I? The Widow cannot pay my parents' passage as well as all of mine. My own full fare was only half of theirs. The Widow meant to pay only half of mine!"

"Can you really believe the Widow will let you be sold, Elizabeth?" he asked.

"What choice will she have?"

"One can always choose to do right—to do kindly. She and I will think of something. Don't worry. God has His hand in this. While He keeps us, no hand can hurt us."

"And what if He gives me up to Taylor?"

The doctor shook his head. "When you're a woman of prayer someday, Elizabeth, you'll know God's love better. I tell you, the Widow is sure she will keep you, and as she knows God's face better than most do, I would trust her opinion."

He pulled the horse to a stop. She leaped out. "I will look at the garden," she said suddenly, keeping her head down.

"The garden?" he asked. "Now?"

"Yes."

He didn't argue. "All right, but stay nearby."

She went out to the garden, then past it to the hillside, still bare of houses, and threw herself down to the ground. "Oh God, have mercy on me and don't let me be sold back into slavery," she begged. "I have no hope but You, now. I've hated You every day of my life, but have mercy on me if You can make Yourself do it, and keep me with the Widow." Then she cried. She cried for a long time, remembering the hold of the ship, the death of her parents, the moaning and the dying and the griefs she had felt. Her sudden memories left her trembling. "Oh please," she added. "If You really

love me, and if You've really wanted my soul all this time, have mercy on me and change my heart. Forgive my sin and save me!"

She looked up. The Doctor was coming up the hillside. "Be of good cheer, girl." He pulled her to her feet. "The Widow's given her savings for you. You'll be all right, now. I will go pay Taylor."

He wiped a tear from her cheek. "She's calling for you."

"Thank you!" Elizabeth exclaimed and ran down the hillside, her soft muslin dress flapping and billowing.

She ran into the house. The Widow was by the hearth.

"You've used up your savings for me!" Elizabeth exclaimed, running and clutching her by her skirt. "Now it will be the poorhouse for you, as sure as we live!"

"Why, you've been crying, child."

"You've bought my life, but you've used your own!"

The Widow sat down in her rocking chair. "I have a pair of hands, Elizabeth. I can save again. Besides, it was God's will to buy you back."

"That way?"

"Yes."

"I've been wicked to you!" she blurted out. "Forgive me, Widow."

"I do, daughter. Come here." She opened her arms, and Elizabeth came into them, closed her eyes, and leaned her head on the woman's shoulder. "I knew that sooner or later God would touch your poor broken heart and begin to heal you," the Widow said.

"Will you keep me, please?"

"I will adopt you," she whispered. "Then it will be settled once and for all."

Elizabeth pulled back a little. "Is that God's will, too?"

"It is." She smoothed the girl's hair. "He may let the heart break in order to bring it to repentance, but then He gathers it back with greater mercies. Wait and see, Elizabeth."

The girl closed her eyes again and hid her face once more on the shoulder, crying tears of remorse and gratitude "I will. I promise I will."

The Youngest Skydiver

Candy Jamison

Warm, honey-colored light spilled through the window and tumbled over a boy bent over his desk. He had his tongue stuck out of the corner of his mouth. He always did that when he was concentrating, and he was deep in thought now. Jon Behn was drawing another picture. This one would probably have to be hung from the ceiling of his room since the walls were already plastered with pictures and posters. They were all pictures of skydivers. As long as he could remember he had wanted to be a skydiver like his dad.

Slowly Jon looked up and gazed out the window that was above his desk. Last night's conversation came back to him as fresh as if it had just happened. His dad might be German and still might confuse a few English phrases, but his meaning was always very clear.

"But Dad, even you said that skydiving is safer than driving."

"Yes, Son. Statistically speaking. But you have to be responsible, and I haven't seen that in you yet," said his dad pointedly, in his frank German manner. "You need to 'get on the bounce.' "

"That's 'get on the ball,' Dad," Jon interjected, then pleaded, "but I'm responsible."

The patient answer came, "And who took out the trash last night?"

"Well, I forgot once."

"What about waiting for your sister after school? Did you forget then too, Son? "

"But Dad . . ."

"Not another word about the matter, Son. If you can prove yourself a responsible young man, then you can go skydiving on your next birthday. You have eight months to show me what you can do."

The memory of Dad's words bit deeply. Jon hung his head and looked at his picture again. According to regulations, he was old enough to jump this year, but his father was correct in saying that he wasn't very responsible. Suddenly he brought his head up and sat straighter; with the Lord's help the next eight months would prove different. Why, just last Sunday his pastor had talked to him about his relationship with Christ and the fact that Christ is always there to help him to do right.

Right then Jon prayed silently. "Dear Father, I know that You are always with me and that You are all-powerful. Please help me always to look to You and to be responsible. I'd like Dad to think that I'm responsible even if he won't let me skydive. I need Your help. Amen."

With a small sigh Jon went back to his picture. God certainly would have to remind him because he always was forgetting to do things.

"Hey, Jon," a voice suddenly bawled.

Sticking his head out of his bedroom window, Jon could just make out the chubby, freckled face that was bellowing from below.

"Hey, Sticks. What ya up to?" Jon yelled back.

"I want you to come see my computer game. You're not going to believe it, but it has parachutes in it."

"Be right there!" yelled Jon.

Rolling up his newest picture and flinging his coat over his arm, he was off. He leaped down the stairs three at a time, and at the bottom he came to a sudden stop.

A small Sunday school card that his sister had made was taped to the inside of the kitchen door. It had a short phrase written in her kindergarten scrawl that said, "God never fails." Jon read the note thoughtfully and then stepped into the kitchen to get the trash on his way out.

In the following weeks Mr. Behn watched Jon. Mr. Behn even invented several little jobs like changing the oil in the power mower and weeding out the garden on Saturdays to see if Jon would remember to do them, and Jon faithfully followed through. His father was so pleased with his progress that one night he praised Jon in front of the whole family.

"Son, you are becoming like my right sleeve."

The whole family broke out into laughter.

"Dad," gasped Peter, Jon's younger brother, "it's 'right arm.' Someday your German mind will get these American phrases."

Mr. Behn laughed good-naturedly, "That's right, Son. It's funny how even after all these years I still get confused. Anyway, as I was trying to say, you do everything I ask you to do. You do it well too, and I'm proud of you." you."

Jon was embarrassed, but very pleased. Still, it wasn't until the following week when they were alone in the truck that his dad mentioned the topic of skydiving.

"Jon, how would you like to sit in on one of my jumping classes today?"

Jon's eyes grew wide, but he didn't dare answer. His dad continued talking, pretending not to notice the silence.

"Yes, I believe that you have proved yourself to be a responsible boy. Usually my students attend only three hours of class before they jump, but I want you to come every weekend until your birthday. This way the material will be firmly rooted in your mind; so in an emergency you can react quickly and confidently."

By the end of the four sessions, the instructions of his dad—his jumpmaster—rang in his head. But he was glad to know them so well. For even though he still wanted to jump, he was beginning to get afraid. But he couldn't let his dad see, so he prayed often that the Lord would give him the strength.

The night before Jon's birthday his uncle came over with a new skydiving poster. His uncle had managed to find one that Jon didn't have yet. Jon was delighted. It suited his mood well because skydiving was all that he talked about that evening.

"Can't you come see me jump tomorrow, Uncle Jim?" pleaded Jon.

"Sorry, Jon, but your dad would have to take me away in a wheelbarrow. I would faint if I saw you falling through the sky. Didn't I ever tell you about the time I had to skydive?"

"No sir. I didn't know you jumped. Tell me all about it," said Jon excitedly.

"There isn't much to tell. I had to jump when I was in boot camp just like your dad did. Only, unlike your dad, I was 'chicken.' They had to push me out. You'd think I would have been used to it, but no. I think they still have claw marks where I tried to hang on. My, oh my. I couldn't help wondering how it would feel to be way up there, falling out of the plane, and find that my chute wouldn't open. But don't you fret; you'll do great, just like your dad."

His uncle's words were like fuel added to the small fire of fear that was already burning inside Jon. Without looking at his dad, lest he guess his fear, Jon said good night to everyone.

Upstairs in the quiet of his room, Jon tried to sleep, but his mind was in a whirl. So many things could go wrong. He began to review the procedures for handling the three landing hazards at the airport. For the telephone wires and the trees, he had to put his feet together and his hands up; but if he landed in the water, he had to inflate a flotation device. If his chute didn't open properly or if his emergency chute that he carried on his chest opened by accident, he'd have a lot more to worry about than just the landing. With these thoughts whirling in his head, he dozed off into a fitful sleep.

Strange pictures formed in Jon's sleeping mind. He could see everyone standing in a circle listening intently to the jumpmaster.

"Be sure to roll out of the plane door if your emergency chute opens accidentally inside the plane," said the jumpmaster. "If you don't, your chute will grab air and it will pull you through the side of the plane. Be sure to roll out, roll out. . . ."

Jon tossed and turned on the bed. "Roll out," he muttered, "roll out." With a sudden jerk he pitched over the side of the bed and landed in a heap of blankets and sheets. Frantically he pushed them aside. He wiped the sweat

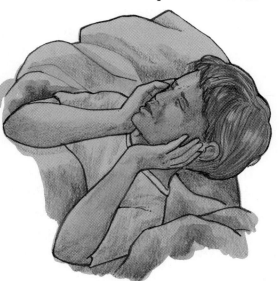

off his face with his sleeve. Rising unsteadily to his feet, he tried to straighten out his bed.

Once more Jon tried to relax and think of something else. Again he dropped off into a fitful sleep. Then his head began to roll from side to side.

"Going to land in water. Blow up the float." And Jon began to snort and puff loudly.

Piercing into the mists of sleep came a voice, "Jon, Jon, are you all right?"

Jon sat up on his elbows, his lips and mouth dry. He had been trying to inflate his pillow.

"Fine," he said hoarsely, "just fine."

"Must be something you ate," said his father with a chuckle.

It seemed like hours before Jon slept again. Moments before his alarm rang, he grabbed the front of his pajama top thinking that he had the emergency ripcord. When the alarm clock rang, Jon pulled hard on the ripcord of his emergency chute. Riiiip! He sat up, blinking in surprise.

The smell of frying sausage floated up the stairs along with the fragrance from the perking coffeepot. Today was Jon's birthday.

Tearing to the shower, Jon nearly collided with his dad.

"Sorry, Dad. I guess I'm in a rush."

"Slow down, Son. The plane will wait for you. Anyway you can't go without me, so take it easy. Besides, that Mom of yours has one big birthday breakfast to eat first," said his dad with a big smile. "That is if you are reaching up to it?"

"Feeling up to it," Jon corrected automatically. "Yes, sir," he added with a slight waver in his voice. "I feel up to it."

After breakfast everyone lined up at the door just as if Jon's dad were going to work. The entire "crew" solemnly shook hands with Jon as he proceeded down the line, but his Mom hugged him till he almost choked.

"Mom," he said, pretending to be disgusted. "I'll be back by noon."

"Oh, I know. Have fun. And listen closely to your jumpmaster. He's the best," was her reply.

The ride to the airport was as familiar to Jon as the paths in his own backyard. But today it seemed like a long ride. Jon didn't even notice the grassy fields. He just stared straight ahead.

The airport was fairly deserted. Only three other people were there with Jon to jump. They gathered around the plane while Jon's dad, the jumpmaster, explained where they would sit and in what order they would jump. Jon was to jump last since he was the smallest and could fit into the back corner.

One by one they boarded the plane. As Jon boarded the plane, his dad patted him on the back. The familiar words printed in faded black letters on the inside of the plane door got Jon's attention.

The message read, "Do you know where you'll go if you die today?"

"At least I know I'd be going up and not down," said Jon with a nervous laugh. Suddenly, beneath his feet and all around him, the small plane rumbled into life. He felt it rolling down the runway, faster and faster, until everything was a roar, and then they were airborne.

The plane was small and noisy. Mr. Behn had to shout to be heard. The door flew open with a snap. The rushing air held it tightly to the bottom of the wing. One by one the jumpers climbed out on the step. Then Jon heard the jumpmaster's yell for him. He moved up into position.

Jon tried to keep his right hand over his emergency chute in the front as he swung his legs out onto the special step. The force of the air caused his legs to flutter up and down like the legs of a doll. He pushed them down to the step and reached for the strut with his left hand. Surprisingly, the air was quite warm.

"Go!" yelled his dad.

He stood up and grabbed the strut with his right hand. Pushing out on the strut as far as he could, he looked down. Jon quickly shut his eyes and gulped frantically. The wind tore at his hands and feet.

Again his dad shouted, "Go!"

Jon looked over his left shoulder at his father. The jumpmaster smiled at him. Jon grinned back. He let his feet lift off the step. He was flying underneath the wing of the plane.

A third time his dad yelled, "Go!"

Jon released his grip on the strut. Arching his back and throwing his head back, he took one last look at his father's face. He tried to grab as much air as possible by spreading his arms and legs out like a big X.

He began to count softly, "1,001, 1,002, 1,003. . . ."

"If the static line doesn't open your chute properly, be sure to abort it after six seconds and pull the ripcord on your emergency chute. " The jumpmaster's words rang in Jon's head while he counted. "After all, you have only a few seconds to decide what to do if your chute doesn't open. The ground comes up fast," he had warned.

Six seconds passed. Jon looked up. The chute formed a white plate against the morning sky. It was nice and round, just as his Dad said it would be. Jon reached up and grabbed the control straps.

Jon took a deep breath and looked down. Everything seemed so tiny. There were little houses with checkerboard lawns. Little cars moved on ribbons of tar across the countryside. Trees were clumped together in big bunches of green. It didn't look far away. It looked as if Jon could reach out a hand and touch the tiny little town. He wasn't falling. At least it didn't seem like it.

Jon looked for the man with a flag. The man had said that he'd stand on a big white target on the ground and help him in. The man would move to different parts of the target, like hands on a clock. If he moved to 9 o'clock, Jon was supposed to turn his chute till he faced 9 o'clock. This way Jon didn't have to worry about which way the wind drew him. This was his first jump, and he had enough to worry about already.

Jon squinted his eyes against the brightness of the morning sun. His heart began to thump loudly. He could not find the man with the flag. He couldn't even find the white target on the ground. He pulled wildly on the left control strap. His parachute rolled quickly to the left. Then he pulled right. Still no man with a flag. Jon frantically pulled with both hands. Then a well-drilled phrase flashed through his mind.

"Son, never pull both control straps at the same time. It will collapse the chute. "

Jon looked up quickly. The chute was still a white circle against the morning sky. He hadn't pulled hard enough to collapse the chute. Relief caused his eyes to mist over. He blinked rapidly to clear his eyes and looked down again.

A flash of bright orange caught Jon's eye. There was the man with the flag to bring him in. Jon quickly pulled his right control strap to pull him to the same position as the man on the ground. Pulling left and then right, Jon closely followed each thing the man did.

The ground came closer and closer. Suddenly it was rushing up at Jon. He quickly looked up at the tree line. He knew that if he tensed up he could break his legs.

He used the tree line to let him know how close he was to the ground.

When it was time, he put his feet together and bent his knees. His feet touched. He melted into the ground, allowing his knees, hips, shoulders, and feet to make contact. Then he flopped over.

He brushed aside the lines and parachute and rose unsteadily to his feet. Across the field came his dad, waving his arms frantically, yelling as he ran.

"You did fine, Son. You followed my instructions exactly. You're a 'nick out of the old rock,' Son!" His dad's arms swallowed Jon in a bear hug. Only then did Jon feel how hard his own heart was beating from the thrill and fear of the jump.

"'Chip off the block,' Dad!" Jon gasped, laughing. "'A chip off the old block!'"

The Beginning of the ARMADILLOS

Rudyard Kipling

Rudyard Kipling was a British writer who grew up in India when it was governed by England. As a boy he heard many of India's folktales and animal fables, and later in life he wrote his own versions of them in two of his books, Just So Stories *and* The Jungle Book. *The following story, written in the form of a folktale, is really poking fun at the theory of evolution. In this story, Kipling jokingly shows his impossible theory of how armadillos may have evolved. Although he pretends to be telling his story seriously, he makes his characters—especially the confused Jaguar—so silly that the reader can see Kipling's sense of humor.*

This, O Best Beloved, is another story of the High and Far-Off Times. In the very middle of those times was a Stickly-Prickly Hedgehog, and he lived on the banks of the turbid Amazon, eating shelly snails and things. And he had a friend, a Slow-Solid Tortoise, who lived on the banks of the turbid Amazon, eating green lettuces and things. And so *that* was all right, Best Beloved. Do you see?

But also, and at the same time, in those High and Far-Off Times, there was a Painted Jaguar, and he lived on the banks of the turbid Amazon too; and he ate everything that he could catch. When he could not catch deer or monkeys he would eat frogs and beetles; and when he could not catch frogs and beetles he went to his Mother Jaguar, and she told him how to eat hedgehogs and tortoises.

She said to him ever so many times, graciously waving her tail, "My son, when you find a Hedgehog you must drop him into the water and then he will uncoil, and when you catch a Tortoise you must scoop him out of his shell with your paw." And so that was all right, Best Beloved.

One beautiful night on the banks of the turbid Amazon, Painted Jaguar found Stickly-Prickly Hedgehog and Slow-Solid Tortoise sitting under the trunk of a fallen tree. They could not run away, and so Stickly-Prickly curled himself up into a ball, because he was a Hedgehog, and Slow-Solid Tortoise drew in his head and feet into his shell as far as they would go, because he was a Tortoise; and so *that* was all right, Best Beloved. Do you see?

"Now attend to me," said Painted Jaguar, "because this is very important. My mother said that when I meet a Hedgehog I am to drop him into the water and then he will uncoil, and when I meet a Tortoise I am to scoop him out of his shell with my paw. Now which of you is Hedgehog and which is Tortoise? Because, to save my spots, I can't tell."

"Are you sure of what your Mummy told you?" said Stickly-Prickly Hedgehog. "Are you quite sure? Perhaps she said that when you uncoil a Tortoise you must shell him out of the water with a scoop, and when you paw a Hedgehog you must drop him on the shell."

"Are you sure of what your Mummy told you?' said Slow-and-Solid Tortoise. "Are you quite sure? Perhaps she said that when you water a Hedgehog you must drop him into your paw, and when you meet a Tortoise you must shell him till he uncoils."

"I don't think it was at all like that," said Painted Jaguar, but he felt a little puzzled; "but, please, say it again more distinctly."

"When you scoop water with your paw you uncoil it with a Hedgehog," said Stickly-Prickly. "Remember that, because it's important."

"*But*," said the Tortoise, "when you paw your meat you drop it into a Tortoise with a scoop. Why can't you understand?"

"You are making my spots ache," said Painted Jaguar; "and besides, I didn't want your advice at all. I only wanted to know which of you is Hedgehog and which is Tortoise."

"I shan't tell you," said Stickly-Prickly, "but you can scoop me out of my shell if you like."

"Aha!" said Painted Jaguar. "Now I know you're Tortoise. You thought I wouldn't! Now I will." Painted Jaguar darted out his paddy-paw just as Stickly-Prickly curled himself up, and of course Jaguar's paddy-paw was just filled

with prickles. Worse than that, he knocked Stickly-Prickly away and away into the woods and the bushes, where it was too dark to find him. Then he put his paddy-paw into his mouth, and of course the prickles hurt him worse than ever. As soon as he could speak he said, "Now I know he isn't Tortoise at all. But,"—and then he scratched his head with his un-prickly paw—"how do I know that this other is Tortoise?"

"But I *am* Tortoise," said Slow-and-Solid. "Your mother was quite right. She said that you were to scoop me out of my shell with your paw. Begin."

"You didn't say she said that a minute ago," said Painted Jaguar, sucking the prickles out of his paddy-paw. "You said she said something quite different."

"Well, suppose you say that I said that she said something quite different, I don't see that it makes any difference; because if she said what you said I said she said, it's just the same as if I said what she said she said. On the other hand, if you think she said that you were to uncoil me with a scoop, instead of pawing me into drops with a shell, I can't help that, can I?'

"But you said you wanted to be scooped out of your shell with my paw," said Painted Jaguar.

"If you'll think again you'll find that I didn't say anything of the kind. I said that your mother said that you were to scoop me out of my shell," said Slow-and-Solid.

"What will happen if I do?" said the Jaguar most sniffily and most cautious.

"I don't know, because I've never been scooped out of my shell before; but I tell you truly, if you want to see me swim away you've only got to drop me into the water."

"I don't believe it," said Painted Jaguar. "You've mixed up all the things my mother told me to do with the things that you asked me whether I was sure that she didn't say, till I don't know whether I'm on my head or my painted tail; and now you come and tell me something I *can* understand, and it makes me more mixy than before. My mother told me that I was to drop one of you two into the water, and as you seem so anxious to be dropped I think you don't want to be dropped. So jump into the turbid Amazon and be quick about it."

"I warn you that your Mummy won't be pleased. Don't tell her I didn't tell you," said Slow-Solid.

"If you say another word about what my mother said—"the Jaguar answered, but he had not finished the sentence before Slow-and-Solid quietly dived into the turbid Amazon, swam under water for a long way, and came out on the bank where Stickly-Prickly was waiting for him.

"That was a very narrow escape," said Stickly-Prickly. "I don't like Painted Jaguar. What did you tell him that you were?'

"I told him truthfully that I was a truthful Tortoise, but he wouldn't believe it, and he made me jump into the river to see if I was, and I was, and he is surprised. Now he's gone to tell his Mummy. Listen to him!"

They could hear Painted Jaguar roaring up and down among the trees and the bushes by the side of the turbid Amazon, till his Mummy came.

"Son, son!" said his mother ever so many times, graciously waving her tail, "what have you been doing that you shouldn't have done?"

"I tried to scoop something that said it wanted to be scooped out of its shell with my paw, and my paw is full of per-ickles," said Painted Jaguar.

"Son, son!" said his mother ever so many times, graciously waving her tail, "by the prickles in your paddy-paw I see that that must have been a Hedgehog. You should have dropped him into the water."

"I did that to the other thing; and he said he was a Tortoise, and I didn't believe him, and it was quite true, and he has dived under the turbid Amazon, and he won't come up again, and I haven't anything at all to eat, and I think we had better find lodgings somewhere else. They are too clever on the turbid Amazon for poor me!"

"Son, son!" said his mother ever so many times, graciously waving her tail, "now attend to me and remember what I say. A Hedgehog curls himself up into a ball and his prickles stick out

every which way at once. By this you may know the Hedgehog."

"I don't like this old lady one little bit," said Stickly-Prickly, under the shadow of a large leaf. "I wonder what else she knows?"

"A Tortoise can't curl himself up," Mother Jaguar went on, ever so many times, graciously waving her tail. "He only draws his head and legs into his shell. By this you may know the Tortoise."

"I don't like this old lady at all—at all," said Slow-and-Solid Tortoise. "Even Painted Jaguar can't forget those directions. It's a great pity that you can't swim, Stickly-Prickly."

"Don't talk to me," said Stickly-Prickly. "Just think how much better it would be if you could curl up. This *is* a mess! Listen to Painted Jaguar."

Painted Jaguar was sitting on the banks of the turbid Amazon sucking prickles out of his paws and saying to himself—

"Can't curl, but can swim—
Slow-Solid, that's him!
Curls up, but can't swim—
Stickly-Prickly, that's him!"

"He'll never forget that," said Stickly-Prickly. "Hold up my chin, Slow-and-Solid. I'm going to try to learn to swim. It may be useful."

"Excellent!" said Slow-and-Solid; and he held up Stickly-Prickly's chin, while Stickly-Prickly kicked in the waters of the turbid Amazon.

"You'll make a fine swimmer yet," said Slow-and-Solid. "Now, if you can unlace my back-plates a little, I'll see what I can do towards curling up. It may be useful."

Stickly-Prickly helped to unlace Tortoise's back-plates, so that by twisting and straining Slow-and-Solid actually managed to curl up a tiddy wee bit.

"Excellent!" said Stickly-Prickly; "but I shouldn't do any more just now. It's making you black in the face. Kindly lead me into the water once again and I'll practice that side-stroke which you say is so easy." And so Stickly-Prickly practised, and Slow-Solid swam alongside.

"Excellent!" said Slow-and-Solid. "A little more practice will make you a regular whale. Now, if I may trouble you to unlace my back and front plates two holes more, I'll try that fascinating bend that you say is so easy. Won't Painted Jaguar be surprised!"

"Excellent!" said Stickly-Prickly, all wet from the turbid Amazon. "I declare, I shouldn't know you from one of my own family. Two holes, I think, you said? A little more expression, please, and don't grunt quite so much, or Painted Jaguar may hear us. When you've finished, I want to try that long dive which you say is so easy. Won't Painted Jaguar be surprised!"

And so Stickly-Prickly dived, and Slow-and-Solid dived alongside.

"Excellent!" said Slow-and-Solid. "A leetle more attention to holding your breath and you will be able to keep house at the bottom of the turbid Amazon.

Now I'll try that exercise of wrapping my hind legs round my ears which you say is so peculiarly comfortable. Won't Painted Jaguar be surprised!"

"Excellent!" said Stickly-Prickly. "But it's straining your back-plates a little. They are all overlapping now, instead of lying side by side."

"Oh, that's the result of exercise," said Slow-and-Solid. "I've noticed that your prickles seem to be melting into one another, and that you're growing to look rather more like a pine-cone, and less like a chestnut-burr, than you used to."

"Am I?" said Stickly-Prickly. "That comes from my soaking in the water. Oh, won't Painted Jaguar be surprised!"

They went on with their exercises, each helping the other, till morning came; and when the sun was high they rested and dried themselves. Then they saw that they were both of them quite different from what they had been.

"Stickly-Prickly," said Tortoise after breakfast, "I am not what I was yesterday; but I think that I may yet amuse Painted Jaguar."

"That was the very thing I was thinking just now," said Stickly-Prickly. "I think scales are a tremendous improvement on prickles—to say nothing of being able to swim. Oh, *won't* Painted Jaguar be surprised! Let's go and find him."

By and by they found Painted Jaguar, still nursing his paddy-paw that had been hurt the night before. He was so astonished that he fell three times backward over his own painted tail without stopping.

"Good morning!" said Stickly-Prickly. "And how is your dear gracious Mummy this morning?'

"She is quite well, thank you," said Painted Jaguar; "but you must forgive me if I do not at this precise moment recall your name."

"That's unkind of you," said Stickly-Prickly, "seeing that yesterday you tried to scoop me out of my shell with your paw."

"But you hadn't any shell. It was all prickles," said Painted Jaguar. "I know it was. Just look at my paw!"

"You told me to drop into the turbid Amazon and be drowned,' said Slow-Solid. "Why are you so rude and forgetful to-day?'

"Don't you remember what your mother told you?' said Stickly-Prickly:

"Can't curl, but can swim—
Stickly-Prickly, that's him!
Curls up, but can't swim—
Slow-Solid, that's him!"

Then they both curled themselves up and rolled round and round Painted Jaguar till his eyes turned truly cart-wheels in his head.

Then he went to fetch his mother.

"Mother," he said, "there are two new animals in the woods to-day, and the one that you said couldn't swim, swims, and the one that you said couldn't curl up, curls; and they've gone shares in their prickles, I think, because both of them are scaly all over, instead of one being smooth and the other very prickly; and, besides that, they are rolling round and round in circles, and I don't feel comfy."

"Son, son!" said Mother Jaguar ever so many times, graciously waving her tail, "a

Hedgehog is a Hedgehog, and can't be anything but a Hedgehog; and a Tortoise is a Tortoise, and can never be anything else."

"But it isn't a Hedgehog, and it isn't a Tortoise. It's a little bit of both, and I don't know its proper name."

"Nonsense!" said Mother Jaguar. "Everything has its proper name. I should call it 'Armadillo' till I found out the real one. And I should leave it alone."

So Painted Jaguar did as he was told, especially about leaving them alone; but the curious thing is that from that day to this, O Best Beloved, no one on the banks of the turbid Amazon has ever called Stickly-Prickly and Slow-Solid anything except Armadillo. There are Hedgehogs and Tortoises in other places, of course (there are some in my garden); but the real old and clever kind, with their scales lying lippety-lappety one over the other, like pine-cone scales, that lived on the banks of the turbid Amazon in the High and Far-Off Days, are always called Armadillos, because they were so clever.

So *that's* all right, Best Beloved. Do you see?

The Hike

Alyssa Ward

"Okay, kids, let's go on a hike!" Those are Dad's famous words whenever we go camping.

"Aw, Dad, do we have to?" That's our famous response. It's not that we don't like hikes, but we've been on a billion of them, and we'd a lot rather ride bikes and play with other kids at the campground.

But Dad insists on at least one hike every time we go camping. So he gets his camera, Mom packs up the baby, and Adam, Annie, and I get the canteen and backpack, make sure we have plenty of water and snacks—we may be gone more than an hour—and we all set off down a trail.

Since this campground is a state park in Florida, there are cypress trees hanging with Spanish moss all around us. When Adam first saw Spanish moss a couple of years ago, he thought it was "spinach moss" because that's what it looks like.

"Everybody walk quietly in case there are animals around," Dad warns.

"Snakes?" Mom asks, her voice quivering.

"No, not snakes, Honey. They'll avoid us," Dad says, then adds, "I hope so, anyway, for their sakes."

Mom once found a snake in our garden at home, and she got

so scared that she called the police and the fire department. Then before they had time to come and get rid of it, she got Dad's bowling ball, took a running start through the tomatoes, and let the ball go, just like in the bowling alley. The ball mowed down all the cucumber vines, three tomato plants, and the snake. When the policemen and firemen got there they took the snake away, but one of the firemen laughed so hard his helmet fell off and smashed the only remaining tomato plant. Dad said our snake was the only snake in the history of the world to be bowled to death. Anyway, whenever we go camping he makes sure to tell Mom that the snakes will leave us alone.

After we walk for a while, Annie points and whispers as loudly as she can, "Look! What's that over there?" Mom jumps, but Dad motions everybody to a halt. "Probably just a raccoon," he whispers.

But beside the path is an animal that looks like a giant rat with armor and a tiny elephant's trunk. He's digging holes and snuffling through them with his snout as he patters through underbrush.

"It's an armadillo," Mom exclaims, surprising Dad with her excitement. "I've never seen a live one before. He's obviously looking for insects for his lunch." So we stop to watch it. Adam screams with laughter at it, and I'm sure the creature will run away. But the armadillo either isn't aware of us or doesn't care. We guess that since he lives around people in the park all the time that he's probably pretty tame.

Just then we see the park ranger strolling along, and we call him over to show him the armadillo. He tells us that they're "exotic"—that is, they aren't native to this area.

"I heard that some fell off a circus wagon in the panhandle in the late 1800s, and that's how they got here from the Orient," he explained. "Other people have said they hid on a ship and came here that way. In the past, settlers and cowboys out West would sometimes eat armadillos when food was scarce. Armadillos taste a little like pork, only better." Mom looks interested, and for some reason Dad seems uneasy. I can see she wants to ask how people cooked armadillos, but the ranger goes on talking.

"They aren't very smart though, and they don't see or hear very well. If you sneak up downwind of them, you can pet them," he said. "They won't bite you."

Adam and I do stoop down to pet this one. Its back feels like a turtle's shell in layers, but its belly is soft.

Before Mom can ask about eating armadillos, Dad sees something farther down the trail and hurries us along.

As we walk, we inspect dead trees as likely homes for animals. "See those holes, Alyssa," Dad shows me. "Birds have tried to peck at insects that live in the dead tree's bark." We see a large hole the size of a silver dollar that was made by a woodpecker.

The water is very low in the river that runs along the path, and the swamps are dirt dry. We can see thick, knobby roots coming up out of the dirt like giant knees. A marker along the trail says that these are part of the roots of the cypress trees.

Every time we pass a cypress swamp, Mom quotes in a dramatic voice, "Blacker than a hundred midnights down in a cypress swamp." It's a line from "The Creation," a poem by James Weldon Johnson that Mom likes. Dad doesn't answer. He's still worried about Mom cooking an armadillo, so he doesn't notice much.

Soon we come to a suspension bridge over the river. Just as we start across, Dad has us stop for an experiment. "Line up and march in step and see what happens," Dad announces. Adam and Annie and I get right behind Mom and Dad. "Left-right. Left-right-left."

After a few steps, the bridge begins to sway from side to side.

"It used to be," Dad explains, "that armies kept in step when they marched across suspension bridges. But too often a suspension bridge would collapse because so many men all shifting their weight at the same time was too much of a strain. So now the troops crossing suspension bridges break rank and go at different paces."

After that, Adam watches my feet all the way across to be sure we're not in step.

On the bank on the other side of the bridge is a marker like a tall yardstick that measures the depth of the water. With so little rain this year the level is way down. "It's on the eight," Adam calls up to Dad and Mom.

"Wow, only eight-tenths of a foot deep. It sure is low." Dad says.

Alongside the yardstick is a locked cabinet. A wooden sign on the cabinet tells us that inside is relay equipment that tells the weather service the depth of the water so they can regulate the reservoir down the river.

"Now that's interesting," Mom says to no one in particular. Then, "Look, kids, up on that branch."

"What is it?" Annie asks, following Mom's gaze to a high tree branch covered with a lush green blanket.

"Just some ferns," I answer.

"True," Mom counters, "but they weren't like that before the rain last night. These probably looked dead and brown like the ferns at last night's campground. After some rain they spring to life. Can you guess what they're called?"

No guesses.

"Resurrection fern." She smiles. "They come back to life. Isn't that appropriate?"

Along the trail we also see

early raspberry blossoms, turtles sunning themselves on logs in the river, poison ivy, grape vines, and raccoon tracks. Finally we arrive back at the starting point. Actually it's been a pretty fun walk, and I guess it's not a bad way to learn things.

Tomorrow we'll look for alligators and climb the fire tower. "No snakes," Dad promises, "and no armadillos."

Literature Lesson:
Types of Fiction

Some stories, like "Fees of Indenture," take place more than a hundred years ago. Some stories take place centuries in the future, like "The Tal-Omega." But many stories that you read could happen today.

• **Modern Realistic Fiction and Historical Fiction**

Many stories take place in the present. They use everyday settings such as a city block, a pet store, or a corner mailbox. These stories include realistic objects and events—a green convertible, an old airplane, the beginning of summer vacation. A story that takes place in the present and uses familiar objects and events is called *modern realistic fiction.* "The Youngest Skydiver," "Big Brother," and "The Surprise" are all examples of modern realistic fiction.

In "Big Brother," Timothy had to learn to love his mentally retarded older brother Brad. The author of "Big Brother" used this story to tell us the sad truth that some people, even Christian children, can be cruel to retarded people. Writers often use this type of literature to show us problems that people have to overcome. But not all modern realistic fiction has been written by Christian authors. Some authors try to teach falsehood in their stories by giving the wrong answers to modern-day

problems. A wise reader will remember that fiction is "made up" by the author, no matter how real the fiction seems.

"Fees of Indenture" took us to the past. Indentured servants, wooden sailing ships, and hand-woven cloth are all a part of history. Stories that show what life was like in the past are *historical fiction*. Historical fiction gives the reader an idea of the differences in the past and present. For instance, the law no longer permits Americans to buy and sell children, nor do children have to pay the debts of their parents. Yet these conditions were a part of life in early America.

Good historical fiction also shows the *sameness* of the past and present. People as cruel as the captain of the slave ship still try to "live off broken hearts" today, though they may not be selling slaves. And, like the Widow, Christians today must still choose to do right, to love the Lord, and to seek lost sinners. Historical fiction should help us to see that the battle between right and wrong never changes in time.

• Science Fiction and Fanciful Fiction

The term *science fiction* usually makes us think of space ships and laser guns. Science fiction almost always takes the reader to the future, just like the story "The Tal-Omega" does. Often the setting used in science fiction is a futuristic world, a distant planet, or a spaceship. But the key to literary science fiction is that it emphasizes science and intelligence in its setting and characters. In "The Tal-Omega," Bruce, Dr. Hanson, and Captain Denton saved the ship by using strategy. They relied on their knowledge of the ship and the doctor's knowledge of chemistry and outwitted their captors.

Fanciful fiction, on the other hand, may take place in the future or in another world, but it does not emphasize science. The author of fanciful fiction creates his own world of make-believe characters and events. "The Beginning of Armadillos" is fanciful fiction. The reader knows that animals don't talk, and certainly he understands that certain turtles and porcupines never taught themselves to change so that they became armadillos. To enjoy fanciful fiction, the reader must allow himself to believe the impossible while reading the story.

Sometimes authors blend science-fiction with fanciful fiction to give us stories that contain space ships and new inventions as well as fanciful characters. It is common for writers to combine these two types of literature.

No matter what the type, good literature always looks at conflict from God's point of view. Good literature will always show love and purity as being good, and it will always show sin as being wrong and destructive.

REGIONS

The True Story
of a
Brave Boy

Robert H. Davis

The following story was told to the author by a man named Captain Crawford, who had traveled west on a wagon train. It is about a white boy who was sent with a flag of truce to receive terms from a band of Indians besieging a party of white settlers they had driven into the bed of a dry river. Ammunition was low in both camps, and the question was, which group could hold out longer. Most of the story is told in Captain Crawford's own words.

You must understand, first, that the settlers had plenty of food in their prairie-wagons and about twenty good horses, also tents and blankets. But they had no water. The Indians were camped at a spring and, being on the chase, had little food and no shelter. Both parties had carried on a sniping engagement for two days, with little advantage to anybody. They were about equally matched in numbers. On the morning of the third day the settlers, who were tortured with thirst, decided to send a fourteen-year-old boy with a flag of truce to ask the Indians what they wanted.

"You had better tell him what to say if they ask questions," said the boy's mother.

"No living man can instruct him. He must face this ordeal alone," said the father. "Self-reliance will give him the strength to do the right thing. I won't tie his hands."

"He is our first-born. The Indians will think you have not the courage to go yourself," replied the mother. "If he should not return?"

"Wife, there are no cowards in our family. Our son is the only hope. If I carry this flag of truce and am slain, God alone knows what will follow. The boy must go. It would be worse than cowardice for me to select another. The Indians will respect his bravery."

"Son?" The pioneer looked into the eyes of his offspring for answer.

"Yes, Father. I am ready," was the firm response.

The mother caught him to her breast, sobbed, and consigning him to the care of God, kissed him on the lips. But the father of that boy, merely holding out his hand man-fashion, said good-by, handed his son a strip of white cloth, and pushed him gently from the barricade into the open. The other members of the party spoke their farewells as the boy walked away, but not once did he look back to his loved ones or falter in his march to the camp of the enemy.

He crossed the open space with the white flag lifted high over his head and arrived among the besiegers, who received him with an invitation to sit down and powwow.

"What do you want?" asked the boy in a calm but strong voice which showed no trace of fear.

An Indian who understood the question pointed to a horse and held up ten fingers. The boy frowned and seated himself stubbornly, shaking his head at intervals. The chief of the raiders

said something to one of his redskins, who withdrew to the spring and returned with an army pannikin brimming with clear, cold water, which he placed on the ground at the boy's crossed feet. The impulse to seize that crystal draft and quench his thirst almost overpowered him, but instead he washed his hands, wet his hair, and threw the water on the grass.

Stunned, but still crafty, the Indians filled another pannikin and held it to the boy's lips. He pushed it aside with the remark, "We got plenty water." Then he picked up his flag of truce and arose as though about to depart. The Indian held up five fingers as a compromise, to which the boy responded with three fingers.

"Yes! You catchum! Mares!" answered the Indian, after reflection. "Catchum grub too."

The boy returned at once to his father and explained the terms. He received some flour and bacon and the three mares, which he led to a distant hill half a mile away from the water hole, the flag of truce still fluttering. The Indians, observing that the terms of the agreement were being carried out and that the boy's presence was a guaranty against reprisal, broke camp, galloped to the neutral ground, received the horses, and disappeared in single file, leaving the young ambassador to return on foot.

"That boy," said Captain Crawford, "did two remarkable things which stamped him as a hero. It took courage to refuse the drinking water that was set before him, but it required brains to deliver the three mares half a mile from the spring. A man can conceal his thirst, but a horse cannot. The boy knew that if those famished animals got within sight of that water hole, nothing could have held them, and that his diplomacy would have come to naught. What a scene must have been enacted at that spring when the white settlers came up to it. The last one of the party to quench his thirst was the boy who bore the flag of truce and made the terms."

Skill Lesson:
Map Scales

• Comparison of Map Scales

Many exciting stories like "True Story of a Brave Boy" took place during the settlement of the American West. Today, many large states make up that western region. One of these large states is Montana.

Look at the maps below. Compare the map of Connecticut, an eastern state, to that of Montana. At first glance, you might think that these two states are about the same size. Actually, Montana is nearly thirty times larger than Connecticut. The reason that the states are about the same size on these maps is that they are drawn on different scales.

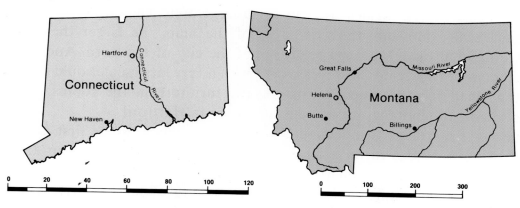

The scale of miles on the Connecticut map shows us that one inch equals 50 miles. We can quickly find that the width of the state of Connecticut is only about 100 miles. Now notice that the scale of miles on the Montana map tells us that one inch on the map represents about 200 actual miles in Montana. By measuring the width of Montana on the map (3¾ inches), we can multiply to find that the width of the state of Montana is about 750 miles.

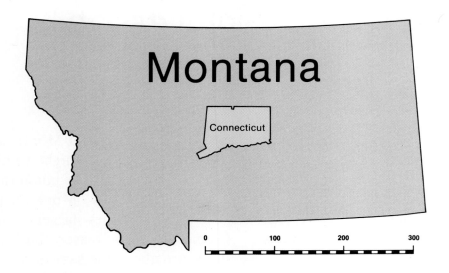

Montana

Connecticut

| 0 | 100 | 200 | 300 |

• Reasons for Map Scales

These maps, drawn on the same scale, show how the sizes of Connecticut and Montana really compare. This scale, however, is too small for the map of Connecticut to contain any details about the state. Connecticut's map must be drawn on a larger scale (fewer miles per inch) if its cities and geographical features are to be labeled.

Maps of the world or of large countries are usually drawn on a small scale so that they can show a large area. The larger the scale of the map, the larger the area of the city of Hartford. And one with a very large scale could show the furniture in the rooms of a house in Hartford.

Look again at the first maps of Montana and Connecticut. Use the map scales to find out whether it would take longer to drive from Helena to Butte in Montana or from New Haven to Hartford in Connecticut.

Stately Verse

Anonymous

If Mary goes far out to sea,
   By wayward breezes fanned,
I'd like to know—can you tell me?—
   Just where would Maryland?

If Tenny went high up in air
   And looked o'er land and lea,
Looked here and there and everywhere,
   Pray what would Tennessee?

I looked out of the window and
   Saw Orry on the lawn;
He's not there now, and who can tell
   Just where has Oregon?

Two girls were quarreling one day
   With garden tools, and so
I said, "My dears, let Mary rake
   And just let Idaho."

A friend of mine lived in a flat
   With half a dozen boys;
When he fell ill I asked him why.
   He said: "I'm Illinois."

An English lady had a steed.
   She called him 'Ighland Bay.
She rode for exercise, and thus
   Rhode Island every day.

The Six Travelers

dramatized by Becky Davis

CAST

Narrator	Runner
Soldier	Friend
Strong man	Merchant
Huntsman	Daughter
Blower	Guard

Narrator: Once there was a soldier who had served hard in a wealthy merchant's personal guard for many years. But when he was finally discharged, he received only three farthings to help him make his way in the world, even though he had served faithfully.

Soldier: Three farthings! A miserable three farthings! The merchant has storehouses full of gold to the ceiling. But for me, who risked life and limb for him, he grants three whole farthings. I shall have to see what I can do to repay him for his generosity.

216

Narrator: As the soldier went on his way through the forest, he saw a man uprooting trees as if they were blades of grass. When the strong man had uprooted two dozen trees, he stopped and noticed the soldier.

Strong man: Well, how now, my fine soldier? You have done with a life of service?

Soldier: A long life of service, with but three farthings to show for it! That is all I have to make my way in the world.

Strong man: Ah, a certain merchant's doing, I'll warrant. I know of how he takes advantage of poor people. He overcharges us till we haven't a cent just so he can fill his own coffers to the brim with gold.

Soldier: Then come with me to seek justice from him. A man of your strength could be a great asset in our plea.

Strong man: You have convinced me! Let me first take this firewood to my mother, and I will join you.

Narrator: So saying, the strong man took up one of the trees and wrapped it around twenty-three others. He disappeared through the forest but soon returned to the waiting soldier.

Strong man: Now we are off to make our way in the world and seek justice from an unjust merchant! Perhaps together we will be able to make our way in the world.

Narrator: The strong man and the soldier traveled on for several miles when they saw a man . . .

Soldier: How now, what is this, my good man? You aim with your gun, but I cannot see a target.

Huntsman: My dear fellow, two miles from here is a fly sitting on a flower petal, and I wish to shoot out its right eye.

Strong man: Ah! An aim like that could serve some purpose in our travels.

Soldier: Surely! Do come with us. We are off to seek justice from an unjust merchant.

Huntsman: Ah, yes. I know of how that merchant takes advantage of poor people. He cheats us of our livestock only so that his barns can be full. I will gladly come with you. Together we will be able to make our way in the world.

Narrator: So the three companions set off. They had traveled several more miles when . . .

Huntsman: What is this? Not a breath of wind, but three windmills all turning!

Strong man: A remarkable sight, surely.

Soldier: Perhaps we will find the answer farther down the road. Let us continue.

Huntsman: There is a man. Perhaps he will know something about the mystery of the windmills.

Strong man: My, what a nose he has! Almost big enough for a man to rest upon. And see how he holds one nostril and blows through the other!

Soldier: How now, my good man? What are you doing with your nose?

Blower: Did you not pass three windmills turning a mile down the road? There is no wind today, so I came out to blow and make them turn. If I had gotten any closer, there is a chance I would have blown them over completely. Sometimes my nose gets out of control.

Soldier: Ah, but what a man to accompany us on our travels! Surely a nose like that would be of some use. Do accompany us. We are on our way to seek justice from an unjust merchant.

Blower: Ah, yes, I know the one.

He takes advantage of poor people. I will gladly come with you. I had best put a clothespin over my nose, though, so as not to blow one of you away by accident. Then together we can make our way in the world.

Narrator: So the unusual group set out once again on their journeys. By and by they came upon two men walking together. One of them, though, was hopping down the road on one foot.

Blower: I must say, that fine fellow can move faster on one leg than any of the rest of us can on two!

Soldier: How now, my good fellow? Why do you have one leg buckled up under you like that?

Runner: And good day to you, sir! If I were to unbuckle my other leg, I would move so fast that my friend here would soon be left in the dust and would probably never see me again. Now that would be a shame, wouldn't it?

Soldier: Ah, a fine man you would be to accompany us on our quest! You never know when a talent like that may have some purpose. We are on our way to seek justice from an unjust merchant. Come with us, and by all means bring your friend along too.

Runner: Ah, yes, my friend and I will gladly come and join the cause of justice. Together we will be able to make our way in the world.

Friend: And so as not to disappoint you by any means, I will reveal that I have a talent too. I must always carry my hat in my hand, for when I place it upright on my head, such a terrible frost comes that trees will fall right over from the ice that forms on them.

Soldier: Splendid! Splendid! Six travelers like us will surely make our way in the world!

Narrator: And so the little group traveled on until they saw before them their destination: the merchant's stately castle. There they heard talk in the streets.

Blower: Ah! The word is that the merchant is looking for a husband for his daughter.

Runner: I have heard that she is beautiful, but just as cruel as her father.

Strong man: People are saying that the man who can win a race with her will win her hand in marriage.

Friend: The racers are supposed to run from the castle to a mountain spring and back again with a cup of water from the spring.

Huntsman: Oh, but if the man loses the race, he will also lose his head. That is part of the bargain. And I have heard that the merchant's daughter is as swift as a deer.

Soldier: Ah, there's always a catch to it. But perhaps we can show the merchant a thing or two about what six "ordinary" men can do.

Runner: Oh, I will gladly race for you, if you do indeed want to win the hand of such a girl. I will unbuckle my leg to be sure to win.

Narrator: So the soldier walked up to the castle to see the merchant.

Soldier: Sir, I am ready to try for the hand of your beautiful daughter.

Merchant: Ha! You are merely a soldier! Better men than you have tried and have not lived to tell the tale. You must bargain to be beheaded if you lose the race.

Soldier: Very well, I would still like to try. However, I would like to request that my servant run for me.

Merchant: Your servant may

run for you, but when he loses the race, both he and you will lose your heads! Agreed?

Soldier: So be it.

Narrator: The race was set. The runner and the beautiful daughter took off. Although the girl was indeed swift, the runner passed her easily. He ran to the mountain spring, filled his cup, and headed back. But he was worn out from all his travels, so he stopped to rest and fell asleep. Soon the merchant's daughter caught up with him.

Daughter: How now? What is this? My challenger—asleep! Well, let us see if he can win the race with no water in his cup!

Narrator: And so saying, she poured out every last drop and raced on, laughing to herself. But fortunately the huntsman was on the castle roof.

Huntsman: Look, my good soldier! I can see the runner from here. He has fallen asleep and the girl has poured out his cup of water.

Soldier: I cannot see him, my good huntsman, but if we do not help him, the six travelers will soon be four travelers!

Huntsman: I will gladly shoot the rock out from under his head.

Narrator: Saying that, the huntsman took quick aim and fired, sending the rock rolling down the hill. The moment the rock disappeared from under his head, the runner awoke.

Runner: Ah, I see that the merchant's daughter has been up to some mischief, but it will not serve her, even so.

Narrator: The runner ran back to the spring, filled his cup again, and passed the girl to win the race with a good ten minutes to spare.

Daughter: *(To her father)* No matter what the rules of the race were, I refuse to marry a common soldier!

Merchant: Do not fear, my dear. You shall not have to. *(To the men)* Come, my good men.

You have won the race, and you shall be honored.

Narrator: So saying, the merchant took the six travelers into a great iron room with walls of iron, doors of iron, and windows with iron bars across them.

Soldier: Ah, a fine treat! You have set before us many wonderful things to eat.

Merchant: Yes, and I hope you will enjoy them immensely.

Narrator: So saying, the merchant disappeared from the room. He hurried downstairs and ordered the cook to stir up a great fire under the room, great enough to heat up the iron and roast the six travelers alive.

Blower: My, but it is getting rather hot in here.

Huntsman: Especially under my feet. I cannot help wondering if the merchant is up to some mischief.

Soldier: I do believe there is a fire under us! And the iron will heat up so hot that we will surely be roasted alive!

Friend: Ah, not necessarily so, my good soldier. Perhaps you have forgotten about my hat.

Narrator: So saying, the runner's friend put his hat upon his head. Immediately the six friends felt the heat no more. Instead they began to shiver. A long time later, the merchant opened the door.

Merchant: Well, two hours have gone by. Certainly they should be roasted by now.

Soldier: Most gracious host, could you p-please let us out? We are s-suffering a mild case of fr-frostbite in this cold room.

Narrator: The merchant was in a speechless rage, but he let the men leave the room.

Daughter: Father, I still refuse to marry that common soldier!

Merchant: Perhaps we can devise another plan, my dear. *(To the soldier)* Good sir, if you were to take all the gold you could carry, would you be willing to relinquish your right to marry my daughter?

Soldier: I think that would be agreeable. But allow me two weeks first.

Narrator: During that two weeks, the soldier hired tailors to make the largest sack in the world. They used all the material they could find to sew it together.

Soldier: I am ready. My servant will carry the gold for me.

Strong man: Here is my sack!

Narrator: When the merchant saw the size of the sack and the strength of the strong man, he turned a little pale, but he ordered a wagonload of gold to be brought.

Strong man: Why, what is this? It barely covers the bottom of the bag! That will hardly do!

Narrator: The merchant turned a little paler at that, but he ordered more gold to be brought.

Strong man: Truly, sir, your men will have to do far better than this.

Narrator: Before long the merchant had emptied every room in his stately castle of the gold that was there. And still the sack was not full.

Strong man: See here, sir. I am not choosy. I will take anything you have to offer in order to fill my sack.

Narrator: So the merchant called for jewels, furs, and fine silk. He called for cups and plates and fine silver. And still the strong man's sack was not full.

Strong man: Ah, well, we must put an end to this sooner or later. And besides, if a man's sack is not quite full, why, he can close it that much more easily.

Narrator: So saying, the strong man hoisted the sack onto his back and walked away with it to join his five friends.

Merchant: What? That man is walking away with all the riches I own! This cannot be! What am I to do?

Daughter: Father! Order your personal guards to be sent out to capture that soldier! Tell them that he stole your riches.

Merchant: That I shall. Guards!

Narrator: And so an entire regiment of guards came to find the six friends rejoicing over all the riches that the strong man had brought back to them.

Guard: You are under arrest for stealing all these riches!

Soldier: Oh, no, good sir. We came by these riches honestly.

Guard: Nevertheless, you are all under arrest.

Blower: Ah! This is where I come in. I was afraid I would not be able to help in this whole great adventure.

Narrator: So saying, the blower removed the clothespin from his nose and gave a little puff with one nostril. Every man in the regiment flew up into the air and floated there under the power of that blast.

Guard: Mercy! Mercy! Let us down!

Blower: Only if you promise to take this message to the merchant: Any man you send to arrest us will also be given a ride in the air.

Guard: We will! We will!

Narrator: So the blower let the guards down gently and fastened the clothespin back on his nose. The guards ran back to the palace, never to be seen again.

Soldier: Well, my good friends, shall we be off? I believe we have succeeded in making our way in the world.

Narrator: And so the six friends lived together happily ever after, using their riches wisely to help not only themselves, but other poor people around them.

Soldier: After all, we knew what it was like to be poor.

Narrator: And what of the merchant and his daughter? Well, they discovered that they did indeed have three farthings left, so we can assume that they also were able to make their way in the world.

P. K.

Karen Wilt

Jay grimaced and slid down into the seat until only the crown of his head showed at window level. "I'll be glad when school's out," he grumbled. "I wish I didn't have to go to sixth grade next year and be in the same part of the building as the high school."

"What happened this time, Jay?" Mom's question was kind, but Jay knew she was getting a little tired of his tales of woe.

"It's that Joe Tally again. Our class was in the dismissal line down at the main entrance, and when the seventh grade kids came by, I read his lips. He called me a 'P. K.' and pretended to draw a halo around his head. He made me so mad, Mom." Jay slouched down farther in his seat. "Maybe Joe'll catch the bubonic plague and won't be back next year," he muttered to himself.

Mom didn't say anything at first, but Jay could tell that she had heard his last remark. He could see the frown that crossed her face in the rearview mirror.

"Jay, the older boys wouldn't tease you if you wouldn't let it upset you so." Mom was turning down Maple Avenue toward their house.

"But Joe shouldn't do that, should he, Mom?" Jay protested. "You wouldn't let me treat Cherry that way."

Mom parked the car and turned to look right at him. Jay knew what she was going to say. He'd heard it before from both Mom and Dad—*You are responsible for your responses.* Why couldn't he keep from getting so mad when the big kids teased him?

"Those boys shouldn't tease you," she began. "Their parents are probably trying to help them overcome that problem as much as we are trying to help you overcome yours. Your job is to control the way you respond to the teasing." Mom removed the

keys and started to get out of the car. "Maybe it will be different when you get to know them better, Jay, and a lot could happen this summer. You'll have to be more careful about your attitude when your cousin arrives next week. If you complain about being a preacher's son, how will she feel about being the daughter of missionaries?"

"Well, she's a girl and she'll probably be too sick from her back operation to bother about my complaining. But I can keep quiet. Not like those kids at school."

The first day of summer finally came. Jay spent the time trying to escape from Cherry, who

toddled after him saying, "Pway me a game, Jay, pwease."

Then just as Mom called everyone for supper, the doorbell rang. Aunt Chloe and Uncle Derrick stood at the door with Dana. Jay had seen Dana at Christmas, before her back operation. He could hardly tell that she wore a metal brace except where it showed above her collar and where it jutted out a little in front of her shoulders.

"Hi, Dana," he said. He felt uneasy. "W-want-want to see the room we fixed for you?"

"Great!" she said. "I saw the new basketball hoop in the driveway. Will you teach me how to play?" she asked, clambering up the stairs after Jay, only a little more slowly than he.

"Sure. Can you play now? I-I mean with your—since your operation ?"

"My back brace won't stop me, as long as you don't play tackle basketball." she replied. "Oh, you painted the guest room. I can't believe I'm really going to have a room of my own with a real bed," she squealed.

"Yep." He felt easier with her. Dana acted like back braces were the most normal thing in the world. "Are you sorry you can't go back to Africa with your folks?" he asked.

"If I did go back, I'd have to go to a boarding school half the year anyway. This year I'll live like a normal person instead of a missionary kid." She bounced on the bed. "No more mats on the floor and eating breakfast sitting cross-legged and having people stare at my white skin. And I won't have to travel fifty miles in a hot jeep to get to a doctor."

Jay didn't say anything, but he wondered if the kids at school would stare at Dana because of her back brace just as the Africans stared at her because she was an American. He could just hear the comments about both of them— a P.K. and an M.K.

"Time to eat," Dad called from the foot of the stairs.

That night Jay heard Dana crying. Before he could decide what to do, Mom's slippered feet padded down the hall to the guest room. Soon the murmur of voices lulled Jay to sleep.

"Jay, Jay," Cherry called from the door. "Get up in da mornin'," she sang.

"It's summertime. Go away, Cherry," he said.

"Come on, Jay," Dana said from the top of the stairs at the end of the hall. "I want to practice doing all the things American kids do in the summer."

"They baby-sit little babies that never sleep late," he grumbled. He pulled himself out of bed and chased Cherry out of the room.

At first Jay wished that Dana had been a boy instead of a girl, but after the first week passed, he found out that it didn't matter. Even with her brace, Dana could still help him build his fort, and she came up with the idea of making a raft for sailing in the swamp. She could pitch a pretty straight softball, and sometimes Jay convinced her to try curve balls to help him improve his swing. She couldn't swing the bat. It pinched her arm. Still, she didn't complain, and Jay was glad for all the extra chances to bat. She soon learned how to shoot a basket, too, though she did it awkwardly. Dana even liked baby-sitting Cherry. Jay couldn't thank her enough for that.

One Saturday in August, Dad planned a fishing day at the ocean. The alarm rang at 4:30 for Jay to get up. He would have missed the trip completely if Dana hadn't thrown a shoe at him on her way downstairs. Then, when his lunch fell overboard, Dana shared hers with him. She said she wasn't that hungry, but Jay knew better. It worked out fine in the end,

though. The food from his lunch attracted a bunch of fish, so they had a full string when they started home.

"You really are American," Jay said as they settled in, sleepy and content, among the rods and fishy smell in the back seat of the car.

"Well, that's on my birth certificate. Really I want to go back to Africa. I'm a missionary, you know. Besides, you can catch super big fish there." Dana held her arms apart to show how big the fish were, but Jay shook his head pretending he didn't believe and then closed his eyes again.

His mind turned to school. Classes would be starting soon. "Dana," he asked, "did it ever bother you that you were the only white kid—I mean you said once you were glad you wouldn't have to be stared at for a year."

"I guess it doesn't bother me so much because I'm glad I'm an American. I love my African friends and I don't want them to think of me as different . . . my family spends a lot of time praying for them, and Dad told me to try not to notice when they look at me and seem to talk about me." Dana rubbed her sunburned shoulder gently. "If Kleestan and Molulu were here now, they'd laugh at my sunburn, but I'd know that they still love me."

"Do you miss your friends there?" Jay questioned.

"Yes," Dana said. "But it has been nice having a brother my age." She paused and rested her head against the back of the seat.

Jay fell asleep thinking how fast the summer had gone by— as fast as the telephone poles swooshing past on the highway. Only two weeks until school would start. Dana had lived with their family over two months. He would feel strange when she left next year. But that was still a long way off. He had school to face before that and the junior-high-school kids. At least he had grown about two inches taller since school closed. Maybe if he started lifting weights the kids would be

afraid to pick on him. Or if he took karate . . . or maybe—Jay's eyes popped open for a minute. He thought about how Dana took care of the problem she had with the African kids. He almost said something, but Dana had closed her eyes and was slumped down inside her brace.

Mom met them at the door as they trudged in, laughing and showing off their catch. She listened quietly. Slowly the talk died.

Dad looked at Mom's anxious face. "What's wrong, Honey?" Dad asked.

"Chloe and Derrick sent a letter through the border guards. There's been a government uprising. The missionaries are being held under house arrest," Mom started crying gently and drew Dana to her.

Dana pulled out a salty Kleenex. "Here, Aunt Julie. Don't cry. The Lord's going to take care of my Mom and Dad."

Jay patted Dana on the back, touching mostly the brace instead. Dana smiled at her cousin. She looked so calm. It crossed Jay's mind that anyone else would think she didn't care about her parents, but he remembered the crying he had heard that first night they left and the conversation he and Dana

had just had in the car. A feeling of pride rushed over him. This was his family. They cared for each other, but they had strength. They had the Lord.

The next two weeks whirled by in a fog. The people in Dad's church had special prayer meetings for Dana's family. Calls came in from foreign embassies at all hours. Then one evening Jay answered the phone to find Uncle Derrick on the other end.

Dana shouted the news through the house. "They burned down the church!" she yelled through the line that carried her voice across the ocean. "Are they persecuting the native Christians?

". . . Are Kleestan and Molulu all right? . . . What can we do? Are you really safe? . . . I love you. . . ."

"They're all right," Dana said, hanging up the phone. "They're going to stay in Africa. Things are calming down."

Mom started crying again. Jay had a lump in his throat too. Dad just smiled and hugged Dana. "I'm all right, Uncle Martin," she said looking up at him. "Listen, I rattle when you hug me."

He laughed. "I know you're all right. You had more faith than the rest of us."

"Off to bed with you two," Mom said. "Remember you have school starting tomorrow."

Dana bounded up the stairs, but Jay felt like a gray cloud had settled over him. A foggy cloud that wasn't nearly as exciting or even as important as Aunt Chloe and Uncle Derrick's troubles.

Jay woke up to a dull, colorless morning. Pounding raindrops hit at the window, mocking him. "P.K., M.K.," they chanted.

Jay introduced Dana to their teacher. Dad had come the day before and rigged up a desk that would seat Dana comfortably during the long school day. No one in the sixth grade class said anything about Dana's brace.

Instead, they asked her a lot of questions about her African school.

At lunch Dana sat with the girls and made Jay feel that he could leave behind a little of the responsibility he felt for her. He dumped his empty lunch bag and headed out the cafeteria door toward the school yard. Out of the corner of his eye he could see Joe Tally sauntering behind him, closely followed by his friends. From a safe distance Joe mouthed the words "Preacher's Kid." Then he pointed back inside at Dana and started walking like a robot.

Joe's friends started laughing. The back of Jay's neck felt hot. What was it to Joe if his dad was a preacher? And mimicking Dana was even worse. They were all supposed to be Christians in this school, weren't they? He could see Dana inside, laughing and talking with the girls around her. "Cut it out!" he heard himself yelling at Joe.

"Jay?" Dana appeared in the doorway.

She saw Joe and tilted her head sideways. "What's wrong with him?" Joe laughed and ran away with his friends.

Jay could have cried. "He was making fun of you!" He turned to Dana. "Can't you tell when someone's making fun of you?"

She shrugged. "Why should I care? I've always been different one way or another, whether because of being an American in Africa or for having my brace. Some people will always make fun of me."

Jay didn't answer her. He knew he was sulking when he frowned and kicked at the concrete with his shoe. "You shouldn't let people make fun of you," he mumbled.

"If you keep getting mad, they'll keep picking on you," she said. "You should know by now it doesn't do any good to yell and scream at them." His mother and dad were always saying that, but it was easier said than done.

He'd heard that before. *You are responsible for your responses.* He felt his face get red. He wondered if he had looked babyish to scream back at them.

"Maybe what they say bothers me too much," he admitted. "I do get pretty mad at them."

She tapped thoughtfully at her side, her fingernail clicking on the metal under her blouse. "But thanks for sticking up for me."

"Thanks to you, too, then. And thanks for staying so calm," Jay answered. "If we stick together and if we start praying for those guys like you did for your African Christians, maybe I'll start being more responsible for my responses."

"Your what?"

"Never mind," he laughed. "Your friends are shooting baskets—go show them how an M.K. with a funny back brace can shoot."

"Okay, P.K.!"

Ma and Muffin

Jamie Turner

The three little children circled their grandfather's big armchair in front of the fireplace and tugged at his sleeve.

"Oh, Grandpa," begged Meg, the oldest, "please tell us a story."

"A story?" said Grandpa. "And what makes you young 'uns think I have another story to tell?"

"You always have another story, Gramps," said Nora.

Grandpa scratched his head. "I reckon I've told you every story I've ever heard at least a dozen times."

"Then tell us one you didn't hear," suggested Mark. "Make one up."

Grandpa tugged at his beard. "Mmm . . . now there is one I hadn't thought about." He opened his eyes and smiled. "How would you like to hear a story about a boy named Micah and his dog?"

"Yes! Yes! Oh, please! Do tell us!" the children all said at once as they sat down around Grandpa's feet.

Grandpa leaned forward to adjust the pillow behind his back, and then he started.

If you had known Micah's ma the way he knew her, you'd understand why he was so fearful of bringing the pup home when he found it.

Micah Ward and his ma lived in Mississippi at the time—right in the heart of the delta, where the land was as gummy black as licorice and as flat as a giant johnnycake. Micah's pa had been a cotton farmer before he died, sharing part of Mr. Deal's land and working for him. After Pa's death Mr. Deal had let Micah and his ma keep living in their little two-room house. To pay their rent, Ma helped Cass Deal in the garden and around the big house.

One day Micah was walking home after school. He had stopped to examine a dead blackbird whose legs stuck straight up in the air in a wonderful way. As Micah was crouched down beside the bird, he heard a shrill, squeaky noise. It was the same kind of sound the Deals' baby girl, Dovey, made when she patted her hands and squealed. Micah thought at first it was coming from the dead bird, and he all but fell backward in surprise. Then he caught sight of an old ripped cardboard box over in some tall grass and saw it wiggle just a little. He left the blackbird and crawled over to the box.

When he lifted the flap on one corner, he saw a pair of the shiniest molasses-brown eyes, a little brush of yellow tail whipping back and forth, and a rosy, grainy tongue hanging out underneath a little wet raisin of a nose. All this was attached to the cutest little flop-eared pup Micah had ever seen.

"Looka' there!" he whispered.

The pup's whole body was wagging in time with his tail. Micah took him out of his box and lifted him up. He was exactly the color of Ma's sweet muffins—the ones she made only at Christmas time because they called for a whole cup of sugar.

"Howdy there, Muffin," Micah said and then let out an Indian whoop. He had him a pup that someone had likely dumped along the highway.

"Let's you and me go home, Muffin," Micah said, tucking him under one arm and picking up his arithmetic book with the other. Muffin was twisting and yipping with excitement as Micah set off at a trot.

Suddenly Micah stopped in his tracks. What would Ma say when he came in toting a pup? He knew she'd think of Muffin as nothing but a pack of foolishness.

You see, Ma was different from other grown-up women that Micah knew. For one thing, she didn't wear lacy collars and smell sweet like honey-suckle the way

Miss Cates did. Miss Cates was Micah's schoolteacher. She had soft brown hair and stepped dainty like a little wren. But Ma moved like a loaded river barge in her heavy shoes, and she smelled mostly like cornmeal and ammonia.

And Ma didn't generally act cheery the way Cass Deal did. Cass was always laughing and humming while she worked, and sometimes she quoted poetry, like "The world is so full of a number of things, / I'm sure we should all be as happy as kings." But Ma mostly grunted and sighed. The only thing she ever quoted was Bible verses when she thought they fit a certain situation. Sometimes she quoted, "The heart is deceitful above all things, and desperately wicked," like when she caught Micah popping blackberries into his mouth instead of putting them in the pail.

Ma didn't tolerate a lick of nonsense, and Micah knew sure and certain what she'd say about the pup. But when he looked down at Muffin, he knew he had to try to convince Ma somehow to let him keep the pup.

He cut across the field at an angle and put Muffin inside the old fenced chicken yard. Then he went inside to face Ma.

As soon as he opened the door, his heart felt as low as the wet floor Ma was scrubbing. Micah had learned from experience that Ma's mood on scrubbing day was not a thing to be trifled with. She didn't even look up or stop when he walked in, but grunted and said, "Now stay out till I'm done, won't you? I left you an apple right by the door. That'll tide you over to supper time."

But Micah, figuring it would be hard for Ma to get up from her hands and knees and chase him with a hickory switch, decided not to put it off. He took a good bite of apple to wet his whistle, swallowed, took a deep breath, and spoke to her across the wet floor.

"Ma, I found me a dog—the cutest little pup, Ma—and his name's Muffin 'cause he's all gold and yellow-brown, and I saw him by the dead bird in the grass, and I think he must be terrible hungry and lonesome, and I can keep him in the old chicken pen out back, and . . . oh *please, Ma!*" The words came tumbling out all helter-skelter, but Ma understood perfectly.

Her scrub brush stopped swishing, and her broad frame rocked back heavily on her heels. The furrows between her eyes got

deeper, and her stormy gray eyes were threatening some mighty bad weather.

"Micah Abner Ward, I can't believe what I'm hearing," she rolled her eyes upward. "Here I am barely able to feed our own two mouths and you bring home an old mutt to stand around with his jaw hanging open. He can't stay, Micah, so just put the notion out of your mind right this instant."

"But Ma, he can eat table scraps, and you won't have to tend to him at all. I'll do it all, I promise!" Micah said.

"Table scraps!" she snorted. "And since when do we have any of those left with the way you eat? No, Micah, he'll have to go."

Ma was a solid woman, as stout as an oak stump, and she had a will to match. Micah stood there with his eyes swimming in tears. Ma's mouth gave a twitch. Hurriedly, she started scrubbing again with fresh vigor. "He can stay out back tonight, but we'll get rid of him first thing tomorrow." She glanced up, adding quickly, "Now that's the end of the matter. Go on out and leave me in peace."

Supper that night was a solemn business, and after Micah had sopped his last chunk of cornbread in his glass of buttermilk, he asked to be excused.

"Go on outdoors," Ma said gruffly, "and since this is the hound's only night here, you might as well take him this last hunk of cornbread to add to the piece you stuffed inside your britches pocket when you thought I wasn't looking. I'm not a mean woman, Micah, but I *am* sensible. Cute little pups grow into horse-sized hound dogs that could eat more than you and me put together. Now say your good-byes to the dog tonight and get it over with."

Grandpa stopped here and reached over to stir the logs on the fire. Then he got his nail clippers out of his pocket and slowly examined his hands. He snipped off a fingernail or two, frowning and whistling all the while.

The children shifted anxiously.

"Go on, Gramps!" one of them said. "Did Micah have to take the dog back where he found him? What happened, Grandpa?"

Grandpa looked up, pretending to be startled. "Oh! I wasn't sure you were listening to me, but I guess I'll go on."

"Please finish it!" they clamored.

Grandpa chuckled a little and plumped the pillow up a bit more. Then he settled back and continued.

Well, after Micah excused himself from the supper table that night, he went out back and gave the pup some water along with the cornbread and then brought him around to the front porch to play with him. A little bit later Ma came out and sat down in her rocker to do a lapful of mending. She grunted extra hard and began to sew furiously.

"Look, Ma," Micah said after a little. "Ain't he a dandy?" He

was grabbing Muffin with both hands and roughing around with him, rolling him over and pushing him in play. Muffin was barking a shrill little yap and coming right back for more.

Ma just grunted and kept her eyes on her sewing.

The next time Micah rolled the puppy over extra hard, he went tumbling over and over and ended up right close to Ma's rocker. Muffin stood up, but this time instead of coming back to Micah for more playing, he set his eye on Ma and started yipping around her rocker and wagging his whole body, trying to get her to notice him. Her stitches got downright violent, and she kept her eyes glued to her lap. Then Muffin jumped up on the side of her rocker, but was so short he couldn't get his paws to catch hold and stay. So he flipped backward and landed in a little squirmy heap and then got up and tried it all over again.

Micah stared with his mouth hanging open, disbelieving the pup's boldness. Ma just kept on sewing.

Then Muffin started nosing around her feet and just plain showing off with little leaps and dog hollers. He even got down on his back and whirled his little legs in the air like he was riding a bicycle upside down. Then when that didn't work, he grabbed the hem of her skirt and gave a little tug. Ma got mad then and kicked her foot at him and swatted the air like she was after a pesky housefly. "Git!" she said.

But Muffin thought she was playing with him, and he just went crazy, jumping back and forth and nipping at her shoe.

Well, Ma was plumb confused about how to act with all of Muffin's goings-on, and she finally let out one giant puff of air, picked up her mending, and stomped on into the house, slamming the door harder than Micah ever did when she fussed at him for doing it.

Muffin ran to the door and stood there yelping and pawing at the screen, with his head over on one side like he thought maybe Ma was teasing him and playing hide-and-seek.

Early the next morning Ma left the house, and when she came back she said to Micah, "Take the pup over to the Deals' house on your way to school. Cass said they'll take him."

When Micah didn't answer, she said, "Be grateful, boy, that you can at least see the critter once in a while. You know we can't afford to keep him, and I done the best I could for ye." She dropped her heavy hands onto his shoulders. Her voice softened as much as Ma's voice could. "It ain't easy t' be poor, Son, but at least you can see the pup now and then."

"But seeing a dog," thought Micah, "wasn't the same as having him for your very own."

He did as he was told, however, and made sure he rubbed the tears off his face before he got to school.

Micah had never had a worse day than that one turned out to be. He got his lessons all mixed up and even labeled his map of Canada upside down. He walked straight home after school without even going by the Deals's to see Muffin. If Muffin couldn't be his, he decided, it would hurt too much to see him.

But that night during supper, they heard a scratching and whining at the screen door. Looking up, they saw Muffin peeking in, and his tail was wagging so fast it was just a yellow blur.

"Muffin!" Micah cried.

"Stay put," Ma said, but she was too late. Micah had already jumped up and run to the door. When he opened it to go out,

Muffin skittered inside faster than a water bug. He headed straight for Ma and started up again. He fell at her feet in a jiggly heap and squirmed and yelped for her to pat him. She tried to pretend he wasn't there, but it was awful hard to do when the pup was going haywire right at her feet.

Just then Cass Deal came panting up the front steps.

"That little feller is quick!" she laughed. Her eyes were sparkling with fun as she picked Muffin up. "Sorry Mattie," she said to Ma. "He shot out the gate before I could stop him." Muffin whined as she carried him away.

The next night Ma and Micah were sitting on the porch after supper. Micah was struggling over a long-division problem, and Ma was darning holes in his socks. Without warning, a little golden fireball streaked up the steps. By the time Cass Deal arrived, Muffin had yarn tangled around his front paws and Ma was flapping her old faded red-checked apron at him and saying, "Scat!"

Things kept going on like this. Muffin was absolutely smitten with Ma, and every chance he got he'd dig or sneak his way out of the Deals' yard and hightail it over to the Wards'. Then he'd bark and

dance around Ma while she tried to shoo him away. Cass finally quit trying to chase him and just waited for Micah to bring him back home.

One day in late October Miss Cates dismissed school a half hour early. Micah hurried home. He was aiming to ask Ma if he could go over and help Cass Deal gather pecans or rake leaves to earn some cash money.

Micah was heading up the front steps when he stopped in surprise. The door was propped open a little way, and inside he could see Ma sitting with her back to him. She was bent over a little and appeared to be talking to the floor.

"You're a little rascal if there ever was one," Micah heard her say. "Yes sir, you're just stuffed full of mischief. Now stop it, you little scamp. I'm gonna whip you good and proper if you don't behave yourself."

And she laughed, really laughed, and then picked up a furry little ball of wiggles and shook it in play. The little fur ball barked in response and tried to lick her face, and she laughed again right out loud. There could be no mistaking that bark. It was Muffin as sure as the Mississippi River was wet.

"All right, you little scalawag," she went on, "it's time to take you back outdoors." And with that, she turned around with the laugh still on her face and her eyes all crinkled at the corners. When she saw Micah, she stopped dead.

At first, she looked embarrassed and then sort of mad, but then finally the corners of her mouth pinched in and she gave a little halfway smile. Then she came on outside and got hold of herself.

"Well, quit your gawking. For pity's sake, what's a body to do when a pup won't leave her alone, but torments her until all she can do is give up and love him? I talked to Cass Deal this morning and told her we'd take the pup back. I aimed to surprise you with him—well, I can see you're surprised, all right. Pick your jaw up, son."

She looked down at Muffin, who was twisting and yipping as if he'd got hold of a firecracker on the Fourth of July. Micah couldn't think of a word to say, but his grin could have lit up the whole cotton field on a moonless night.

Grandpa looked into the fire a minute, and the children sat quietly. Meg sighed contentedly.

"So Micah got to keep Muffin for his very own dog, Grandpa?" asked Mark.

Grandfather nodded. "Yes, sir, he did. And Muffin was the best little dog a boy ever had. He lived almost thirteen years with Micah and Ma, and no one cried harder than Ma when the little fellow died. I can still see her stroking his tired little head tenderly and crying without shame the day he died. I keep remembering too how Muffin won Ma's heart when he was a pup by just being nice and steady as the sun shines. She finally *had* to give in and be nice right back." Grandpa chuckled softly.

"Grandpa," said Nora. "Micah had the same last name as ours, didn't he? I think you must have known that boy and his little dog. Did you, Grandpa?"

"Yes," said Grandpa, smiling at his grandchildren. "I knew that little boy very well—about as well as I know my own self."

Common
SALT

Candy Jamison

• Salt Makes a Difference

Does a bite of pickle appeal to you? What about a soft pretzel, fresh from the oven, or a big plate of French fries from your favorite restaurant? One thing that makes pickles, pretzels, and French fries taste so good is the salt in these foods.

In parts of the world where people eat mostly cereals, vegetables, or boiled meats, they usually add common salt to their food. This common salt is sodium chloride. It is important to health. For example, a strong, steady heartbeat depends partly on the sodium from common salt. In the United States we "iodize" our common salt before eating it. Iodized salt contains a small amount of the compound potassium iodide. This compound helps keep the thyroid gland healthy and prevents the illness called *goiter*.

Meat-packing companies use salt to preserve some foods. Most bacteria cannot survive in large amounts of salt. This method of food preservation has been used by people since Bible times. Christians are called "the salt of the earth" in Matthew 5:13 because their presence in the world holds back corruption.

People who live in northern climates use salt to melt the ice and snow on roads in the winter. When salt is added to water or ice, a salt-water mixture forms.

This mixture freezes at a much lower temperature than pure water does. Because this mixture freezes at a lower temperature, early car owners added salt to the water in radiators. This did help prevent the water in the radiator from freezing in the winter. But it also made the radiator rust faster. Today car owners use anti-freeze to protect their radiators.

• Salt Is Everywhere

Seawater

Common salt is the most abundant kind of salt in seawater. Common salt and other salts enter the seas through the water cycle. In this cycle, water follows a series of steps over and over again. First, water evaporates. Then it precipitates as snow, rain, or sleet. Next, water flows through or on the ground to the lowest place it can. It will drain into rivers and streams first. These rivers and streams dissolve minerals and salts from the land over which they flow. Eventually they will empty into the sea, depositing their dissolved cargo there. Finally, water evaporates again. When water evaporates from the seas to enter the water cycle again, the salts are left behind.

The seas are growing a little saltier every day as streams and rivers bring salts to them. Evolutionists once thought that they could judge the earth's age by figuring out how fast this salt accumulated. But did the seas start out *without* salt? And have they always gotten saltier at the same rate? Evolutionists assume the answer to both of these unanswerable questions is "yes."

Even with these assumptions, though, their calculations told them that the earth was only a few million years old. Their evolutionary theories required the earth to be billions of years old. They gave up attempting to judge the earth's age from the accumulation of salt in the seas.

Natural brines

Water that contains large amounts of salt is called *brine water*. Seawater can be called brine water. But the term usually refers to waters containing more salt than is in seawater. The Dead Sea (really a lake) and the Great Salt Lake are both examples of natural brines. They both receive salt from rivers. But in each example the evaporation of fresh water is faster than the supply of fresh water from the rivers. This fact makes both "lakes" much saltier than the seas. If you swam in either the Dead Sea or the Great Salt Lake, you would notice the high salt content right away. You would find it easy to float in the salty water, and any cuts that you have would sting as soon as they touched the water.

Rock salt

When common salt crystallizes, it is called *rock salt*. Rock salt is found either in great flat beds or in salt domes. Although salt beds are found in Pakistan and in Iran, not much salt is removed from them. Salt is removed, however, from the salt beds in the United States and Canada. Salt is also removed from salt domes, which are humped salt deposits from one thousand feet to two miles across and several thousand feet deep. Some salt domes in North America extend more than three thousand feet, and some in Europe are believed to extend downward fifteen or even twenty thousand feet.

Evolutionists have a theory of how salt beds and salt domes came to be: salt-water seas or lakes evaporated very slowly to form salt beds, sometimes very deep in the ground; then great pressure or high temperatures made some of these deep salt beds come to the surface and form salt domes. But the evolutionists face a problem that they don't want to admit: there is no evidence to back up this theory.

Creationists believe that God made the salt beds when He made the land, and the salt domes formed as a result of the Flood. Evolutionists say that we hold this belief by faith. However, they were not present to observe the formation of the salt beds either, so they must accept their ideas by faith, too.

The difference between the evolutionist and the Creationist is what they put their faith in: man's ideas or God's truth. The Bible tells us that God made the earth by speaking it into being. Just like everything else in nature, salt formations remind us that He is the Creator.

WHY THE SEA IS SALT

Peter Asbjörnsen and Jorgen Möe
translated by George Dasent

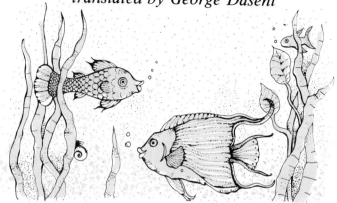

Until the brothers Grimm published their book of fairy tales in 1812, most educated people regarded folktales as something to amuse unlearned peasants or children. The works of these two German men became so famous that people from other countries became interested in reading folklore and exploring its history. Scholars all over the world researched their own cultures for folktales. Peter Asbjörnsen and Jorgen Möe led the way in Norway by working together to write down a collection of folktales. Their works were translated into English a few years later by George Dasent.

Once upon a time, but it was a long, long time ago, there were two brothers. One of the brothers was very rich but the other was very poor. One day the poor brother didn't even have a crust of bread to eat, so he went to see his rich brother.

"My wife and I haven't even got a crust of bread for our dinner," he said. "Surely you will give us something."

"I will give you a whole flitch of bacon," his brother replied. "If you will do what I ask you."

"Why, of course," the poor man said. "I will do anything you say."

"Here is the flitch of bacon then," said the rich one. "And now go straight to the land of Nowhere."

The poor brother always kept his word, so he took the bacon and started off, trying to find the road to the land of Nowhere. He walked and walked and at last, in the evening, he came to a place where he saw a very bright light shining through a house made entirely of glass.

"Maybe this is the place," he said to himself.

So he stopped and looked around, and he saw an old, old man with a long white beard chopping wood.

"Good evening," he said to the wood chopper.

"The same to you," the wood chopper replied. "Where are you going so late in the evening?"

"Oh, I am going to the land of Nowhere," the poor man told him, "but I don't know the way."

"You are very lucky then," said the wood chopper. "For that is the land of Nowhere right behind the glass walls. When you get inside, everyone will want to buy your bacon, for meat is very scarce there. But be sure you don't sell it unless they give you the little quern which stands behind the door. It can grind out anything in the wide world you want. That is, if you know how to work it.

And when you come out again, I will teach you how."

So the poor man thanked the wood chopper for his good advice and then he knocked on the big glass door of the glass house. When he got inside, it was just as the old wood chopper had said. There were hundreds of little gnomes about, all working busily, but when they saw the flitch of bacon they stopped working and wanted to buy it.

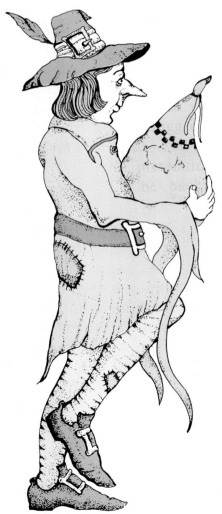

"I want this bacon so that my wife and I can have a good dinner," the poor man said, "but I will give it to you if you give me that little hand mill that stands behind the door."

At first the gnomes would hear of no such bargain, but the bacon looked so good to them that they finally gave the poor man their hand mill. Off he went with it, and the old wood chopper showed him how to work it. He thanked him kindly and then went home as fast as his legs could carry him.

When he got to his own door, he called out, "Come here, Wife, and you shall see what you shall see."

His wife came to greet him, and he put the quern on the table. Then he started it working and made it grind out a tablecloth and meat and cakes and every good thing he could think of to eat for dinner.

Husband and wife had a fine feast, and so it went every day, all through the winter. Then one day they decided to have a specially fine feast and to invite all their friends.

All the neighbors came, and everyone enjoyed the party except—as you may suppose—the rich brother. When he saw all the wonderful food on the table and all the food in the kitchen, he became very jealous. Of course he had plenty of food in his own house, but he didn't want his brother to have any.

"Where did all this wealth come from?" he asked angrily.

And his brother showed him the remarkable little hand quern which could grind out anything in the whole world.

"I must have that quern!" the rich brother said to himself, and he begged and coaxed until finally it was his—for the price of three hundred guilders.

He was so afraid that his brother would change his mind that he paid the three hundred guilders and took the mill home as fast as he could. He went *so* fast, in fact, that he forgot to ask how it worked.

The next day, at dinnertime, he said to his wife, "Now you go into the parlor and sit down while I get dinner ready."

He took the hand quern into the kitchen and bade it grind out herrings and broth. It was very easy to get the quern to work. Herrings and broth started pouring out of it, filling up all the bowls on the table. But it wasn't so easy to get the quern to stop. Herrings and broth started flowing all over the table itself, and then onto the floor. Herrings and broth, herrings and broth poured out of the mill till at last the kitchen was filled to the ceiling. Then herrings and broth started to pour into the parlor and into every room in the house.

The man did everything he could to stop it, but it would not stop. So he took it to his brother's house, running as fast as he could while herrings and broth kept pouring out all over the road.

"Here, take this thing away from me," he shouted when he got to the door. "Take it and make it stop or else the whole countryside will be flooded with herrings and broth."

The brother took it, but only after he had received three hundred guilders more.

Now, you see, he had the money and the quern besides. He lived comfortably with his wife for many years, and every time they wanted something the little quern would grind it out for them.

Naturally everyone was curious about the remarkable mill, and people came from far and wide to see it. It became famous all over the country—all over the world, in fact.

One day a sea captain came to see the quern, and the first thing he asked was whether it could grind salt. When he heard that it could, he said that he must have it no matter how much the cost.

"For then," he thought, "I won't have to take those long sea voyages to distant lands just to bring back salt."

At first the man wouldn't dream of parting with his precious quern, but the sea captain begged and coaxed so hard and offered so much money that he finally consented.

The captain was afraid that the man would change his mind; so he paid his money and went away with the little mill as fast as he could. He went away so fast, in fact, that he forgot to find out how to work it.

He got on his boat and, after he had sailed far out to sea, he bade the mill to grind salt. Now, as you know, it was very easy to start the quern working but very hard to make it stop. So it started grinding salt, and it ground and it ground till the whole deck was covered. Still, it kept on grinding, till the whole boat was filled with salt and, try as he would, the captain couldn't make it stop.

So, of course, the boat being filled with salt, it was heavier than you could possibly imagine and it sank to the bottom of the ocean. There it lies to this very day while the quern keeps right on grinding. And that is why the sea is salt.

An Incident of War

Jeri Massi

The following story is based on the journals of a man whose parents were killed in the Korean War. Orphaned when he was only nine years old, he learned the truth about Communism and how it quickly removed compassion and kindness from its followers. Although some American soldiers were unkind to war refugees, the South Koreans thought of most Americans as heroes and friends, and many American GIs and marines proved their friendship to the civilians that they helped. Unlike the Communist soldiers, the Americans were governed by a special code of laws meant to ensure good treatment of the victims of war.

"Son, today is a swimming day."

From his own window Chung could see the soldiers marching by, directing the jeeps and tanks, shouting orders back and forth.

"I'm afraid to go out there, Father," Chung said.

"Chung Hyong," Father replied gravely. "These are days when every man must master all his fears." He put his hands on his son's shoulders. Chung saw that his father's eyes were wet.

He clung to his father's waist. "Please don't make me walk past the soldiers. At least walk with me, Father, and then I will go swimming."

Father shook his head. "The Communist soldiers won't let me out of the village. You know that. They must be too afraid of spies. But you can go because you are young. Kiss your mother goodbye and go swimming."

"Yes, Father." Chung knew better than to argue. His father was a softspoken man and very gentle, but he had to be obeyed in every point. Chung quickly gathered some old clothes for swimming. His mother was in the small front room. She, too, was looking out the front window, with her back to the door.

"For three days they are here," she said as Chung entered. She thought he was Father, not Chung. "The trees are in full bloom and the branches are heavy. And our village is so tiny."

"Mother, Father is sending me to go swimming."

She started a little, then smiled. "Take your fishing pole, Chung," she said. "But come and kiss me goodbye."

Chung sensed their fear. Not long ago he and his family had all been herded out by the Communists to see what happened to anybody who supported the old Korean government. Hundreds of people had been gathered at the great, powerful waterfalls five miles from the village, where the cataracts of strong water had been crashing down for thousands of years. Great pools almost two hundred feet deep had formed there over the centuries. The Communists had brought their prisoners—men who had served minor positions in the government—had tied them up, and had thrown them into the pools to drown. And Chung had watched, numb with horror.

He had returned home with his family, terrified of the fierce men called Communists. He did not understand what they believed, but he knew what they did.

For weeks afterward he would see them in his sleep, their visored caps pulled down over their harsh faces, their guns ready. Night after night he woke up in the darkness, crying out for his parents.

Mother or Father always came, surrounding him with comfort, holding him close in the sinister darkness. "Chung, Chung, you're dreaming. Wake up, my son." And then he would wake up and see the familiar walls, perhaps feel the softness of his mother's evening robe, and everything would be all right again.

At the beginning of the week, a whole caravan of Communist soldiers and trucks had come into the village on its way south to join the forces at the front. The Communists ate up much of the food, and they refused to let any of the adults out of the village at all. But otherwise they were too busy to do much damage. Chung desperately wanted to stay out of their way. But every single day Father made him go swimming. And every single morning when he left, Mother kissed him goodbye, and he sensed her deep, deep fear as she pressed him close.

"Have a nice time, my son. Bring me home a big fish." She hugged him and kissed him on both sides of his face. "My dear, brave Chung." And she smiled at him and smoothed his lank black hair.

"I am not brave. I am afraid," he said.

"So are we all," she answered.

Father came in. "Stay until dark," he said. And then he picked Chung up in his strong farmer's arms and hugged him. "After the soldiers leave, I will go swimming with you."

Chung obediently trudged out of their thatched-roof house. Mother came outside and waved. He waved back, not knowing he would never see her again.

The soldiers on the road ignored him. They were used to him by now, running down to the lake every single day with his fishing pole.

Once he was out of sight from the village he slowed down. He had to walk a mile before he got to the lake. The sky was clear, but it was not always so. Every day the American planes came overhead. Chung used to wave at them, wondering if they could see him. Father had told him that the Americans were their friends. But now with the Communists in the village, Father looked at the American planes with dread. He was afraid they would attack the Communists right there in the village, and he didn't want his crops and home ruined.

For a long time Chung swam in the water hole. He climbed on the rocks and dived in. After a while he became bored with swimming; so he set up his fishing line and drowsed in the sun until finally the shadows in the swimming hole lengthened. Crickets began to sing. The trees and bushes rustled comfortably. Chung picked up his pole and began the walk back home.

The country still smelled fresh. Mother was right about the trees—they were heavy with leaves now, very thick. "Why did that frighten her?" he wondered.

Overhead in the dimming light a plane droned by and then swept toward the village. He watched it. It was American. It passed low over the village and then began to climb into the sky. Chung saw other planes approaching, a whole formation of B-52s, and his heart swelled a little bit with their beauty and power. He had never seen an American soldier, but he had seen their planes.

Chung watched the formation come down low, closer than he had ever seen them pass before. Suddenly the planes dived and the droning turned into a terrible roar. The grass and trees bent and rippled under them like sea water. He realized that they would be sweeping right over the village. Chung's knees became weak. He had never seen the planes come this low. He wanted to run away from the loud, diving planes, but he burst into a run toward the village.

Just as he crested the hill overlooking his village, the planes opened up their bellies and an explosion shook the very ground Chung was standing on. A hard, hot force like a fist knocked him to his knees. Billows of black smoke erupted from the village like volcanic clouds. Explosion after explosion rocked the valley. There were gunshots from below—the Communists. Chung fell onto his face and covered his head with his arms. Over and over the bombs fell, until there were no more gunshots, no more jeep engines, nothing but explosions. And then even the explosions died away.

He lifted himself onto his hands and knees, but he couldn't lift his head in that awful silence. How long had the bombing lasted? He tried to put it together in his mind. How long? It had silenced all the Communist soldiers. And there had been so many.

Shaking, he stood up. He forced himself to run down the hill, but all he could manage was a shaking sort of limp.

The smoke was clearing. The jeeps and trucks in the streets were on their sides like huge crushed insects. But along the streets there were no houses any more, no trees. Everything was twisted and smoking. Some of the piles of thatch were burning. There were Communist soldiers lying in the street as though they were sleeping.

For a long moment Chung only looked at everything, for-getting all his fear in the wonder of how anything could be so completely destroyed. His mind was numb, but slowly he remembered his fear. He ran to where his house had stood. There was only rubble there now. "Mother!" he screamed. "Mother!" Chung fiercely grasped a piece of timber and heaved back on it. It didn't budge, and he fell over. "Mother!" he screamed again, and threw himself against the smoldering heap. "Father!" But nobody answered.

* * *

The crickets had come back. Chung rolled his head back on the dusty street. He could hear them singing.

The trees. They had hidden most of the village. The citizens had been locked indoors all day. And so the Americans had seen only the trucks and jeeps, the empty fields, and they had thought it was all a Communist camp. And they had destroyed it as duty commanded.

Chung lifted his head. As soon as he did he began to cry again. But he had already cried himself into a stupor once. Now he must get up and act. He had no food and no money. Nothing but a fishing pole. He stood up. Chung heard something, the smack of a

rifle; something like the wind brushed by his face. Before he could even react to that first shot, a sharp pain knifed into his knee and he collapsed onto the ground, writhing in pain. Nearby a hoarse voice spoke in Chinese, then stopped suddenly.

Liquid fire was pounding against the inside of his knee. The hoarse Chinese voice began again. Chung managed to lift his head to look for his danger. Not far away, one of the soldiers was staring at the sky and talking, delirious from his injuries. He had a rifle gripped loosely across his chest. Imagining himself surrounded by enemies, he was shooting every few seconds.

Chung let his head drop back into the dust, and he tried to move, but his knee was badly injured from the rifle bullet. For a long time he lay still, breathing hard and trying not to groan. The pain began to feel far away. He soon fainted and then dropped into a fitful sleep. The next thing he knew, the sky was pink.

When Chung tried to move, pain shot up his leg, and he cried out before he could stop himself. Heart pounding, he waited for the next rifle shot, but the Communist soldier was asleep or unconscious. Far away, he heard voices.

"Now I am delirious," he told himself. "Who could be talking here?"

The voices continued. Chinese voices. Chung understood little of their words. He lifted his head and saw two soldiers coming, holding their guns ready. They saw him and ran up to him. One of them spoke harshly to him. He shook his head and pointed to his knee. "Please help me," he said in Korean, but tears came into his eyes. He knew that they wouldn't help him. The Communists were too savage. They had killed hundreds already. Life meant nothing to them.

The other soldier lifted his rifle straight up, ready to bring the butt down like a club, to kill him, for he was of no use to them because he was wounded. But just then the delirious soldier fired his rifle again, and the two men ran over to him. Chung fainted again. When he awoke, they were gone.

"They had been part of a reconnaissance team," Chung thought. Were the Americans advancing? He raised his head again. The wounded soldier was still lying there across the wide

dusty road. But his gun was gone. Chung looked around and saw that the Communists had taken all the weapons. He called to the wounded man, but there was no answer.

Fighting the pain in his knee, Chung dragged himself along the dusty street. He wanted water, and he had to find it to live. His tongue was swollen inside his mouth, and when he tried to work his lips, dry sharp pains split them like many needle points.

He had to stop, exhausted after only a few feet, but he kept on as much as he could, resting often.

Soon, he came to a puddle in the dirty street. It was muddy and foul, but he put his swollen lips into it and drank from it. When he had revived a little, he cried again for his mother and father. He knew now why they had sent him swimming every day; they had sent him away from the village to save him, but, he told himself, "It would have been better to die with them."

Then he fainted again.

Chung woke up with a fever. He saw that the puddle had evaporated while he had been unconscious. The muddy scum that was left in it was undrinkable, even to him. He tried to move and the fire in his knee tore at him so badly that he knew he must die from it. He sobbed and then cried out.

"Over here, that boy. It was him."

"Could be delirious. See if he's hurt."

Chung stopped his screaming in surprise and fear. He didn't understand the words of the voices nearby. They weren't Chinese. He looked up in time to see a soldier bending over him. Normally the pale eyes and big nose would have been a source of wonder to him, but the green uniform was enough to terrify him. He remembered the Communist soldier, the one who had intended to kill him, and he screamed again, trying to wiggle away from the GI.

"No, sonny, don't do that. Hey, you, Jim! Come and say a few words!" the GI called, getting a grip on Chung to keep him from moving. Chung fought desperately, trying to beat against the soldier with his fists.

Another soldier rushed to the boy's side.

"Friend," he said in Korean. He pointed to the U.S. stamped on the pocket of his uniform. "Americans. We will help you. Don't be afraid of us." Chung

paused from his struggles at the wonder of hearing his own language so unexpectedly.

"Give him water, Lincoln," the man named Jim said in English.

Chung saw the first GI slowly unscrew a canteen. He held up Chung's head and gave him a drink from it. "There you go, old sport," the soldier named Lincoln said gently. "Take a few sips of that." The cool, clean water washed down his throat, and Chung realized that these men wouldn't hurt him after all. Help had come at last. He lay back, panting.

"There, there, little boy, ain't nobody here going to hurt you," the GI said. "I wonder how long you been lying here, poor kid." But Chung, unable to understand the man's words, only looked at him, watching the American's face for some sign of what would happen next.

Meanwhile, the man named Jim Sharpkin walked through the village, shaking his head. "Why did the Reds keep 'em locked up? If only we'd seen 'em in the fields!" he exclaimed to himself.

There was no answer—only the piles of smoldering thatch and

one badly wounded little boy. Sharpkin called his men together around Lincoln, who was kneeling by Chung. The boy had to be taken care of. "Take him by jeep with Redding to the Mobile Hospital," he told Lincoln. "We'll go south and rejoin the platoon." He glanced around. "The only thing I can figure is that the Reds meant to hold the people hostage, but they did their job too well when they kept the villagers locked up."

"Yes, sir." Lincoln looked down at Chung. "He's an orphan, I guess," he said. "Here sonny,

take some more. It's going to be a long trip for you." He offered the canteen again to Chung, who drank from it eagerly.

Chung soon found himself securely fastened to a make-shift stretcher of charred wooden beams and blankets. The soldiers took him to a jeep and laid him across the back seat in the stretcher. A soldier with his head wound in a huge bandage was in the passenger seat. Lincoln drove. He looked back at Chung and smiled. But Chung was too feverish and sleepy to smile back.

He woke up a long time later. There were people moving back and forth, big people with big noses and light skin. Chung saw that he was in a bed that stood on four legs like a wide, flat turtle. His leg was tightly wrapped and felt much better. At first the relief from pain made him grateful, but then he began to be afraid again. To his eyes, the Americans looked goblinish and foreign. There were no friendly, familiar faces like in the village, and worst of all, his mother and father were dead. The grief struck him afresh. No bandages could heal this wound, this shock of having seen the horrible planes drop their belly-loads of bombs. Chung let out a wail. "My mother and father!" he screamed. He didn't even care if the Americans beat him for it. "Come back to me!" he called. "Don't take them away from me!"

Suddenly two big blue eyes looked right into his face and he stopped with a gasp.

"Poor little friend," a kind voice said in Korean. "They cannot come to you now."

Breathless from surprise for a moment, Chung studied the face of the American in front of him. He was clean-cut, with brown hair the color of chestnut shells. He was dressed in a real uniform, pressed and clean, with shining buttons. The soldier wore a patch that was an American flag.

"I am an orphan now," Chung lamented. Deep inside he hoped the American would talk to him, perhaps tell him that none of it was true. Like all his other nightmares, perhaps it had been only a dream.

The American man sat down on the edge of the bed and carefully picked Chung up, cautious of the boy's injured knee. The huge American GI held him on his lap as though Chung were just a little boy. But he told Chung the truth. "Little friend, I not speak Korean well yet. I understand not everything you say. But I know that your family is dead. You survived the bombs alone. I am sorry."

He held Chung tightly while the boy cried, and at last he wiped Chung's face with a white handkerchief that he carried in his pocket. "I also was an orphan," he whispered. And suddenly, as though the idea had just occurred to him, he added, "I will help you."

"He did speak funny," Chung thought. But he was kind. Snuffling and catching his breath, Chung curled up against him and hid his eyes in the uniform. The kind American didn't move after that, and Chung fell asleep in his arms. After that, the soldier set him back in the bed and walked away.

When Chung woke up, a Korean man was by his bed. He talked to Chung about the Communists and how bad they were. Chung agreed. He told the man some of the things he knew about the Communists. Then Chung asked him about the future: what would become of him and how would he live?

The man asked if Chung had any relatives anywhere.

"On the southern coast," Chung said.

"Then you must make your way to them," the man said.

"How?" Chung asked.

"You must find a way."

"I have no money, no food. Can't anybody help me?"

"Our country is filled with little boys and girls just like you. There is no help. We must all find a way to survive until the Communists are thrown out. When peace comes, your family will care for you, or there will be an orphanage for you."

The man went away. Happily for Chung, the American doctors and nurses tried to keep him as long as they could. He could not speak to most of them, but he knew that they were trying to help him. A big bald doctor whose mustache was long and smooth and twisted on the ends like the horns of a bull often spoke to him in Korean.

"Where is my American friend?" Chung asked him.

"Who is that, Chung?"

"The man who took me on his lap my first day here. He wore a patch, a flag."

"That was part of his uniform. What did he look like?"

Chung did not know what to say because all of the Americans looked alike to him. Some of them had brown eyes and some had blue eyes, but other than that, they seemed alike: big, awkward, with bony, pale faces.

"He had shiny buttons," Chung replied at last. "Shiny buttons?" the doctor said in English. He shrugged.

One day the nurses wheeled in a man with a black face and smooth black hands. Chung stared at him all day long while the man, recovering from a brief attack of typhus, slept. Finally Chung himself fell asleep, but when he woke up, the black man was awake and smiling at him.

The black man, named Corporal Johnston, as Chung later discovered, laughed at Chung's wonder. He swung his feet out of the bed and pulled a silver dollar from one of the boots under his bed. He held it in front of Chung. Then he tossed it up, caught it, and opened his hand. The coin was gone.

"Ah!" Chung exclaimed.

Johnston reached behind Chung's ear and pulled the coin out again. He did more tricks for Chung—coin tricks and then tricks with a shoelace from his boot. Finally he lifted Chung onto his back, careful not to bend the bandaged knee, and tried to walk around the ward with him, but he didn't get very far. Johnston was still weak.

After the nurses made them return to their beds, Johnston took the Korean boy onto his knee to show him magazine pictures of America. Chung realized that to the gigantic Americans he must seem younger than he really was, but he wasn't offended by them. As Johnston flipped through the magazine with him, Chung touched the brown face in wonder, then stroked his own, comparing them. He put his hand against Johnston's hand, then lifted his sleeve and compared his arm to Johnston's arm. Chung, who had never seen a non-Korean until a few weeks ago, suddenly had an idea of how huge the world must be. The black man was an American, yet his skin was very different, as different from the white Americans' as Chung's skin was.

Johnston smiled, guessing the boy's thoughts. There was no way to explain it to him, not in English, anyway.

"Has my friend come back?" Chung asked at last.

Johnston shrugged. He couldn't understand Korean.

"My friend," Chung said in Korean. "Shiny buttons," he said in English. It was a phrase he had picked up since coming to the hospital.

"You know somebody in the army with shiny buttons, huh?" Johnston asked. "Well, that narrows it down to about six thousand."

The doctor with the big mustache was walking past. He stopped and said, "He met an American soldier who promised to help him, but that was two weeks ago, and the man hasn't been back. I don't know who it could have been, but the man was in uniform, and Chung remembers the shiny buttons."

Johnston recovered quickly from his illness, and he soon returned to the front. Chung was sad to wake up and find him gone, but to his surprise he found that under his own pillow Johnston had tucked the beautiful silver dollar, a bootlace, and some army money. One of the nurses carefully sewed the army money and silver dollar into Chung's shirt. It would help him on his journey. Chung felt grateful to Johnston, but the sight saddened him. Soon even the doctors and nurses could not keep him, and he would have to leave. "If only my friend would come back," he thought, "he would help me."

When the doctor visited him that day, he brought good news. "I have found a place for you not far from here," he said. "An orphanage. They will take you until the war is over."

"Will somebody adopt me after the war?" Chung asked.

The question caught the doctor off his guard. "I hope so," he said cheerfully. "You are a very good boy." But Chung saw that his heart was sad. Korea was a poor country. Who could afford to adopt a child?

Chung's third week at the hospital drew to a close. He knew that he must leave within a few days. Although the nurses kept many bandages on his knee whenever they could, it was much better. He could limp around the ward to the billowy canvas walls and back. One day he even went through the weatherproof plastic doors and looked around at all the huge army tents in the sunshine before limping back inside when some planes flew overhead. He no longer liked planes.

And so the doctor told him at last that tomorrow a jeep would take him to the orphanage. The nurses found candy to bring him, and they took turns hugging him good-bye and kissing him. Many people left army money for him, and the night nurse sewed it all into his shirt for him.

Chung lay down in his bed. He wondered how his friend would find him. He must make sure to leave word with the doctor. At last he fell asleep.

He woke up much later as somebody was picking him up. Buttons glinted in the faint light from the nurse's desk. "Shiny buttons!" he cried in English.

"Shhhh, Chung." The American soldier gathered Chung's clothes and carried Chung, the blanket, and the clothes out into the starry dimness of the very early morning. He put Chung into the waiting jeep. The doctor was standing nearby.

"I was just told that you are taking Chung," the doctor said.

The soldier nodded. "My name's Frank Barrett. Have you been looking after him, sir?"

"Yes. He was my charge, and I did my best to help find a place

for him. I hope the orphanage is a safe place."

"I appreciate what you did. I'll be keeping an eye on him when I can."

"But why him? How did you know about him?"

"A buddy of mine, Jim Sharpkin, found him while on reconnaissance with an army unit.

He told me about Chung. After I found him, I knew I had to help him."

"But why?" the doctor asked. "There are hundreds of war orphans over here. Why Chung?"

"I guess because Chung called out to me. What else could I do?"

"I wish all men believed that way. The best to you, Captain," the doctor said. "I mean to look you up after it's over to see how the boy is doing."

"Goodbye, Doctor." Barrett climbed into the waiting jeep with Chung.

"Are we going to the orphanage?" Chung asked in Korean.

"Yes. You will stay there while it is safe."

The jeep slowly rumbled through the camp. Safe with his friend, Chung glanced up at the sky and for the first time let himself remember his old friends and his past life in the village. For one brief moment he let himself remember the Communist soldier who had wanted to kill him. Then he let his eyes take one last look at the American camp.

Dawn was coming up over the mountains, and two privates were hoisting an American flag up the squeaky flagpole. The breeze snapped it stiff and straight—a banner of red and white stripes spread out for a moment in the glow of the morning sky.

When the battlefront moved and Chung Hyong again found himself in danger, he traveled with a band of war refugees and followed the American army from place to place. After the war, he entered an orphanage for a short time and then trained himself to become an athlete. In the early 1960s he won several athletic events and received a student visa to come to the United States. He graduated from college in South Carolina and became a citizen of the United States. Here he started his own family and lived close to the former American army officer who had befriended him as a war orphan.

DAMON
AND
PYTHIAS

adapted by Becky Davis

Long ago two friends named Damon and Pythias lived in Syracuse, a city in Sicily ruled by a strong and cruel tyrant named Dionysius. Because they were good young men who loved truth, Damon and Pythias both chafed under the rule of Dionysius. In fact, one day Pythias spoke against King Dionysius in public.

When he heard of it, the king was furious. Immediately he ordered that Pythias be thrown into prison and sentenced to die in one month. And so it was.

When Pythias heard that he was to be executed in one month's time, he was brave enough to request audience with the cruel king to make a request.

"O Dionysius," he said, "I realize that I am sentenced to death in one month. I beg, though, O King, that I may be granted leave to sail home to my parents to say good-bye to them one last time."

Dionysius listened intently until the end. Then he threw back his head and laughed loud and long. "Young man, you are braver than any man I have ever seen." His face grew hard. "You are also more foolish. Only a very stupid ruler would allow a prisoner to leave at all. And you want to travel far away for an entire month! Back to the dungeon with you. There you will sit until the day of your death."

When Damon heard that Pythias had been denied his request, he too begged audience with the king.

"O Dionysius," he said, "I beg that you hear my petition. Let Pythias go to his home to say good-bye to his parents. I will stand in his place until then. If he has not returned by the day appointed for his execution, I will be executed for him."

For a moment Dionysius was speechless. "Now I have seen a man even more foolish than Pythias," he said. "Yes, I will grant your request. But I'm sure that

you will never see your friend again. In one month you will die."

"Pythias will return," Damon answered confidently. "He is a friend that I trust in everything."

So Damon was cast into the dungeon and Pythias was allowed to go free. He boarded the ship and sailed far away to bid his parents good-bye. And day after weary day Damon sat in the dungeon, trusting in his dear friend Pythias to return.

Finally the day appointed for the execution arrived. Pythias had not returned, and Damon was summoned before the king. "Your friend has not returned!" Dionysius sneered. "What will you do now?"

"I am sure that he has been detained beyond his will," Damon replied stoutly. "He will come if he possibly can."

"In the meantime, though," Dionysius shouted, "*you* will go to the executioner!"

But just as Damon was being led to the executioner, he heard a clatter of hoofs and a familiar voice.

"Stop! Stop!" the voice called. It was Pythias! "My ship was detained in a storm," he panted.

"I have done all I can to arrive in time. Do not allow Damon to die in my stead. I have returned." And he ran to the executioner to take his place.

King Dionysius watched in amazement. Just as the execution was about to take place, he ordered, "Halt! We will not execute either of these just men. I will spare their lives. They have been nobler than I." He covered his face with his hands and said, "I only wish that I could be worthy of such a friendship as the one that I see between Damon and Pythias."

Literature Lesson: Legends

Damon and Pythias would have lived over two thousand years ago. Do you think their story is true? History does tell us that there was a tyrant named Dionysius who was harsh to his people. Dionysius, we know, exacted heavy taxes and believed in his own absolute power. But what about Damon and Pythias? Were they real?

Cicero, the famous Roman statesman, was one person who made the story of Damon and Pythias famous. It's likely that the two friends really existed, but different details of what really happened have been told and retold so that you might hear several versions of their story with no two versions being exactly alike.

In some of the versions of this story, Pythias arrived in Syracuse from a conquered land, already a prisoner, to be condemned to death by a whim of Dionysius. Other people tell the story so that Pythias was a noble citizen who took part in a plot to kill Dionysius and was caught. Stories that contain some truth and are passed down from generation to generation are called *legends*.

A legend can be almost completely accurate or almost all fiction. "Damon and Pythias" is close to being accurate, unlike the stories of Robin Hood, for instance. Although a real Robin Hood probably existed, story-tellers and songwriters created most of his adventures for him—in stories and in songs.

King Arthur is another example of a man who has become a part of legend. Historians think that Arthur was a successful general who lived in the sixth century. Yet we know him as a king and as the head of the Knights of the Round Table. If the legends are true, Arthur filled his days with jousts and tournaments, slayed dragons all over England, and rescued fair maidens. What is more likely is that he spent his life fighting off invaders who wanted to conquer his land.

People enjoy legends because legends provide them with heroes.

Damon and Pythias symbolize friendship. Robin Hood was the symbol of what English farmers admired: generosity, courage, and wit. And King Arthur stands for true, unselfish kingliness as well as dignity and fearlessness.

Legends usually grow up around famous people. Think of the stories you have heard about George Washington and Abraham Lincoln. The story of Washington chopping down his father's cherry tree is a modern example of a legend. Even today people are passing down to their children the stories of great men.

Some Special Day

Marie C. Poley

Jesse poked his digging stick a little farther into the dirt, wriggling it in little circles as it went deeper. Again, nothing! He'd been searching most of the morning, getting his sneakers wet and his pants muddy to the knees, and still no arrowheads, not even a piece of flint. He rubbed a grimy fist across his hot face and wished for a drink. "Best be getting back," he said to himself.

As he turned toward home, he whistled for Rusty, the crossbreed farm dog that served as watchdog, hunting dog, and companion. His dad called him the "Heinz dog" after Heinz 57 varieties. Jesse smiled and squinted toward the last place he had seen Rusty. Sure enough, down through the plowed field came his buddy, head to toe in burrs and muddier than Jesse himself, with his pink tongue sliding out of one side of his mouth.

"You didn't find anything either, huh, Rusty?" asked Jesse. He knew the dog had been digging into ground-hog holes all along the field near the fence. That was the best place to look for ground hogs, rabbits, and arrowheads!

Hunting arrowheads, flints, and other Indian relics was Jesse's hobby, something he had learned to enjoy while sitting on the tractor fender as Dad did the farm work. His dad had been farming here in Pennsylvania all his life and had found many relics in the fields as he worked. As he was plowing or harrowing, or even while harvesting, he had a good vantage point from the tractor seat to spot the shiny pieces of quartz. Jesse's mom had taken great care in arranging the Indian relics that Dad had collected over the years. She had bought a piece of hunter-green velvet and then laid the arrowheads in a pattern that was spaced with small pieces of flint. Dad had spent several snowy evenings one winter building a glass-topped table for the collection, and it now sat in a place of honor near the fireplace where, when the fire was roaring, the pieces of quartz caught and reflected the light and shone like gems against the soft, dark velvet.

Jesse enjoyed scanning the table, spying out his favorite pieces. He hoped he could collect enough of his own to display someday. If only he could find some rare pieces that weren't somehow chipped or damaged. It was very hard to find a perfectly shaped arrowhead. So far, he had seven arrowheads, five of which were pure white quartz, and two black flint pieces. Only two of the quartz stones were whole, and the one was worn so smooth that it was hard to tell whether it was a true arrowhead.

"Mom, I'm home!" Jesse called into the kitchen. Mom was setting the table. She smiled at her son. "Any success with the great exploration?" she asked. "You were gone quite awhile today, and by the looks of you and Rusty, not too much dirt was left unturned."

Jesse grinned and put his arm around her while he helped himself to a piece of sliced carrot from the table. "I didn't find anything and neither did Rusty, but I sure am hungry, and I think he is, too. What's for supper?"

"I made potato salad, and we'll grill pork chops on the grill," she replied. "We'll eat as soon as Dad comes in with the plow." No sooner had she spoken than they could hear the rumbling growl of the huge tractor and the clanking sound of the plow rolling behind.

Jesse pushed open the screen door, leaped off the porch, and ran to his dad, who slowed the tractor enough for Jesse to scramble onto the seat beside him. They rode the last few hundred feet together, with Rusty jumping and barking and biting at the big tires as they rolled past.

"Won't he ever learn?" Dad

called good-naturedly above the roar of the tractor. He pulled to a stop and "killed" the engine.

"He just wants to come too, Dad!" Jesse hollered, then realized too late that the great engine had been turned off. He laughed. "Rusty gets jealous because I get to ride and he has to stay on the ground," he added. "Someday I'm going to give him a ride!"

"Well, that will be some special day when I let that Heinz dog ride on my tractor," Dad teased. "And it'll be some special day before I let you drive this tractor alone, Son." Jesse knew Dad was serious about that part.

He sighed. Other kids got to drive tractors for their dads. Jesse's father had done it himself as a boy . . . and had wrecked the family tractor by driving it over a riverbank. That was why he wouldn't let Jesse do it.

"Sorry, Son," he would say. "But it takes responsibility to drive a machine—especially a big, tough machine like a tractor. You'll have to wait."

The Petermans enjoyed the dinner and the cool evening together. Jesse recounted his adventures with Rusty and assured his dad that his chores were done. Then Dad read the Scripture, and each of them prayed in turn. The evening went by quickly, and around nine-thirty they all went to bed. Sunrise on the farm came early.

Jesse groaned and rolled over in bed. He had heard Mom calling his name and, as usual, stayed where he was until she sounded insistent. Knowing he had only a few minutes to get washed and dressed, he hopped out of bed, pushing Rusty off the bed as he did so.

"Are you ready for us to find our treasure today, boy?" he whispered to Rusty as he scratched the dog behind his ears. Rusty looked agreeable and scurried toward the steps. It was a mad race as boy and dog bounded down the stairs. As always, Rusty's feet hit the hall floor first and Jesse's hit a split second later.

"You win again, you 'woofy' dog," laughed Jesse. He could see Rusty was pleased with himself. He always had been since they had started this game four years ago when Rusty was a puppy.

"When you're done with breakfast, Jesse, you need to get the calves fed and watered and make sure *all* the eggs are gathered. Mom said you missed a few last time," Dad reminded him during their breakfast. "And start coming the *first* time your mother calls

you. Concentrate on the important things as much as you do on your fun. I'm glad you're interested and excited about a hobby, but your chores come first. Never make a hobby so important that you lose sight of your responsibilities or put the Lord second in your life, all right, Son?"

"Sure, Dad, but—" Jesse thought of how inviting the farm was. He wished his Dad could see how wonderful it was to call his time his own, forget everything, and go roaming over the farm, looking for arrowheads.

"No excuses, Jesse. If you want to do things like run the tractor and help with the important work, you have to show me you're dependable. Now, no arguments."

Jesse looked down and nodded. He knew Dad was right. "Yes sir."

Suddenly Dad put his arms around Jesse's shoulders and gave him a big bear hug. "Wanna' wrestle?"

Jesse could barely squeeze out a reply but nodded his head very hard before wriggling, without success, to try to get a grip on his dad's great forearms. Soon they were both wrestling around the maze of living-room furniture as Mom looked on.

"I don't know, Dad," she said, "but I think you'll have met your match soon. I only hope you two don't ruin any furniture trying to prove who's stronger. Then you'll both have to deal with me," she warned them laughingly.

Dad gave Jesse a "Dutch Rub" by rubbing his knuckles hard across the top of his head. Jesse whirled around and punched his dad's shoulder one last time. He breathlessly wrapped his arms around Rusty, who had been whining and furiously wagging his tail.

"It's okay, boy. I beat him this time!" Jesse teased.

"Oh boy!" Dad grinned and said, "It's just one of my off days. I'll be heading down to the river field in about an hour. You can ride down with me if you've done your chores right."

As they went out the door, Jesse answered, "I'll try to do better, Dad. I promise."

About two hours later, as Jesse was following a small trail through the woods—one that he had even read about in a historical book about Pennsylvania Indian trails—he heard Rusty barking

excitedly and crashing in the underbrush a few yards away.

Knowing the bark of his dog in the chase of wildlife, Jesse scrambled over a few branches and dived through bramble bushes.

"Get him, Rusty, get him!" he encouraged the dog even before he could see what Rusty had cornered. Then, as he crashed through the trees on the bank of the stream, his eyes opened wide at the sight of the biggest raccoon he had ever seen. The angry animal was spitting and growling at Rusty, who kept bounding at

the stump it was balancing on. The stream at the base of the stump rushed by. The water swirled and foamed around some of the roots that were thrust out from the bank. The stream fell into a small pool before gradually winding through the woods.

Jesse knew that coons could be vicious when cornered, so he tried to pull Rusty away by his collar. "Not this time, boy," he murmured. But the dog, determined to finish off his prey, bounded back toward the coon. As he landed on the stump, it gave way a little from the bank. Just then Jesse saw a glint of quartz at its base. A couple of pieces of arrowheads lay right in the hole that was laid bare. Jesse was so excited that he got down on his knees to grasp at the treasures, but just then the whole stump crashed into the water, taking the dog and most of the bank with it. Jesse's heart sank as the arrowheads fell into the water too. But he had little time to think about them when Rusty gave a terrible yelp from the stream where he was struggling with the coon. The big coon had clenched its teeth into the side of the dog's neck.

Both animals went under water, thrashing wildly about. With little thought of what the coon could do to him, Jesse leaped into the stream. He started screaming and hitting the coon with his digging stick while trying to pull Rusty up. He remembered hearing Dad say that a coon could drown a dog, even one as big as Rusty. The water was one of a coon's best defenses.

He clenched his teeth and pounded the coon again. This time it let go, growling and showing its teeth, but just as the dog was gaining his footing, the coon flew at him. The dog yelped again and tried to turn to face the attack. But again the coon's sharp teeth found their mark, this time on the dog's ear. Both animals were in deadly combat now as the coon dragged Rusty under water.

Fear and excitement overtook Jesse as he scrambled into the current and lifted the largest rock he could find. Then, stumbling and tripping, he got right over the two animals as they rolled near the surface. It was all Jesse could do to stand up straight and land the rock squarely on the coon's back, but the big coon just reared its head back and went down on Rusty's head again.

The dog wasn't fighting now; he was crying. Jesse hit the coon again, this time on the head. That last effort had stunned the coon, and it rolled downstream with the current as Jesse summoned all his strength to pull and lift his beloved dog from the stream.

As he stumbled and tried to gain footing on the bank, Jesse desperately prayed that Rusty would be all right, wondering whether the dog were even alive. Blood and water oozed off the dog's head and neck, and he didn't move at all.

Jesse crumpled to the ground and cradled Rusty's head in his lap, murmuring and stroking him gently. Rusty stirred then, but had no strength to move otherwise.

Jesse knew he had to get help quickly. He took off his shirt, spread it on the ground, and gently laid Rusty on it. Then he grabbed both sleeves and, as quickly as possible and trying not to hurt the dog, pulled him up the trail toward the open field.

As he got into the cleared field, Jesse spotted his dad on the tractor, creating a cloud of dust with the moving equipment. He left Rusty where he lay and ran as fast as he could over the uneven ground. Once he fell and, gritting his teeth against the pain in his knees, scrambled to his feet and continued the desperate run.

Dad saw Jesse coming and slowed the tractor to a halt. He quickly switched it off.

"Dad," Jesse called, "Rusty's hurt real bad 'cause he tangled with a coon. I'm not sure if he's going to live. He doesn't even move or make any noise. Help me, Dad, please!" He quickly climbed up with his father. Dad switched on the huge engine, and the big tractor rumbled down to the woods.

Dad's face was strained as he looked at the injured dog. "Son, you'll have to drive the tractor while I sit on the fender. Rusty's too heavy for you to keep hold of while you try to keep yourself on," Dad said. "Think you can do it?"

Jesse had never driven the tractor alone. Now it scared him. "I'll drive slow enough so it won't hurt Rusty," he suggested with a gulp, hoping his dad would advise him.

"Right. Nice and easy, Son, over the smooth ground, but take the bumps slow."

Together they positioned Rusty on the tractor and Dad held him securely. Jesse climbed up onto the high, hard seat. He cautiously pulled the throttle

down a notch, ready to hit the brake if the tractor jumped out of control.

"It's not engaged!" Dad yelled. "Hit the clutch, Son!"

Jesse pressed the clutch, and the big giant slowly lumbered across the field. He wanted to glance back and see how Rusty was, but he decided not to risk taking his eyes off the route in front of him. Instead, he drove out of the woods onto the smooth field and up the wide path, trusting to his sense of feel to make sure the tractor wasn't bumping too much.

When Mom heard the tractor so early, she ran out to meet them. Jesse pushed down slowly on the brake, trying not to let the big

machine jerk to a stop, afraid of hurting Rusty even more. But it was hard to stop it that way, without using a lot of strength. He hurriedly hit the clutch to disengage the engine and switched the tractor off. All three worked together to lower the dog to the ground. "Kate," Dad said, "call the vet and tell him we're bringing in a badly injured dog. I'll get the truck."

In a short time, although to Jesse it seemed like forever, the three of them were pulling into the veterinarian's drive; an assistant came out to take Rusty. Dr. Bradley, the vet, told them to stay in the waiting room as he examined the dog. In a few minutes he came out.

"Well?" Jesse asked anxiously.

"Oh, it's going to take a lot of repair work," the vet said. "Plenty of stitches, and it's hard to know how all that water's going to affect his lungs yet. But he's strong and healthy; he's got a good chance to recover. I can give you a better answer tonight."

In the pickup on the way home, Jesse gave his dad an account of the episode at the stream. When he came to the part about the stump's breaking off into the stream, he remembered the arrowheads that were lost.

"They were beauties, Dad, but I don't even care about them now. I won't care if I ever find another arrowhead as long as Rusty will be all right." Jesse glanced at his dad with sadness in his eyes. "Do you think he'll be all right, Dad?"

"I don't know, Son. We'll have to leave it in the Lord's hands."

After they got home, Dad pointed to the tractor. "You want to take it to the barn, Jesse?" He held out the keys.

Jesse shook his head. "No." He looked away from the keys in front of him, and Dad slowly put the keys in his pocket. Jesse felt his father's eyes on him.

"Why not, Jesse?"

"It scared me up there. I knew I had to be careful of you and Rusty and keep going and everything, but you were right. I'm not old enough."

Suddenly Dad smiled. "You *felt* responsible," he said. "And that means you *are* responsible." He pulled the keys out and held them in front of Jesse in his big hard palm. "Now you can see it's no joke to drive a tractor. Maybe it's a little scary, but you just tell the Lord you're scared, and you ask Him to guide you. Pretty soon you'll see how much you've depended on Him all along, and then you won't be scared anymore. That's what it is to do the Lord's will. It means depending on Him for everything and trusting Him." He hesitated, then asked again, "Won't you take the keys, Son?"

Jesse looked up. This time he nodded. "Yes, Dad. I guess I will." And he took them.

"It isn't going to be easy if Rusty dies, Jesse, but sometimes even that is part of growing up. Go on now. You park that thing and come inside."

The doctor called that night while Jesse was helping Mom with the dishes. Dad talked to him. Jesse stood by, forgetting the dish in his hand.

Dad hung up and smiled. "Rusty's come through the worst of it, and the vet expects him to make it. We can probably bring him home at the end of the week."

Mom gave Jesse a hug. "Thank the Lord. Rusty's been a good dog. Pretty soon everything will be just the same again," she predicted happily.

"I wonder," Dad said, and looked at Jesse, who smiled for the first time since that morning.

As they settled back into the farm routine the next couple of days, Jesse stayed around the farm, played some ball with some of the neighbor boys, and waited anxiously for Rusty's return. Several times he went down to the field with his Dad to watch the planting, or he scouted out new places where the chickens were hiding their eggs. He was even on time for breakfast.

When Dad came in for dinner one night, he pulled out a soiled handkerchief and laid it near Jesse's plate. "I finished up in the river field today because I'll be planting behind the barn tomorrow. Here's something I found as I was coming back tonight. It was just downstream from where that raccoon fought with Rusty. It's for you, Jesse."

He winked at Mom as Jesse opened the soiled cloth. There, lying inside the dusty white folds was a beautiful—and yes perfect—arrowhead! Jesse gasped as he picked it up and fingered it gently. "It's one of the arrowheads from under the stump, isn't it? Thanks, Dad," he managed to get out. "It's the best one I've ever seen, and just when I wasn't going to look for any more."

Dad put his arm around his son's shoulder and hugged Mom

with the other arm as he said, "I know, Son, and I'm glad you were able to realize they're not the most important things. The Lord tested you to show you what was important. You saw that you might have lost Rusty because of your love for arrowheads."

Jesse set the arrowhead aside. "Thanks a lot, Dad. Nothing's been just the same since Rusty got hurt. You told me what responsibility was, but that was the first time I ever really knew what it was."

Mom smiled. "Dad always said it would be some special day when you drove the tractor. I guess he was right."

Dad took the arrowhead and set it on the kitchen counter. "I'll put that in the case tomorrow after I bring Rusty home."

"I'll help," Jesse offered. He grinned at his Dad. "Can I go park the tractor?"

SHOWDOWN IN DUST RIVER GULCH

Timothy N. Davis

WANTED!

GRUFFLE O'BUFFALO
ALIAS
"GRUFF"

"GUILTY OF CRIMES AGAINST THE PEOPLE"

Now don't get the notion that the folks in Dust River Gulch were a bunch of softies. Nothin' could be further from the truth. Dust River Gulch was inhabited by some of the wildest characters west of the Mississippi. Few human-type outlaws would test a town whose sheriff was a thoroughbred mustang. But this here Gruffle O'Buffalo—now there was a different sort of outlaw. He was wanted in seventy-eight counties and half a dozen zoos—it was no wonder the folks of Dust River Gulch were feelin' a mite queasy when they heard he might be passin' through.

It wasn't that folks didn't have confidence in Sheriff J. T. Saddlesoap. No doubt about it, he was an awe-inspirin' figure—a mighty good lawman and a fine-lookin' horse to boot. Many's the wild and woolly outlaws he'd driven out of town. But, y' see, this was different. This was Gruffle O'Buffalo.

Well, seems as if it was old Tumbleweeze McPhearson that mostly started stirrin' up the townsfolk. Over at Rosie's Restaurant, he was a-gobblin' down some grub when he leaked out the rumor.

"Yep, 'bout this time tomorrow, I reckon most folks'll be sittin' in their houses with the doors bolted up."

Old Bo, the lizard, leaned over from the next table. "Whatcha talking 'bout, Weeze?"

"Nothin' other than Gruffle O'Buffalo and his gang of bum steers," replied old Tumbleweeze with a snort.

"Gruffle O'Buffalo!" Old Bo got so startled that he dropped his spoon—per-clunk.

Well, the murmurin' started up mighty quick-like all through the restaurant. 'Fore long every ear in the house was tuned in to old Tumbleweeze. (It was the usual way news got around in Dust River Gulch.)

The old weasel continued, "Yep, word has it old Gruff an' his gang are comin' to town tomorra."

"Tomorrow?" squealed Rosie, who kept the restaurant as tidy as her own kitchen. "Somebody go get J. T.!"

As a wild-eyed prairie dog went a-scamperin' after Sheriff Saddlesoap, Old Tumbleweeze kept on a-stirrin' up the folk.

"I heard the last town old Gruff and his gang passed through—the folks haven't nearly recovered yet."

While some folks were tremblin' and whisperin', Bo asked, "Why haven't they?"

"Well, he an' his gang done humiliated the sheriff an' his deputies so bad that they high-tailed it outa town. So then the folks were so scared they just did whatever old Gruff was a-mind to ask 'em." Tumbleweeze paused to munch a spell. "Nearly stole the town blind, they did."

A scrawny buzzard asked, "You think Sheriff J. T. can take 'em on?"

Tumbleweeze shrugged. "I don't know. Gruff's ruined plenty of sheriffs in his day."

Well, at that comment the mutterin' an' murmurin' got near a deafenin' pitch there at Rosie's Restaurant. Some folks were sayin' they'd been a-plannin' to be out of town the next day anyway. And the rest started makin' such-like plans.

But Miss Rosie, she wouldn't have none of it. She started a-scoldin' and a-shamin' those folks for not trustin' in Sheriff J. T. like they should've. 'Course, everybody knew she had a sweet spot in her heart fer J. T., but they took the scoldin' to heart anyways.

The little lady mustang kept on a-going. "Why, he's the finest, bravest sheriff you'll find in any county, anyplace! No outlaw's gonna run him outa this town! No, not J. T. . . ."

Then the doors swung open. In walked none other than Sheriff J. T. Saddlesoap himself. "Why, thank ya, Miss Rosie. That's mighty sweet of ya."

Miss Rosie turned sorta pink-like as J. T. smiled over at her. "Well, it's true, isn't it, J. T.?" she said. "You're gonna stand up to that there Gruffle O'Buffalo an' his gang, aren't you?"

J. T.'s smile looked a mite strained, an' he swallowed mighty hard. But he said he would. If nothin' else, he wouldn't make Miss Rosie into a liar.

Well, tomorrow came a mite sooner than Sheriff J. T. was a-hopin'. Seemed like most folks decided to stay in town after all,

seein' as how Sheriff J. T. was a-gonna stand up to Gruff an' his gang. They weren't about to miss that, now were they?

Round about noontime, old Tumbleweeze was out in the street with his ear to the ground. Lots of folks was a-watchin' real quiet-like. Perty soon he spoke up. "They's a-comin'! I kin hear the rumble!"

Everybody cleared the street and waited. They was a-lookin' out windas an' peerin' 'round barrels. Miss Rosie's Restaurant was jammed with folks, eatin' and strainin' their necks to see 'round each other outside.

No doubt about it, that cloud of dust on the horizon was gettin' closer every second.

J. T. was a-waitin'. He wouldn't start no trouble—but as sure as he'd promised Miss Rosie, he wouldn't stand for none either.

So into Dust River Gulch they came—old Gruffle O'Buffalo an' his gang of bum steers. They did a little hootin' an' hollerin' an' then they headed to Rosie's.

Everybody was actin' as calm as they could inside—but most folk were sweatin' like it was two hundred degrees. Then in sauntered Gruff and his steers.

"We's hot!" rumbled the big, mangy buffalo. He turned to

Rosie, standing behind the stove. "You there, give m' boys some milk shakes."

Rosie went right to it an' served those five bum steers real quick-like. They started a-slurpin' an' a-sloppin' it like the no-'count critters they were. Meanwhile, ol' Gruff, he was a-saunterin' 'round the place like he was king. He plucked the cherry right off the top of one buzzard's sundae. Gruff smiled an' rubbed his straggly-lookin' beard whiles he ate that cherry. The buzzard didn't say nothin'. Fact is, the only sound in the place was the slurpin' an' sloppin' of those bum steers, startin' in on their second round of milk shakes.

Finally, Gruff seemed 'bout strutted out, an' he found a table to his likin'. So old Gruff, he took a seat. Poor old Bo, the lizard, he was already a-sittin' at that same table. Gruff sorta gave him th' eye an' rumbled, "I prefers a private table, myself." An' Bo, he pert near melted to the floor an' slithered over to the next table whiles Gruff chuckled to himself.

"Hey, gal," Gruff yelled out real sudden-like. "I's ready t' order." So Rosie, she hustled on over to his table. "Give me a gallon of the sourest, smelliest, most curdled-up milk ya got," growled the shaggy outlaw.

There was some quiet-like oohin' and ahhin' at that, an' Gruff sat back in his chair with a satisfied snort.

Then Rosie just said, "Only *one* gallon, sir?" in a smart-alecky sort of way.

Gruff, he raised himself up and rumbled out, "Nah, make it *three* gallons, gal! An' quick-like!"

Perty soon Rosie came back with the sourest milk you ever smelt! Gruffle sorta chuckled an' drank it all down like it was nothin' to him. Course, everybody at Rosie's couldn't hardly believe it.

The old buffalo let out with a hiccup an' yelled over to his gang of bum steers (still a-slurpin' an'

a-sloppin'), "C'mon, boys! We's a-goin'!"

So the whole bunch of 'em started for the door. Most of the folks started breathin' normal-like again—that is, till Miss Rosie spoke up. She said, "Sir, you an' your boys haven't paid your bill."

Then Old Gruff turned around real slow-like an' looked Rosie in th' eye. An' it got quiet—terrible quiet. Then the bum steers started a-laughin' an a-snortin' like nobody's business, an' out the door they went. And Gruffle, he started a-saunterin' out, too.

Then Rosie (she was a mighty plucky lady mustang) said flat out, "Sir, you haven't paid."

The bum steers couldn't hardly take it, they were laughin' so hard. Old Gruff strutted over to poor old Bo an' picked him up by the kerchief an' set him on a table by Rosie. He blew out some sour milk breath and said, "My friend here says he'll pay." An' the bum steers started a-howlin' with laughter.

But the laughin' didn't last long this time. 'Cause who do you think came through the swingin' doors? None other than Sheriff J. T. Saddlesoap.

Gruffle smiled an' said, "Well, if'n it ain't the sheriff!"

J. T. just looked at Rosie an'

asked, "What's the trouble here, Miss Rosie?"

Rosie told him, whiles Gruffle sorta snickered an' rubbed his mangy beard. The bum steers, gettin' mighty interested in the goings-on, sauntered back into Rosie's. One of the mangiest of 'em spoke up. "Whatcha gonna do about it, Sheriff?"

J. T. puffed up his chest an' replied, "Gruffle, you're not gettin' away with anything in Dust River Gulch. Pay up an' get outa town."

Gruff sauntered over till he was 'most in J. T.'s face an' breathed out in sour-milk breath, "Who's gonna make me, Sheriff?"

"You're lookin' at him."

Well, Gruff, he started smilin' an' rubbin' that mangy beard of his.

"Maybe we can make a deal with this here sheriff, eh, boys?"

The bums a-snorted an' a-snickered. "Yeah, boss. Maybe."

"You boys want a little entertainment?"

"Yeah, boss!"

Gruffle smiled real mean-like an' said, "How 'bout we have ourselves a little rodeo, Sheriff, just you an' me?"

"What're you sayin', Gruff?" asked the sheriff. The steers commenced their laughin' again.

"We'll have a rodeo. You ride me an' I ride you. An' the one who stays on the longest is the winner, see?"

Well, now, that mangy buffalo musta had nearly a thousand pound on J. T., but one glance in Miss Rosie's direction, an' the sheriff figured he'd accept the challenge. "If I win, you'll pay up an' get outa town, right?"

Gruffle snorted his approval. "Gladly, Sheriff. But now, if you might just happen to lose, you'll do the same?"

J. T. nodded.

". . . that is, if'n you kin still walk." An' at that the bum steers started a-snickerin' an' a-snortin' like nobody's business again.

"Let's go, Sheriff," grunted Gruff.

So out went the outlaw an' the lawman, followed real close-like by the snickerin' steers. An' then 'most the whole town gathered 'round in front of Rosie's Restaurant.

Gruffle an' J. T., they stood on opposite sides of the street, a-loosenin' up an' eyein' each other real fearsome-like. They decided old Tumbleweeze would keep time, along with one of the smarter bum steers (or at least one of the less dumb ones, that is). J. T. would ride Gruffle first, then vicey-versey.

Gruffle, he had a sneaky, sly sorta smile on his face like he was up t' somethin'. An' wouldn't you know it—he was. When nobody was a-payin' no mind, he slipped one of the spurs off his boot an' hid it in the thick, mangy hair on his back, real secret-like. He whispered what he'd done to his no-'count steers, and they started some fearsome snickerin'.

Meanwhile, J. T. was developin' a perty sizable lump in his throat. He hadn't never ridden no buffalo before. 'Specially not when it counted fer so much. Miss Rosie, she musta' sensed it, 'cause she ran over t' him an' planted a big, sweet kiss on th' end of his nose an' said sweet as anything, "Whoop him, J. T.!"

With a spark in his eye, Sheriff J. T. Saddlesoap called out, "I'm ready, Gruffle! Are you?"

Gruffle O'Buffalo, he smiled an' snorted out, "Yep." An' there he stood, ready t' be ridden.

All the folks held their breaths. Then J. T. galloped over an' hopped onta Gruffle's back.

"Start a-timin', Weeze," called out Miss Rosie. An' he did.

The mangy outlaw started a-buckin' an' a-snortin'. He ran 'round in a circle front-wise an' back, sendin' some folks fer cover. Up he reared an' down he tramped whiles J. T. was a-bouncin' 'round on his back like a jackrabbit.

"Ride'm, J. T.!"

"Yahoo!"

"Whoop'm, Sheriff!"

"Ride him right outa town!"

Meanwhiles, the bum steers was a-snickerin' a mite less. But Gruff was a-snortin' up a storm. He was a-twistin' in contortions an' a-kickin' like a mad billy goat.

J. T. was a-feeling like a sack of pataters that's been bounded downstairs, but he was still a-holdin' on. Then he hit that spur.

"Yee-ooowww!"

The spur sent J. T. up past the roof of Rosie's, an' down he landed in a cloud of dust. But one glance in the direction of his favorite gal, an' he claimed he was just feelin' a mite sore.

"One minute an' forty-two seconds!" announced Tumbleweeze.

Old Bo, the lizard, was so excited, that he yelled out, "Beat that, you outlaw, you!"

But Gruffle, he shuffled over inta Bo's face an' blew out enough sour-milk breath to send old Bo into a coughin' fit.

"Heh, heh." Gruffle turned to J. T. an' snorted, "Yer next, Sheriff. Now I ride you."

So J. T., he dusted himself off and stood in position, still a-catchin' his breath.

Gruffle reared up an' took a flyin' leap onto J. T.'s back. Whomp! J. T. was squished as flat on his face as a bearskin rug.

"Start a-timin', weasel," chuckled Gruffle. An' he did.

Thirty seconds went by, an' the bum steers was all smiles. Y'see, Sheriff Saddlesoap hadn't got up off his face yet.

"C'mon, J. T.!"

"Buck him, Sheriff! Buck him!"

"Git up, J. T. You can git him yet!"

The bum steers was a-laughin' like nobody's business by now 'cause J. T. was still a-squirmin' underneath the big buffalo.

But how was old Gruff a-doin'? Seemed like he shoulda been laughin' louder than them all. But he weren't. Nope, instead he was a-lookin' kinda greenish.

One of the bum steers noticed it. "What's wrong with the boss?"

"Dunno. He's lookin' mighty queasy, though."

An' sure 'nuff, he was. His face was a-puckerin' an' a-twitchin'. Seems like that three gallons of sour milk had got mighty churned up. He was groanin' an' moanin' an' holdin' his stomach. Then he let out with a hiccup and rolled right off J. T.'s back, howlin' like a shot coyote.

Folks' mouths dropped open. They was so shook up they couldn't hardly say nothin'.

Sudden-like, over the moanin' of the sickly buffalo, old Tumbleweeze spoke up an' said, "One minute an' twenty-nine seconds."

Then what a ruckus there was! All kinds of cheerin' an' yellin'!

"You did it, J. T.!"

"You won!"

"Way t' whoop him, Sheriff!"

J. T. he stood himself up an' brushed off the dust. Folks was jumpin' 'round him an' shakin' his hoof, congratulatin' him like he was a livin' legend or somethin'.

Seein' as how they was licked fair an' square, the bum steers started sorta sneakin' outa town with their moanin' boss slung over their shoulders.

"Hey, boys," yelled out Rosie, "You haven't paid!"

"Ain't paid!" shouted some old prairie dog. "Why, we oughta tar an' feather 'em!"

"That's too good for 'em," yelled Bo. "We'll let J. T. take 'em on!"

"Yeah, but let me get a piece of 'em first," hollered some burly mountain goat.

The bum steers emptied out their pockets as quick as a flash an' started runnin' like fresh-branded cattle clear outa Dust River Gulch.

An' the cheerin' an' celebratin' commenced all over agin. The folks carried J. T. into the restaurant. 'Most everybody wanted to buy him a sundae er a shake er some such-like thing.

"Don't spoil his appetite now," said Rosie, "'cause I'm gonna cook him the best-tastin' supper he ever laid eyes on . . . ," she glanced kinda shy-like over to J. T. ". . . that is, if'n he'll accept my invitation t' supper."

"Miss Rosie," replied the Sheriff, "I wouldn't miss it fer nothin'."

Well, nowadays folks still listen to old Tumbleweeze tell 'bout the time old Gruffle O'Buffalo an' his gang of bum steers came to town whiles they're a-slurpin' down their milkshakes at Rosie Saddlesoap's Restaurant. An' Rosie, she an' J. T. keep plenty of sour milk on hand, just in case.

CREATURES
GREAT AND SMALL

The Ship of the Desert

Becky Davis

You can go for a ride
When it isn't high tide
  On a specially different kind of a ship—
Far across desert sands
In Arabian lands
  Take a rolling and rollicking holiday trip.
    For he'll roll and he'll rock
    When he's not safe at dock—
      The unusual ship of the desert.

He will kneel on his knees
Just as nice as you please
  So that on his broad back you can easily jump.
But when he stands up tall,
Hold on tight—or you'll fall
  From his lumpity, humpity, bumpity hump.
    For he'll weave to and fro
    When he's walking, you know—
      The remarkable ship of the desert.

He can close up his nose
When the desert wind blows.
  He can go without drinking or eating a snack.
So for many a mile
You can travel in style,
  For he carries his food in the hump on his back!
    Though he may kick and bite,
    You had best be polite
      To this wonderful ship of the desert.

Shady's Fourth

Joanne Hall

We found her on the Fourth—our dog, Shady, I mean. We always spent the Fourth at a family picnic at Grandpa's. His fireworks displays were the envy of his neighbors. Throughout the long day we would sit around the yard with all our cousins, eating fried chicken, potato salad, and the other good things that Grandma made. Maybe in the afternoon we'd get a ball game started, but really we were all just waiting until dark when Grandpa sent up his fireworks display.

Everything went well. Grandpa's fireworks were beautiful, and we'd had a good time trading baseball cards with our cousins. We started for home at ten o'clock in the evening. When we got back, there was a dog sleeping under the shade tree in our back yard. How she got into the yard was a mystery, because it was surrounded by a six-foot chain-link fence and the gate was closed.

The next day Dad looked for a hole in the fence or in the hard-packed earth around the fence, but he couldn't find any sign of how the dog had entered. One of our neighbors told Dad that maybe the dog had jumped the fence to get into the yard. Dad wasn't sure about that. It was a high fence.

"Well, she still might have done it if she was scared enough or angry enough," our neighbor said.

One look at the strong, slender dog and her friendly, alert eyes told us that she could never be *angry*. But what could have frightened her?

My twin brother, Jeff, and I loved her at sight and begged Dad to let us keep her. Her warm brown eyes and wagging tail told us she wanted to stay.

But Dad said, "No, boys, we'll have to advertise that we've found a dog and see if someone claims her." That was that; we knew we were going to lose her. Anyone with such a beautiful and graceful dog would want her back. But the dog had already become Shady to us, named after the shady spot where we had found her. That same spot was already Shady's favorite place in the yard.

When we told Mom and Dad what we had named the dog, Mom reminded us, "She's not ours, remember?"

Our older brother and sister laughed at her name, but Shady didn't seem to mind, and so Shady she was, forever. No one ever did answer the advertisement that Dad put in the paper, so Shady stayed with us in our big fenced-in yard. After coming to live with us, she never seemed able to jump the fence, though Jeff and I often coaxed her to try. She always insisted on leaving and entering the yard through the gate.

Then the next Fourth of July came. We went to Grandpa's again and stayed to watch his fireworks display. We knew that this year there would be fireworks in our own neighborhood, but nothing could compare with Grandpa's setup. We left Shady penned up in our yard where we knew she would be safe.

That night we returned from Grandpa's house as usual and ran to say goodnight to Shady. We looked everywhere in the yard, around the house, but we couldn't find her. Shady was gone! She had disappeared as mysteriously as she had come.

The next day we went from door to door asking people if they had seen our dog. And again our neighbor told us that Shady must have had some reason to try extra hard to jump that fence. "She was either scared or mad—one or the other," he insisted. "Something put her half out of her senses, so she hopped the fence. Hope she didn't hurt herself."

We felt glum after talking to him. But when we got back to the house, the man who took care of a swimming pool near our home called to tell us that a stray dog was at the pool. Jeff and I raced each other to the pool. There lay Shady under an umbrella table. She almost knocked us to the ground with her greeting, wiggling and squirming with happiness. Well, she was no happier than we were, but Jeff noticed that she was limping, favoring her back left leg as though she'd strained it by jumping too high.

"Why did you disappear like that?" Jeff asked Shady. "We've left you alone before and you never left the yard. How did you get out?"

Shady only wiggled harder and licked his hands. How and why she left the yard remained a mystery. It was hard to imagine good-natured, gentle Shady becoming angry enough to try a ferocious trick like leaping the fence. And we didn't know of any animal or person big enough to scare her into doing it.

After the next school year was over, we moved eight hundred miles away to a different house, a different town, a different state; no more summer picnics at Grandpa's we thought, not for a long time, anyway.

Shady loved the new house and settled right in. After a few weeks, she acted as if she had been there for years. We quit worrying about the unfenced yard and enjoyed the summer. About the second of July, our cousins came to visit, bringing a big supply of fireworks with them. We checked with the police about the laws concerning the use of fireworks. "Sure it's legal to set off fireworks in your backyard," the officer told us. "There'll be no trouble unless your neighbors complain."

Well, Mom and Dad didn't want to bother the neighbors, so they asked around. No one minded; in fact, they said they would like to watch!

So we really treated them to a show. Toward the end of our fireworks display, our high-school-age cousin set off a whooping big firecracker that brought all the neighbors out of their houses! The man at the store had told him it was a good one to use last. "It'll be a gigantic array," he had promised. But my cousin never would have bought

it if he'd known how gigantic it was! At first he had wanted to keep up with Grandpa's reputation for terrific fireworks displays. But the first crash of explosions made the windows in the house shudder and gave my ears the feeling that I'd been hit—a stunned, aching feeling. The explosions went on, louder and louder, while sprays of red rained down around us. The colors were pretty enough, but the thunderous explosions were almost too much for just neighborhood fireworks.

The noise went on and on— crash, bang, crack, pop, boom! Somebody's baby started crying. Fire and sparks kept spraying high into the air and falling on the grass and bushes. There was nothing anyone could have done to stop it, or, believe me, my father would have! When the show ended, we knew that was the last fireworks display we would have. The commotion we had caused had been the end of our fun. We were all embarrassed, especially our cousin.

After we cleaned everything up, we looked for Shady. She was gone again! Jeff went down the street, whistling and calling for her, and I went up the street, doing the same. But there was no sign of her. For days we expected her to come home, back to her food and back to the ones who loved her. But she didn't.

"Why does she run away?" Jeff asked. "We take good care of her and we love her. I know she loves us!"

"Of course she does," Dad said, "but have you two ever thought about *when* she runs away?"

I blinked. "Why—on the Fourth of July!"

"Yes," Jeff exclaimed, "We found her on the Fourth and she

has run away every Fourth since then!"

"She's afraid of fireworks!" we both said at the same time.

Well, the truth had dawned on us, but it was too late. Shady was gone and probably lost in a strange city. We'd never see her again! Oh, why had it taken us so long to realize how terrified Shady became when fireworks began to flash?

We didn't give up. We looked and looked. We cried and prayed all week. Then one bright day, about a week later, I was in the car with my older brother on a busy highway on the other side of town. He was driving and trying not to look too proud of himself for having his license. I was staring out the window,

looking at the pedestrians, when suddenly I saw a familiar sight— a flash of brown and tan disappearing among the legs of all the people.

"Stop! Stop!" I yelled, grabbing at my brother Louie.

"What's the matter?" He slowed down, but kept on driving.

"That looked like Shady!" I exclaimed, pointing at the crowd.

My brother gave me a disgusted look. "There's no way Shady could be this far from the house. We're twenty miles from home. That's some other dog."

But when I insisted, he stopped the car. I ran back down the sidewalk, yelling, "Shady! Shady!" I dodged through the crowd and called for Shady, all the while apologizing for brushing past people. "Excuse me, excuse me," I would say, and then yell, "Shady, Shady!" I caught sight of her again. "Shady, come back!" I called.

The dog stopped and looked back at me. I was so afraid she would run again. I called and called. Finally the dog's tail wagged; then she turned and began to run—toward me! Shady charged down the sidewalk, scattering pedestrians on the way. She practically knocked me down, lapping my face joyfully. I kept saying, "Shady, it's you! It's really you!"

By this time, my brother had parked the car and had caught up with us. "Okay, I was wrong. It's Shady," he said and I looked up at him triumphantly. "Let's take her home."

Still shaking his head in amazement, he herded us back to the car while the people stared. Shady leaped into the car without being told and we joined her, heading for home.

Where Shady had been going, we don't know. She was just running away from the "rockets' red glare" and the "bombs bursting in air," I guess. Maybe she thought she was going home to Illinois, the home she had found when she settled under our shady tree that first Fourth of July. But it didn't matter. Shady was home to stay. You'd better believe we would be more careful when the next Fourth of July rolled around!

The Silent Witness

adapted from a true story by Carl Trevor

Cato lay still in his hammock and listened to the whisper of early morning waves on the beach. Closer by came the whirr of night insects and the fluttering of the birds that roosted in the thicket outside the hut. Turning his head, Cato could see the pale rectangle that framed the dawning light.

Outside, the sky would be flaming pink and orange over the sea, but inside the hut, night shadows still cloaked familiar objects. Something stirred in the darkness. Cato's eyes followed the movement, knowing it had been made by his wife's black and tan short-haired dog. There had been no children to bless his marriage to Mera. Years ago, when Cato had brought home the fuzzy, roly-poly puppy, the dog had changed Mera's heart. Now, old and silver-muzzled, the dog she called Punik seldom moved more than a few feet from his mistress, still returning her love with devotion and protection.

Cato's eyes moved upward from the dog, seeking the sleeping form of his wife. As he watched, her hammock swayed. The shadows shifted as Mera's feet sought the floor, gently sliding over the dog to rest on the dirt floor.

The pale light touched her face and silvered the gray in her hair as she bent down to pat the old

dog on the head. Punik's thin tail happily thumped the floor. Then, wrapping her shawl around her shoulders, Mera left the hut. Punik got up and padded after her. Cato stirred restlessly. Mera would be gathering driftwood to start a cookfire. By the time the fire burned hot, others in the village would be awakening. The smoke from the cookfires would drift through the thicket, and the deep, rich smell of corncakes would bring the men from their hammocks.

Cato took a deep breath of the sea air. "A good day for fishing," he thought, and sighed. For six days of the week, his friend Tali fished with him. Today was the seventh day and today was different. Today was the day Tali, his wife, Belee, and Mera called Sunday. On Sunday they went to the mission church outside the village. And every Sunday Cato fished alone. Not that they didn't ask him to join them. No, even good-natured and easy-going Tali was often persistent in trying to persuade Cato to go to the church and hear the missionary.

Outside, the fire crackled and blazed up. The roosting birds screeched and beat the air with their wings as they left the thicket. Cato swung his feet over the hammock and stood up in one easy motion. He left the hut and walked to the fire. When he stopped beside Mera, she fanned the smoke out of her eyes and smiled up at him.

"Will you go with us today, Cato?" she asked.

Cato looked away. "There will be many redfish today. Perhaps some other time."

The smile left Mera's eyes but she nodded. "We will be ready to eat soon," she said.

Cato strode down the sandy path to the beach and leaned down to check his boat. Light and long, it lay on the sand beside the boats of the other villagers.

Satisfied, Cato walked to the edge of the sea and looked out over the water. As always he marveled at the brilliance of the sun as it rose from the night, paling the dark water to pink and silver, then to blazing gold and blue green. The waves crashed on the sand, spinning the shining foam almost to Cato's feet, then breathing the foam back into the water. Cato breathed with the ocean, feeling its pull in his own body. Impatient to be skimming over its surface, he turned away and hurried back up the path to the hut.

Punik looked up and wagged his tail as Cato climbed over the ridge of sand and rock that separated the village from the open beach. When he reached the hut, Mera took the last corn cake from the cookfire. Cato ate hungrily, enjoying the crisp texture of the fried cakes.

"Where will you fish today?" Mera asked.

Cato swallowed his last bite. "There'll be some redfish near the lagoon," he said, knowing she worried about him when he went out without Tali. "I'll fish there. Maybe get some lobster," he added with a smile. "You can take some to Pastor Sam."

Mera smiled too. All the villagers knew of Mr. Sam's love for the sweet meat of the lobster. Even those who didn't attend the church would sometimes bring the missionary his favorite treat, for the missionary was well-liked in the village.

He had often visited Mera and Cato, but he had been unsuccessful in his efforts to get Cato to accept Jesus Christ. However, the two men respected each other, and Mera still had faith that one day Cato would walk with her down the road to the little mission church. But for years now, she had gone with Tali and Belee, with Cato's permission, but without Cato. Even Punik went to church with her, obediently curling up by her feet and nobly refraining from joining in with the singing of the small congregation. Tali, always merry, often told Cato of how Punik would lift his head at the first note of music, his throat trembling with restrained howls. Punik had always enjoyed singing, but he behaved himself in the church.

Mera watched her husband as he reached for his battered straw hat and gathered up his fishing net. Although age and the sun had burned wrinkles deep into his skin, his movements were still swift and sure. His years of fishing had kept him supple and strong,

and his knowledge of the sea gave him a wisdom that made the young men of the village seek him out for advice. "A natural leader," the missionary had told her once. "What a witness he would be for Christ in the village!" But despite the testimony of Mera, Tali, and others in the village, Cato held back. And so did most of the young men.

Mera put her hand to her head and rubbed it, a motion she had been doing often lately. Cato frowned as he stopped beside her. "What's wrong?" he asked.

"Only a little headache," Mera answered. "It'll go away soon."

Cato hesitated. "Shall I stay with you today?"

Mera shook her head. "I'll be all right. Punik is here, and Tali and Belee are nearby. You go ahead."

"Well—" Cato bent down to rub Punik's head. "You take care of Mera for me, Punik."

Punik thumped the sand with his tail. He and Mera watched as Cato disappeared down the path to the beach. Then Mera went back inside the hut, hoping its coolness would ease the throbbing of her head. Punik whined as she lay back down in the hammock. Then he curled up below her and put his head on his paws. He looked up and wagged his tail when Tali and Belee stopped by for Mera. Belee touched Mera's hot forehead.

"She's sick, Tali," Belee said. "You go on to church and I'll stay with her."

"Should I get Cato?" Tali asked quietly.

Belee hesitated and Mera spoke from the hammock. "No," she said, "It's only a headache. I've had them before. Just ask Mr. Sam to pray for me."

Tali nodded and left the hut.

After church Mr. Sam came with Tali to see Mera, carrying his bag of medicine and his Bible.

"She's worse," Belee told them. "And she's calling for Cato."

"I'll take my boat and go for him," Tali said, hurrying from the hut.

By the time the two men returned, shadows had crept into the hut. Mera lay quiet in the hammock, pale and weak. When she heard Cato, she opened her eyes and spoke to him. He leaned closer to listen but when he tried to speak, her eyes closed and she was still. Punik stirred underneath the hammock and whined.

Mr. Sam touched Cato's shoulder. "She has gone to be with the Lord, Cato."

"You mean she's dead!" Cato exclaimed. He stared at the still form of his wife, then back at the missionary, as though expecting him to do something.

"Yes," the missionary replied quietly. "To us, she's dead; to Christ, she's alive."

"Don't talk riddles to me," Cato cried. "Just leave us alone!" He pointed to the door. "Go. All of you. Leave us alone." Again, Punik whined and pushed his head against Cato's knee as the others silently walked out.

Weeks later, long after the funeral, Cato was still alone. He refused to see Mr. Sam. He avoided Tali and Belee and he left Punik alone at the hut. Cato spent his days on the ocean, returning home late at night.

One day when Mr. Sam and Tali came to visit, Cato saw them coming. Grabbing his net, he hurried down to the beach. His two friends watched him leave.

"He has a great anger," Tali told Mr. Sam. "And a great hurt. It will take time to heal."

"I understand," Mr. Sam answered. "He has no faith that he will see her again. If only we could reach him with the gospel!"

On the ocean the sun still burned down as brightly as ever. Its rays sparkled over the surface of the water in an ever changing pattern of light and dark. Cato lay in his long boat, cocooned in the heat, bobbing gently on the swells of the ocean. But inside him the ice left by Mera's death still lingered, cold and sharp. It had been a Sunday, just like this Sunday, when she had died, he thought. When he closed his eyes to sleep, her last whispered words seemed to drift on the sea breeze, "I'm going home, Cato. I'm going home." Sighing, Cato sat up and began to paddle toward the shore. It was still early—Tali would not be back from church yet—but Cato was tired of fishing alone.

When he reached the empty hut, Cato stopped. He stood for a moment in the door, remembering the warm welcome Mera had always given him. Cato turned away from the dark doorway and walked out into the thicket, calling for Punik. No answering bark broke the quiet of the hot afternoon. Cato rubbed his face in a tired motion, then walked stiffly back into the hut. He climbed into the hammock and put his arm over his eyes to shut out the light. He let his other arm dangle over the edge of the hammock.

He awoke when something touched his hand. Opening his

eyes, he looked down and saw Punik.

"Where have you been, Punik?" Cato asked, puzzled. The dog looked at him with its sparkling dark eyes and lay down beneath Mera's hammock. Cato drifted back to sleep.

For a week, Cato remained at the house. Tali came by, and Mr. Sam. This time Cato let them in. They talked for a long time.

Still, when Tali stopped the next Sunday and asked if Cato wanted to go to church, Cato shook his head, wanting only to lie in the hammock, and listen to the sounds around him. But just as Tali left, Punik got up and trotted to the door. At the door he stopped and looked back into the hut. Then he barked, looking at Cato. Cato looked up, surprised, but when he didn't move, Punik trotted outside.

The dog didn't come back. Cato lay without moving, watching the door. When he heard the sounds of villagers arriving from the mission church, Punik trotted into the hut. Cato swung his feet over the hammock and sat up. "Punik, where have you been all this time?" he asked.

The next Sunday Punik followed the same pattern. Tali stopped to visit, then Punik disappeared. Cato got up and followed the dog through the thicket and out onto the dusty road.

At the mission church, the dog entered the open door without looking back. Cato followed slowly and stopped in the doorway. In amazement he watched as Punik trotted down the aisle and curled up underneath an empty space on the bench beside Tali and Belee. As the singing began, Mr. Sam saw Cato and motioned him inside. Cato went in slowly and sat beside Belee. Punik shifted to rest his muzzle on Cato's foot.

Cato listened as Mr. Sam preached about Jesus and how he died on the cross for the sins of the world. After the service, he asked his friends why Punik came to the church.

"He always came with Mera," Belee explained. "She always sat there and he lay beneath her seat through the whole service."

"Yes," Tali added, "you know he was never far from her."

Cato nodded. The bond between Punik and Mera had been strong. Punik had felt the loneliness too.

When the villagers stopped to speak to Cato, he responded with relief. He had missed their

companionship more than he had thought.

The next Sunday Cato dressed carefully. He and Punik left the hut together. Punik trotted along beside Cato, stopping occasionally to look up at him. Mr. Sam met them at the door of the mission church.

"Hello, Cato," Mr. Sam said. "Welcome."

Cato nodded, shaking the missionary's hand. "I enjoy your sermons, Mr. Sam, but I have some questions. There are some things I don't understand."

"Why not wait after the service?" Mr. Sam asked. "You can eat with me and we can talk then."

Cato greeted a few young men who had not been at the service the last Sunday and walked up the aisle to sit beside Tali.

After the service he and Punik went to the missionary's house.

Punik lay down on the porch as Cato and Mr. Sam went into the kitchen. Cato helped Mr. Sam boil shrimp and cook rice, marveling at the refrigerator that kept the food cold and at the electric stove that cooked so much faster than the fires.

When the last shrimp was eaten and only crumbs remained on the bread plate, Mr. Sam took out his Bible and spread it open. For hours they sat at the little table, searching the Word of God for the answers to Cato's questions. The first one he asked was why Mera said she was going home. The last one he asked was how he could be saved.

When the moon lit up the evening sky, Cato left the missionary's house a new creature in Christ. As Cato stepped off the porch, Punik stretched and yawned. Then he padded down the steps and followed Cato home.

Eagle on a Leash

Milly Howard

Brent Thompson finished cleaning Rama's cage and carefully shut the door. When the golden eagle gave a protesting screech, he laughed and said soothingly, "Now, Rama, take it easy. I'll be back in a little while. Dad is going to let you fly today."

Rama tilted her head to one side and made a twittering sound deep in her throat. "I promise, Rama. Dad said before noon." Brent latched the door of Rama's eight-by-twenty-foot cage and picked up his tools. Instead of going straight back to the house, he stood enjoying what his father called Rama's domain. Her cage was located back of the house on the canyon rim. Both the eagle and Brent had a clear view of the canyon below.

The high canyon walls cast early-morning shadows on the rolling green hills of the canyon floor. A moving wave of white caught Brent's eye. He watched as a flock of sheep was herded back into the Culpeppers' sheepfold. Suddenly his gaze sharpened as he realized it was too early for the sheep to come back from the pastures. He saw the small figure of the shepherd stop at the Culpeppers' ranch house. Then a taller figure came out on the porch, listened to the younger one for a minute, and disappeared inside. He reappeared; then both figures went around the side of the ranch house. A few seconds later, a jeep left the Culpeppers' ranch, spinning a cloud of trailing dust as it churned up the dirt road toward the Thompsons' house.

When the jeep screeched into the front yard, Brent was waiting. Three weeks of vacation at the new house had left him eager for company. The Thompsons had bought the canyon-rim house just before school had let out for summer vacation. Although they had stopped at their nearest neighbor's house several times, there had been little response. The older Culpeppers kept to themselves, responding curtly to the friendly advances of the newcomers up on the rim. However, their thin, sun-browned boy was about Brent's age. Jasper seemed shy but cheerful. Although the interest in his clear gray eyes hinted at friendship, there had been little time to be together. The Culpeppers were sheepherders and Jasper was often away with the sheep.

And now, as the man and boy strode toward him, Brent realized this was no friendly visit. Jasper's face was as tense as his father's. Brent looked from Jasper to the tall dark man beside him. His startled gaze took in the work jeans and boots before it settled on the rifle in Barlow Culpepper's hands.

"Dad!" Brent called.

The screen door opened behind him and his father spoke quietly. "It's okay, Brent. I'm here."

Barlow's voice was harsh. "My boy lost a lamb this morning," he said sharply. "Carried off by an eagle. Folks tell me you have an eagle up here."

"Yes," Noel Thompson said. "We have a license to keep a golden eagle for research. But since the territory is new to Rama, we haven't flown her free yet. She's still on jesses and a leash. Are you sure it was an eagle?"

Mr. Culpepper scowled and thrust out an object he had been holding in his hand. The light glinted on a feather—the white-splashed tail feather of a young golden eagle. "It was an eagle all right."

"It looks like one of Rama's, but she's still in her cage," Mr. Thompson said slowly. "It's a strong cage, Barlow. She couldn't get out by herself."

Mr. Culpepper's gaze settled coldly on Brent, and the boy felt a shiver run down his spine. "Perhaps your boy let her out."

"I never—"

"Brent has been responsible for Rama ever since we got her," Mr. Thompson said calmly. "He would never let her out without permission. She's still in her cage."

Jasper stood half behind his father. He shifted uneasily, scuffing the toe of his boot in the dirt. For one moment his troubled gray eyes met Brent's; then he stared down at his dusty boots.

"Mind if I take a look?" Barlow Culpepper's tone was challenging.

Mr. Thompson stepped back. "Not at all," he said evenly, "follow me, please."

The Culpeppers followed as Mr. Thompson led the way to the cage behind the house. Rama was perched inside on a branch of gnarled pine, preening her feathers. When she caught sight of the procession of men and boys, her head lifted. Her beak opened slightly. Ignoring the others, her eyes fixed unwaveringly on Barlow Culpepper. Slowly the golden feathers on the back of her neck lifted. The rest of her feathers flattened tightly. Her eyes glittered.

Shifting his grip on the rifle, Mr. Culpepper stepped forward to check the construction of the cage. He inspected the latch and rattled the cage door. With a wild screech, Rama flung herself across the cage, talons first. Her weight thrust the mesh net cage wall a full two feet out from the side. Brent smothered a grin as both Barlow Culpepper and his son leaped back.

"Don't be alarmed," his father said quickly. "She can't get out."

"She'll be a goner if she does," Barlow said bluntly. "Look, Thompson, something's been attacking my lambs. If it turns out to be your eagle, her flying days are over, and that's no idle threat!"

He turned and stalked back to his jeep angrily, thrusting the rifle into the back.

Jasper followed more slowly. He had taken off his hat and was turning it around and around in his hands. Looking at Brent, he hesitated, then began to speak.

"I'm sorry—"

"Jasper!"

Sighing, Jasper turned and hurried quickly to the jeep. He had barely climbed in before the jeep roared out of the driveway and down the dirt road toward the canyon.

"Why pick on Rama?" Brent asked indignantly. "She wouldn't hurt a lamb!"

"If she weren't well fed and well trained, she would, Son," Mr. Thompson replied. "And any sheep man will shoot an eagle that attacks his sheep. He would be within legal rights to do it, too. Barlow is only doing what he thinks is right to protect his flock. To him, eagles are predators that cost him his livelihood."

He looked at Rama thoughtfully. She stared back, the wild glitter in her eyes gone, the perfect example of a gentled bird. "I wonder if there is another eagle in this territory."

"Wouldn't we have seen it by now?"

"Maybe not," Mr. Thompson said slowly, "but Rama should have. The other bird would defend its territory. We'll wait a little longer before letting Rama fly free."

"But Dad, I promised her she would get to fly this morning," Brent protested. "We had already made plans to fly her!"

"Not today, son," Mr. Thompson said, shaking his head. "Let things simmer down a little."

For that day and the next few weeks, Rama was exercised only on the jesses and leash. Brent and Mr. Thompson continued with her training, using the lure. The tethered flights were unsatisfactory, not only to Rama, but to her trainers also.

"She's ready to fly, Dad," Brent insisted.

"A little longer, son," his father

replied. "I know both of you are impatient, but it's better to be safe than sorry."

Rama, perched on Brent's fist, tensed when he approached the cage. Mr. Thompson turned to Brent. "We can make a perch out here on the rim and tie her to it. She'll feel more free at least. We'll have to keep an eye on her, though," he continued as Brent raced to get the materials to build another perch. "If there is another eagle and it discovers Rama, she would be helpless against an attack."

Saturday dawned hot and dry. Brent made sure Rama was secure in her cage before he joined his parents for a ride to town. On the weekend, the small town of Cottonwood overflowed with farmers, ranchers, wives, and children. They came from miles around to buy the week's groceries and visit with each other. The Thompsons were no exception. While Mrs. Thompson shopped

for groceries, Mr. Thompson and Brent headed for the hardware store to pick up some fencing. Across the road Jasper was sitting on the soft-drink box outside the gas station, drinking an orange soda. His tanned face turned away as he saw Brent. In a lot of ways Jasper Culpepper was just like his father.

He slid off the box and silently pushed the lid back. Mr. Thompson smiled at Jasper and handed Brent some change before crossing the street to the hardware store. Brent leaned over the box, letting the blast of cold air cool his face.

"Hot as a firecracker and it's only July," he said as he carefully pulled out a chocolate drink. He dropped his money into the coin box and pried the cap off the drink. Then, leaning against the drink box, he looked at Jasper. "Aren't you hot?"

At last Jasper grinned. "I'm used to it, I guess. You'll get used to the heat, too, if you stay." He looked at Brent shyly. "It gets pretty lonesome out here. There aren't any other boys close by."

"I'd like to be friends," Brent said, "but what would your father say?"

"Pop hasn't always been like this," Jasper said slowly. "He's just worried about money lately. We've lost a lot of lambs, one way or another. Now, the eagle—"

"It wasn't Rama!"

"Maybe not," Jasper replied uneasily, "but you'd better keep her penned up good. Pop will shoot any eagle right now. He won't take chances. It wasn't too long ago that ranchers hunted eagles from airplanes. Pop's been fussing ever since he heard you had an eagle."

"Maybe we could prove it isn't Rama," Brent said thoughtfully, putting his empty drink bottle into the case beside the drink box.

"How?"

"Catch the other eagle, that's how!"

"You know how to catch an eagle?" Jasper stared at Brent.

"Sure, I helped Dad catch Rama," Brent replied. "Course, she was just a fledgling and we got her from a nest. But I've read lots of books about eagles. We can use Dad's bow net and a lure. It won't hurt to try, anyway."

"Okay," Jasper said. "Pop always takes the sheep to the far pasture on Thursdays. He gives me the day off. Why don't you meet me at the ranch then? We can stay the whole day."

"All right!" Brent agreed enthusiastically.

The next Thursday, he was up early. He finished his chores and made sure Rama had water and food. Then he gathered up the bow net and one of Rama's lures, a dead squirrel. Fastening them to his bicycle, he pedaled down the dirt road. Although it was folded, the net was unwieldy. Brent's progress was slow and clumsy. When he finally reached the ranch, Jasper was waiting on the porch.

"Let's go!" he said eagerly, reaching for his bike.

The two boys rode slowly northwest to Sunset Crag. Propping their bikes against the red rock, they looked up. "It's high enough," Brent said in satisfaction. "We should be able to see every direction from the top."

"And the eagle can see us," Jasper said. "Hey, are you sure this is all right?"

"Sure," Brent said with more confidence than he felt. "It's done all the time. Anyway, we've got to do something to prove to your father that Rama is okay. She can't stay in that cage forever."

Jasper said no more, and the boys began to scramble up the crag. By the time they reached the top, they were out of breath. Brent wiped his face and looked around. "Just look at that!"

Sunset Crag was higher than the canyon rim. To the east he could see his house clearly. He and Jasper watched as Mr. Thompson took Rama from her cage and tied her to the perch outside. Then he went into her cage.

"He's going to build another section onto Rama's cage," Brent told Jasper. "That'll give her a little more room, anyway."

"They look like dolls," Jasper said. He walked over to the north edge of the crag. "I wonder if I can see Pop. Yes, there he is!"

Brent came over to look. Far below, in a box canyon, he could see sheep milling around a pool. A movement at the edge of the flock caught his eye. He just made out the Culpeppers' sheepdog; then his gaze focused on Barlow Culpepper. The shepherd moved along the edge of the flock, herding them up the canyon to the grassy floor. The sun glinted off the rifle in his hand.

Sighing, Brent looked up, scanning the sky for some movement. To the left, a hawk circled lazily in the heat. Nothing else moved.

"Well, let's set it up," he told Jasper.

The boys struggled with the bow net, trying to get it just right. "It looked a lot easier in the book," Brent grumbled as the net collapsed for the third time. Jasper just shook his head and stopped to watch a bird in the sky. "See anything?" Brent asked as he spread the net again.

"Another hawk," Jasper said, turning to watch Brent.

Brent released the net slowly. This time it stayed. He tied the squirrel inside the net and looked at it doubtfully. "It'll just have to do," he said wearily.

He straightened up. "A hawk?"

Jasper pointed to the bird circling in the sky. "There."

Brent watched for a moment as a large bird spiraled in the sky, riding an updraft. Then he caught his breath. "That's not a hawk! It's the eagle!"

"Get down!" he hissed as the wild bird banked and swept toward them. Just over the crag, the eagle swung and circled again, its wings outspread. "Look at the size of those wings!" Brent shivered, partly from excitement, partly from fright. The eagle was big, bigger than Rama. Its wingspread must have been about eight feet. "It's seen the lure!"

The eagle tightened its circle, then—folding its wings—it dived. Straight down it came, right on target. The boys scrambled behind the rocks as the whistle of air through its feathers became a roar. Then, talons outstretched, the eagle struck. The net sprang together sharply, slinging itself sideways. The eagle's wings spread, beating the air fiercely. With a wild shriek, it rose into the air.

"Missed!" Brent could have cried from disappointment.

"It didn't get the squirrel, either," Jasper said, shrinking back against Brent. "And it's mad!"

Jasper was right. The eagle flew back over the crag, shrieking with anger. And from the east came an answering shriek.

"Rama!" Brent turned to look.

He saw his father appear at the cage door just as Rama flung herself into the air. She hit the full length of the leash with all her strength. With a sinking heart Brent saw the leash snap. Rama was loose!

Noel Thompson dropped his tools and ran for the truck as Rama launched herself from the canyon rim. Riding the updraft, she rose quickly, seeking height from which to attack. The other eagle responded immediately, closing the gap between them.

"They're going to fight!" Brent groaned. Grabbing the squirrel from the net, he swung the lure, trying to bring Rama down. It was no use. The birds swept back over the crag, ignoring the lure. They had no thought for anything except each other.

Rama attacked. Diving, she rapidly approached the wild eagle. It rolled over in the air, warding off the attack with out-thrust talons. The two birds broke away. Again they circled, each trying to

gain altitude over the other. Again a sharp dive, then breaking away, then another dive. This time, with a flurry of wings and talons, they closed together.

For one wild moment, they tumbled over and over in the air, falling. They broke apart and began climbing again. Angry screeches and harsh challenges vibrated through the hot air.

Desperately, Brent and Jasper scrambled down the crag. At the bottom they met Brent's father who had just arrived in the pickup. A white-faced Brent quickly explained what had happened.

Mr. Thompson listened grimly, then turned his attention to the battle in the sky.

Huge wings beat the air as the birds, one wild and one tame, fought for a killing hold on each other. Closing again, they clutched at each other. Feathers drifted downward. Tumbling end over end, they released their holds only when the ground rushed up to meet them.

This time they circled higher and to the north. Jasper pointed down at the canyon floor. "They're flying over the box canyon where Pop is!"

Brent and his father looked at each other. "If they don't kill each other, Barlow will do it for them! Let's go!" Mr. Thompson motioned both boys into the pickup. A red cloud of dust rose behind them as they raced toward the north pastures.

They found Barlow Culpepper standing apart from his sheep, rifle ready. His eyes didn't leave the fighting eagles as the pickup approached and the man and boys leaped out. He took careful aim. His finger tightened on the trigger.

"Pop!"

Mr. Thompson hushed Jasper's anguished shout. They stood motionless as the barrel of the rifle followed the flight of the birds.

Brent held his breath. The birds broke apart. Rama's jesses and leash showed clearly against the blue sky as she turned to attack again. She and her enemy plunged into each other and tumbled behind the sturdy stone peaks that closed off the deeper part of the canyon.

Slowly, Barlow lowered the rifle.

"Pop," Jasper said again and went to stand beside his father. "Thanks for not shooting."

"Guess I've been too hasty in my judgments lately, Son," Barlow Culpepper turned to look at the Thompsons. "You were right. Two eagles. I guess one of them would be yours."

Noel Thompson nodded. "She broke her leash when she saw the wild eagle. They'll fight to the death."

"The wild one killed our lamb, of course."

Noel nodded, turning to scan the empty sky. "It's a young female, too. This must be her territory. She has the advantage, but Rama is giving her a good fight. Maybe Rama feels like she is protecting Brent, here. Nothing else would give her the confidence to invade another bird's territory."

"Brent and I were going to capture the wild one," Jasper told his father. "Then you would know that Rama didn't kill the lamb."

Brent was surprised at the look of sympathy on Barlow's face as he swung around to look at him. "Sorry, son. I wasn't thinking how much you cared for your eagle." He rubbed his face. "I never thought of eagles as pets."

"Dad explained why you don't like eagles," Brent said in a choked voice. "I understand, but it doesn't change anything. What I did may cost Rama her life."

"We'll wait, Son," his father said quietly. "You should have talked to me first, but what's done is done. There would have been a fight sooner or later anyway. We were just prolonging the time by keeping Rama penned up."

"But what can we do?"

Mr. Thompson shook his head. "Just wait. It's up to Rama now."

When late afternoon came, neither bird had returned. Mr. Thompson and the two boys helped herd the sheep back to the ranch. Then Brent and his father returned to the house to wait.

Early the next morning Brent and his parents went out to Rama's cage. They stood quietly, looking out over the canyon rim. Slowly the sky lightened. The rising sun edged the ridges in deep red and spilled golden light into the night-darkened canyons. Night shadows faded into the purple and pink of a new day. Still there was no sign of Rama.

Down below, they saw Jasper and his father out by the corral, watching the morning sky. At last they turned away and entered the ranch house. "We might as well go in too," Mr. Thompson said. Silently, Brent and his mother followed him to the house.

The sun had been up several hours before Brent started down the dirt road to the Culpepper ranch. As he rode around the bend in the road, he could see Jasper, shouting and waving excitedly. Brent looked up at the sky. A large bird was approaching, flying low. Brent's heart thudded, then he realized the bird was moving too slowly and too low to be an eagle.

Still, he stopped and watched.

The bird came on, wings pumping up and down, up and down. Suddenly Brent realized it was Rama. She was flying out of pure determination, too tired to lift herself. Her line of flight would take her to the ranch at the bottom of the cliffs, but not high enough to reach the rim.

Brent began to pedal. He reached Jasper about the same

time Rama reached the ranch. She landed at their feet, exhausted. Mr. Culpepper came out, shaking his head in amazement. Without a word, he went back into the house to telephone Mr. Thompson. When Brent's father arrived, Barlow helped load the wounded eagle into the back of the pickup. Rama watched him fiercely but made no move to attack.

When they were ready for the trip back up to the rim, Mr. Thompson tried to thank the Culpeppers. "Don't mention it," Barlow Culpepper said gruffly. He turned to Brent. "Never thought much of eagles before. Maybe when Rama is well, you can show me and Jasper how those jesses and stuff work?"

Brent grinned from ear to ear. Even Jasper smiled. Reaching out to shake hands, Brent replied, "I surely will, Mr. Culpepper. I surely will!"

King of the Birds

Marilyn Elmer

King of the birds! Ruler of the sky! Majesty in the air! You might see the eagle circling endlessly against the blue of the sky or sitting motionless upon the highest limb of a tall tree. You might see it pouncing furiously upon some unwary prey or patiently feeding and training its young. Large, swift, powerful, fierce, faithful—all these words describe the eagle. It rightfully deserves to be called the king of the birds.

There are forty-eight kinds of eagles in the world, but the best-known in the United States are the golden eagle and the bald eagle. The bald eagle got its name years ago from early settlers, who used "bald" to mean *white*. Because of its strength and splendor, the bald eagle was chosen to be the symbol of our country.

Eagles are mentioned in the Bible over thirty times. From Genesis to Revelation, the writers of Scripture described characteristics of the eagle that we can still see today.

Job, Jeremiah, and other biblical writers described eagles as being swift. Both bald eagles and golden eagles have been found to travel at almost one hundred twenty miles per hour in a dive after prey. Birdwatchers have seen these masters of flight almost ten thousand feet above the earth.

Once, a bald eagle detected a fish three miles from where it was soaring and captured it after one long, slanting dive.

Moses lived in the desert and the wilderness for eighty years. He probably viewed eagles at close range for long periods of time. In Deuteronomy 32:11-12a, he compared God's care of the Israelites to an eagle's care for its young. "As an eagle stirreth up her nest, fluttereth over her young, spreadeth abroad her wings, taketh them, beareth them on her wings: So the Lord alone did lead him." Both the golden eagle and the bald eagle parents mate for life. The male and female stay together throughout the year instead of just in the breeding season as so many pairs of birds do. They arrange and rearrange their nesting materials. They spread their wings to protect the young from rain, the burning sun, and the biting wind. Occasionally an adult bird will let a faltering eaglet rest upon its back as the youngster is learning.

Bald eagles build their nests in tall trees; golden eagles prefer high cliffs. The nests, called *aeries,* are built mainly of sticks. They are lined with leaves, grass, feathers, moss, and other soft materials. Eagles use the same nesting site year after year. They build one nest on top of the others. Since these birds live from thirty to fifty years, the nests become enormous. One nest in a blown-down tree near Lake Erie weighed over four thousand pounds, which is two tons.

The female eagle lays two or three white eggs. The eggs are not much bigger than chicken eggs. Over the next thirty-five to forty days the parents take turns sitting in the nest until the eaglets hatch.

When the babies are first hatched, the adults put food directly into their mouths. Soon, however, the parents show the youngsters how to tear the food into pieces and feed themselves.

Eaglets spend much of the first few weeks of their lives preparing

to hunt and fly. They learn to grasp objects with their talons. They exercise by flapping their wings, jumping up and down, and stamping about. Finally when they are about three months old, they are ready to take their first shaky flight from the edge of the nest. If they are too slow about starting to fly, the parents coax them with pieces of food held just beyond their reach. As they become more skillful in flying, the growing birds spend less and less time in the aerie. However, the parents supply their food until they are about a year old.

Eagles are carnivorous, or meat-eating. Much of its diet is fish, but the bald eagle also eats small birds, mammals, and other animals. Eagles are called predators because they often kill their own food. They are also scavengers because they eat animals that have been killed by cars or have died from other causes.

Eagles have to consume a certain amount of fur, feathers, and bones if they are to remain healthy. These indigestible items roll up to a ball in the bird's crop. The ball is called a *casting*. The ball acts like a brush to clean the crop. Each morning the eagle regurgitates the casting. Scientists collect eagle castings, pull them apart, and study them to find out what the bird has been eating.

The eagle's weapons are his beak and talons. The hooked beak is from two to three inches long. The razor-sharp claws may be the same length. The talons continue to grow throughout life as our fingernails do. The eagle sharpens and trims them by constant use.

Mankind must be careful in his care of these birds. As farmers and ranchers well know, eagles present a threat to young livestock, and in certain areas the number of eagles has to be controlled. But hunters and eagle-egg collectors have greatly decreased the overall eagle population. Some pesticides caused the female eagles to lay eggs with thin shells that were easily broken. This, too, reduced the number of eagles in our country.

Laws now protect these magnificent birds. It is against the law to kill, shoot at, or capture an eagle for sport. It is also illegal to molest or take eggs from a nest. If these laws are strictly enforced, the eagle will probably not become extinct.

Isaiah 40:31 says, "But they that wait upon the Lord shall renew their strength; they shall mount up with wings as eagles; they shall run, and not be weary; and they shall walk, and not faint." This promise that God made to his people centuries ago is for us today, too. Whenever you think of an eagle, remember that God will strengthen you as you look to Him.

Literature Lesson:
Fiction and Non-Fiction

Most people enjoy reading fictional stories like "Eagle on a Leash." Unusual settings and new characters appeal to a reader's sense of adventure. Informational articles like "King of the Birds" are nonfiction and often help readers better understand stories that they read. All of what we read can be put into one of two groups: fiction or nonfiction.

Fiction

We usually think of fiction as anything that is made up and told in the form of a story. Fiction began long ago with oral folktales and grew into written novels, plays, and short stories that we enjoy today.

Fiction gives pleasure. We read it to be entertained. Fiction helps us to rise above everyday chores like homework, setting the table, and sweeping the garage and to take part in great adventures—battling giants, soaring through space, defending the paths of justice. The pleasure and excitement in fiction relax and refresh our minds.

Fiction also gives us *insight*. In "Eagle on a Leash," we came to understand Brent's love for his eagle, Rama. Very few people own such an unusual pet, yet through reading the story we understood what it is to own and love a golden eagle. And like Brent, we wanted Rama to be safe. But in the same way that we understood Brent, we came to understand Barlow Culpepper and his distrust of the predatory birds. We could see that Culpepper wasn't a cruel man. He wanted only to protect his sheep. The story helped us to see that there are two sides to every question. We gained this understanding by looking first through Brent's eyes and then through Barlow Culpepper's eyes. Fiction often brings us into a character's mind so that we can compare his thoughts and feelings to our own thoughts and feelings. In this way fiction helps us to understand people—their desires, experiences, and beliefs.

Nonfiction

The goal of nonfiction is *to inform,* and in this way it differs from fiction. Although fiction may use facts, the goal of fiction is still to give pleasure and insight. The writer of fiction uses facts only to make his plot and characters be fully appreciated by the reader. But the goal of the nonfiction writer is communicating the factual knowledge itself—to set the knowledge in order, keep it clear, and make it enjoyable to the reader.

The writer of nonfiction uses pleasure to lure the reader into gaining new information. The author of "King of the Birds" described the beauty of eagles to attract the reader's interest. The writer of "Common Salt" in the previous unit started the article by talking about soft pretzels and kosher pickles—a sure way to get a reader's attention! But both writers gave us factual knowledge. We didn't enter a character's mind in these two articles. Instead, we learned facts about salt in one article and facts about eagles in the other.

Nonfiction may be enjoyable because it satisfies our desire *to know,* but it's doubtful that nonfiction would move people to tears or make them laugh helplessly. Occasionally a writer gives a true account of something very sad or funny, but even "true" stories are mixed with some elements of fiction and are not completely informational.

Fiction like "Eagle on a Leash" and nonfiction like "King of the Birds" are both interesting and enjoyable and can often be used together to give us a good experience with reading.

The **Eagle**

Alfred, Lord Tennyson

He clasps the crag with crooked hands;
Close to the sun in lonely lands,
Ringed with azure world, he stands.

The wrinkled sea beneath him crawls;
He watches from his mountain walls,
And like a thunderbolt he falls.

The Leaves Rustle

Jim Kjelgaard

The summer days faded like golden shadows one into the other, and the first frost came to leave a riot of color behind it. Danny climbed mountains and traveled streams, blazing with his axe every place where a trap might take a fur-bearing animal. When he was not doing that, he was abroad with Red.

The big setter no longer chased whatever ran before him. Slowly, bit by bit, he became woods-wise.

The dog heeled perfectly, lay down on command, and remained there until instructed to get up. With difficulty Danny taught him to return to the house, leaving Danny in the woods, and started him retrieving with a soft ball. And when he was finished, he knew that he was going to have a partridge dog.

With Red frisking before him, Danny tramped out of the beech woods on a frost-tinged evening in early autumn and into the cabin. Ross was sitting at the table, his chin in his hands, staring out the open door at the haze-shrouded peak of Stoney Lonesome. Ross's four hounds had come out of their kennels, and each sat at the end of its chain staring at something that only they could see. Danny grinned. It was this way every year. When summer started to fade, Ross worked hard and long to prepare for the trapping season. But little by little he became impatient, and by the time the first frost struck, impatience would be a raging fever within him. Then he must take his hounds and go into the mountains for the season's first varmint hunt.

"Danny," said Ross, "do you think the trap-lines are in good shape?"

"Sure they are. We got a right handy lot of trappin' laid out for us." Danny grinned to himself.

His father resumed his staring out the door while Danny busied himself preparing the evening meal. Ross was a hard worker, and little was ever permitted to interfere with essential work. Because varmint hunting was his pleasure, he hesitated to go while there was other work to be done.

"Supper's ready," Danny announced.

Ross moved moodily over and sat down, staring at the food before him. He was still trying to convince himself that there was work to be done on the trap-lines and he could not possibly take a varmint hunt.

Danny stopped eating and said carelessly, "Pappy, if the hounds are goin' to be in shape for the winter, they got to have some chasin'."

"Yeh, I know," Ross said absently.

"Then," Danny continued, "why don't you take 'em out for a varmint hunt, come mornin'?"

"Well, there's a little work to be done on the Lonesome Pond line. . . ."

"You can't be caught in the winter with soft hounds," Danny warned.

Ross slapped the table with his fist. "That's right, Danny. Guess I'd better take 'em out!"

"Sure. It's just as important as trappin'. You catch a lot of varmints with those hounds."

"That's right," Ross repeated. "Can I take the Red dog with me, Danny?"

Danny fidgeted. "That Red, I gotta work him some more."

"Mebbe so. I'll take him the next time."

Danny washed the dishes and read the latest issues of the outdoor magazines while Ross prepared happily for his hunt. Danny went to bed early, and when he awoke Ross had taken the four hounds and gone into the mountains. There was a roughly penciled note on the table:

"Danny, don't worry if we ain't back tonight. If we jump a long runner, we may stay two days."

Danny went out on the porch to look at the weather. The maple tree in the pasture had streaks of red running through its leaves. The leaves on the beeches hung listless and yellow. A cold wind blew down from Stoney Lonesome, and Danny whistled happily. Autumn was surely the finest time of all. Partridge season opened in just a little more than three weeks, and he could go shooting with Red.

Danny prepared breakfast, fed the big setter, and did the few other chores that needed doing. Then he took a pack basket from its hooks on the shed wall, and dumped thirty number-one steel traps into it.

Danny shouldered the basket, and the big setter frisked happily before him as he set off through the beech woods. The cold wind sighed down from Stoney Lonesome, and far off Danny thought he heard the mournful baying of a hound. He stopped to listen, but the sound was not repeated. Red walked toward a small hillock that was carpeted with winter-green, and looked invitingly over his shoulder. But Danny snapped his fingers.

"Come back here, dog. There's work to be done."

He strode up the valley, following the course set by Smokey Creek through the huge beeches. A buck deer, with the last shreds of summer velvet gone from its branching antlers, stood silently as a wraith in the trees before him. The buck snorted, stamped the ground with a forefoot, and bounded away. A couple of crows cawed raucously from the top of a beech. Then

Danny broke through the last of the beeches on to Lonesome Pond.

The pond itself was a mere widening of Smokey Creek, a mile and a half long by a half mile wide. Lonesome and sluggish, it rested between the acres of reeds and was flanked by the straggling tamaracks. It was a desolate place, but the little conical houses that muskrats had built were strewn thickly wherever there was shallow water, and freshly cut reeds floated almost everywhere. Every year Ross and Danny took a hundred muskrats from the pond, and caught eight or ten mink on the little mud paths around it.

Danny deposited his pack on the bank, and went to one of the tamarack trees. With his knife he cut half a dozen forked branches from it, and from a grove of willows beside the pond took twenty more. He returned to the water, took a trap from the basket, and thrust one of the sticks through the ring at the end of its chain. He drove it deep into the bank, pounding the fork down until nothing showed, and cast the trap into the water. Even muskrats were sometimes wary and hard to take. But they would become accustomed to the trap by the time the season opened, and pay no attention to it when it was set.

Danny worked slowly around the pond, leaving an unset but firmly staked trap at every likely place. The sun was sinking when Danny straightened up from the last trap and swung the empty pack basket to his shoulders. He sighed, and stretched his cramped muscles. But the Lonesome Pond line was finished and ready. There remained only the setting of the traps. Danny grinned down at Red.

"I feel like supper. How 'bout you?"

He wandered back to the house, cut chops from a side of pork in the spring house, peeled a kettle full of potatoes, and brewed fresh coffee. The day had been pleasantly warm, but the night was definitely cold, so he stuffed two blocks of tough oak wood into the stove. The lid glowed red, and the pleasant aroma that wood fire always creates filled the cabin. Danny put the potatoes over to boil, and laid the pork chops in a skillet. Probably Ross would not come. But he might, and if he did he would expect a hot meal ready. When the potatoes began to bubble, Danny moved them to a

back lid and put the pork chops in their place. If Ross didn't come to eat his share, Danny could always make breakfast on whatever might be left.

He stood over the stove with a fork in his hand, and was just about to turn the sizzling pork chops when Red sprang to his feet. A little growl bubbled in his throat, and his hackles raised. Danny shoved the pork chops to the back of the stove and went to the door.

A moment later he saw Ross swing out of the forest into the clearing and start across it. Danny swallowed the lump that rose in his throat and went quietly back to the stove. His father's hunt had gone amiss. Of the four hounds that had started out with him that morning, only three were coming home. The missing one, Danny knew, lay somewhere in the mountains and would never hunt again.

Twenty minutes later Ross entered the house. Danny had known that he would be that long; having had hounds in the mountains all day, Ross would take time to feed and care for them before attending to his own wants. Red rose, and padded politely across the floor to greet this other occupant of their home. Danny turned from the stove to smile at his father. He knew better than to question Ross about his hounds.

"Hi, Pappy. I didn't know for sure whether you'd get home or not."

"Yep. I got here."

Ross's face was haggard, as were his eyes. Wearily he hung his rifle beside Danny's, sloshed water from one of the two tin pails into a tin basin, and washed his face and hands. He dropped on a chair and sat staring dully across the table. Danny tended busily to the already cooked pork chops,

and glanced furtively at Red. Ross Pickett set a lot of store by his hounds, and it always cut him deeply to lose one. With the long fork Danny put the pork chops on a platter, and emptied the potatoes into a dish. He set them on the table along with butter, milk, and bread.

"Supper's ready, Pappy. How'd it go today?"

Ross Pickett shook his head. "Bad, Danny, bad. I lost a hound."

"No!"

"Yes," Ross corrected. "The likeliest of the three pups it was, too."

"How'd you lose him?"

"Killed by a varmint, a cat varmint. We jumped him in that sag just under Stoney Lonesome, and I heard the hounds bay him a mile back in the brush. Time I got there, they'd gone. The pup lay by a rock, ripped to ribbons. We followed the varmint all day, but I never got a shot."

Danny said, "I'm right sad about it, Pappy."

Ross pecked at the food before him, still staring aimlessly across the table. Danny busied himself with his own food, avoiding his father's face. Whoever hunted dangerous game with hounds was sure to have one killed once in a while. But Ross always grieved over such mishaps, and blamed himself for them. He picked up a pork chop, gnawed on it, and put it back on his plate.

"It's a big cat varmint, Danny," he said. "A big lynx or catamount."

He resumed his vacant staring over the table. Never given to futile outbursts, he would not now storm and rage. But Danny knew that his present moodiness was not wholly grief. The varmint that had killed the hound was still running free in the mountains. And even while he mourned the loss of one of his cherished dogs, Ross could still lay plans to avenge it. Danny knew that he was plotting the varmint's downfall now, and also that he was quite capable of pursuing it until he finally did overtake it, regardless of when that might be. No varmint of any description ever killed a Pickett hound and went scot-free.

Danny finished eating, and sat silently at the table until Ross, by pushing his plate aside, signified that he wanted no more. Danny flipped the half-eaten pork chops to Red, and the big setter carried them to the porch where he lay gnawing on them. Ross turned the kerosene lamp a little higher. He took his best hunting knife, one that he himself had made of tool-steel and that was always reserved for special occasions, and began to whet it on the fine side of an emery stone. The next time he went into the mountains he would carry that knife, and its next function would be to remove the pelt of the varmint that had killed his favorite pup.

Quietly Danny gathered up the dishes, poured hot water from the tea kettle into a basin, and washed them. He glanced dubiously at his father, still sitting at the table whetting his knife to a razor edge. Ross raised his head, and stared fixedly at the flickering lamp before he spoke.

"Danny, I think that's a bad varmint."

Ross rested his chin on his hand. "I do think so," he said, more to himself than to Danny. "It's no ordinary cat. It trapped that hound, and waited until it could trap it without hurt to itself. Then it got slick and clean away. It's a cunnin' thing, and a big one, and I think it aims to make itself boss of Stoney Lonesome. Danny, do you go up there, you carry a gun."

"I won't go without I'm ready for it," Danny promised.

"Don't," Ross admonished.

He fell to whetting the hunting knife again, and Danny stood uneasily watching him. Tomorrow morning, with his three remaining hounds, Ross would be again on the trail of the varmint. There was no use in even asking to accompany him because Ross would flatly refuse all aid. The varmint was a personal affair, and one that concerned him only.

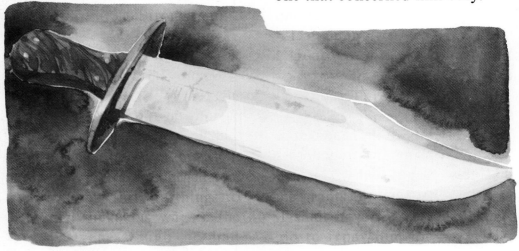

In the black hours of the next morning, so early that the first hint of dawn had not even begun to show in the sky, he was awakened by Ross kindling a fire in the stove. Danny lay sleepily on his cot, and reached over to caress Red, while he watched his father prepare breakfast. Ross ate and made a small pack in which he put bacon, salt, bread, and tea.

He rolled the pack in his fringed hunting jacket, slung it across his shoulder, strapped the knife about his middle, and took his rifle from the rack. Quietly he stole out the door and closed it behind him.

Danny heard Old Mike, the leader of the hound pack, whine eagerly as Ross went to the kennels to release the hounds, and his father's gruff command to be quiet. Then there was silence, and Danny turned over to sleep until a more reasonable hour. There was nothing special to do today, aside from splitting a little wood, and therefore no reason to be up so early.

When he awoke again, sunlight was streaming through the windows and a bluejay in the maple tree was shrieking at the mule. Red padded over to Danny's bed and scratched with his front paw at the blanket that covered it. Danny looked at Ross's empty bed, and the space on the deer horn rack that was usually occupied by Ross's rifle, and sighed. Ross would be far back in the mountains by this time, looking for the trail of the varmint that had killed his hound. Danny swung out of bed and opened the door to let Red make his usual morning tour of the clearing. He washed, put on his clothing, and was preparing breakfast when he heard Red bark.

Danny reached for his rifle and went to the door. Red stood just at the edge of the clearing. There was motion within the trees, and Red trotted forward with his tail wagging. A moment later John Bailey, the game warden who patrolled the Wintapi, broke out of the trees and with Red beside him started toward the cabin. He paused at the bottom of the steps and grinned up at Danny.

"Are you going feuding?"

Danny grinned back. "Pappy had a hound killed by a varmint yesterday, and he allows it's a bad 'un. When I heard Red, I just thought I'd be set for anything. That's how come I got a gun."

John Bailey nodded. "What kind of varmint?"

"A cat varmint. Pappy's back in the hills huntin' it now."

"Hope he gets it," the warden said thoughtfully. "We can't have any cats killing deer in the Wintapi. Danny, are you too busy to do a little job for me?"

"Reckon not. What do you want?"

"There was a big buck hit by a car on the highway yesterday afternoon. Almost certainly he has a broken leg and internal injuries. But he isn't hurt so badly that he can't run. I tracked him a ways, to Blue Sag up on Stoney Lonesome, and marked where I left off with a handkerchief. He laid down three times, and there was blood in each bed. Do you want to pick up the trail and finish him?"

Danny nodded. It was far better to put the buck out of its pain as swiftly and mercifully as possible.

"Sure," Danny agreed. "Red and I'll go after him."

John Bailey reached down to tickle Red's ears. "Aren't you afraid the dog will learn to hunt deer?"

"No, sir," Danny said stoutly. "That dog hunts just what I want him to."

"Okay. When you get the buck, bring him here to your house and I'll come get him. Of course the meat will have to go to a hospital or the county home, but I'll pay you for your time."

"Sure thing."

John Bailey disappeared back down the trail, and Danny took his own rifle from its rack. He gave Asa a measure of oats, milked the cow and put the milk in the spring house, packed a lunch, and with Red careening happily before him set off through the beech woods toward Stoney Lonesome. A gray squirrel scampered around the side of a tree, and Red looked interestedly at it but let it go. He glanced back at Danny, and grinned foolishly. Danny grinned back.

Danny toiled up Stoney Lonesome's steep slope, and halted before a huge, gray-trunked beech to get his bearings. Red stopped beside him, sitting on the ground with his plumed tail outstretched. A woodpecker hammered on a tree, and a chipmunk with his cheek pouches stuffed full of beech nuts dived backward off a stump. A little gust of wind blew across the forest floor, and ruffled the fallen leaves. Danny cut a little to the left, and came to the edge of the shallow gully that was called Blue Sag. He stood on the rim, his eyes roving up and down. Red walked into the gully, sniffed interestedly along it, and raised his head suddenly to stare toward one of the big blue rocks from which the sag took its name. Danny's gaze followed his, and he saw a corner of John Bailey's white handkerchief beside the rock. Danny snapped his fingers and called Red to him.

"Heel," he ordered. "If there's tracks, I don't want 'em messed up."

With the dog walking behind him, he made a slow way to the rock and knelt to study the ground. A low whistle escaped him. John Bailey hadn't exaggerated when he called this a big buck. The imprints of its cloven hoofs were huge and plain beside the rock. But there was a little line where it had dragged one hind foot, and it had fallen twice in climbing out of Blue Sag. Danny put his hand in the scuffed leaves and brought it away wet with blood.

"He's hurt, right enough," he murmured to himself. "It looks like he's hurt mortal bad. But he might go a smart piece yet."

He followed the trail to the top of Blue Sag, and stood pondering. Badly injured, the buck would not be likely to climb any hills or seek any other hard going. He would choose the easiest way, and that was straight around the rim of the mountain. If he deviated from that course he would go downhill. Danny followed the trail, walking swiftly.

By late afternoon they were far around the side of Stoney Lonesome, in a region of big and little boulders. The buck was walking more slowly now, and lying down more frequently. But he was only a little way ahead, floundering and working mightily to keep away from the pursuer that he knew was on his trail. Danny kept his rifle poised, ready for the first shot that might offer.

Then he walked around the edge of a boulder and placed his foot within six inches of the prostrate buck. For one brief second he had a glimpse of a huge, tortured gray body surmounted by a superb rack of horns. In split-second decision he raised his rifle and shot. At exactly the same second the buck, able to run no more and prepared to fight, hurled himself up and over. Danny scrambled wildly, and felt his flailing hand brush the side of the boulder. His head thudded against the rock and blackness enfolded him.

When he awoke it was night. His head throbbed painfully, and a great weight seemed to be crushing his right foot. For a few seconds he lay quietly. There was a motion beside him and Red's anxious whine sounded in the darkness. Danny flung out a hand, found the dog, and felt Red's wet tongue licking his arm. Slowly he raised himself to a sitting position, and as soon as he did that his head cleared.

But when he tried to move his right foot, he could not. It was bent around the boulder and held there in an unbreakable grip. Danny fumbled in his pocket for the box of matches that he always carried, and struck one against the boulder. In its wavering glare he saw the buck's head, upper body, and one of its huge antlers. The other antler was pressed tightly against the rock. Danny gulped. The antlers ended in a wide fork, and when the deer had thrown itself over on its back the fork on the right antler had closed over his leg, then wedged itself deep into the earth and against the rock to form an almost perfect trap.

Danny moved a little down the hill to ease the strain. Sweat rolled from his forehead, and sharp pain traveled the length of his body as he strove with all his strength to pull himself loose. But the dead buck did not even move; the antler that pinned his foot was firmly wedged. Danny sat up, and leaned forward. By extending his fingers he could reach around the edge of the rock and touch the dead buck's throat and muzzle. But there was nothing on which he could get a firm hold. He lay back down.

"No time to lose your head, Danny," he murmured to himself. "You can't do a thing by flyin' off the handle."

A sharp wind blew around the side of Stoney Lonesome, and fluttering leaves rustled. Red snarled fiercely and rushed, barking, into the night. Danny whistled him back.

"Don't get excited," he murmured. "Little old leaves a-blowing', that's all. Take it easy, Red."

Suddenly Danny was afraid. That wind would carry all along the side of Stoney Lonesome, and blow leaves before it. It would cover whatever trail he had made so thoroughly that nothing could follow it. Nobody, not even Ross,

could guess exactly which way this buck had come or where he was. A search party would certainly be organized and in time would find him. But how much time would that take? Danny felt as far as he could in every direction, but his groping fingers could not touch the rifle. Probably he had flung it when he fell.

He snapped his fingers. Almost immediately Red stood over him, half-seen and quivering in the darkness. The dog lowered his cold nose to touch Danny's cheeks, and whined. Danny lifted a hand to stroke his shoulder.

"Listen," he said, slowly and emphatically. "Listen careful, Red. Go home!"

Red whined and backed away. Danny waited eagerly, an unsaid prayer in his heart. If Red went home alone, Ross would know that something was amiss. He would also bring Red with him when he came to look for Danny, and almost certainly the big setter would lead him back here. But Red only sat on his haunches and bent his head down.

"Go home!" Danny ordered angrily. "Go home!"

Red whined again, and stood up to face into the darkness. Another gust of leaves blew around the side of the hill. A snarl

rippled from the big setter's throat, and again he raced, barking, into the darkness. Danny felt cold despair creep through him, and then anger. For the first time Red had shown a flaw. Afraid of leaves blowing through the darkness! Danny choked back the sobs that rose in his throat. Red emerged from the night to lie beside him, and Danny brought his right hand up to cuff the dog on the head.

"Go home!" he yelled. "Go home!"

Red backed a few feet away and sat down uncertainly. Danny writhed on the ground, but the antler that imprisoned him could not be moved. He was as helpless as if he had been tied.

"No time to lose your head," he repeated. "If that fool dog won't go home, think of somethin' else."

But there was nothing else except the darkness, the great pain in his foot, and the long, endless minutes. He bent his head toward the dog, and snapped his fingers.

Red came cringing in to lie beside him, and Danny stroked his back.

"I'm sorry, Red," he muttered, "sorry I hit you. But, oh dog, if you'd just go home!"

The long night hours dragged painfully by, and twice more the leaves rustled. Each time Red ran, barking, into the darkness. At long last gray morning spread itself across the sky. With it, so suddenly and unexpectedly that Danny jumped, came the clamor of hounds. They were very close, baying within a few hundred feet of where Danny lay. Ten minutes after they arrived there was the sharp snap of a rifle. Danny sat painfully up and shouted.

"Hall-oo-oo!"

And he heard Ross Pickett's answering, "Hall-oo!

Danny sat very still, listening to the rustling leaves that told him his father was on the way. He saw Ross, followed by the three hounds, appear among the trees and toil up the hill. Ross knelt to examine Danny's foot, and the concern on his face changed to a grin.

"It's what you get for shootin' deer out of season. But you ain't hurt bad. How long you been here?"

"All night."

"I'll get you out."

Ross caught the dead buck's antlers and heaved upward. Danny felt his foot come free, and rolled gratefully over. He sat up and leaned forward to watch Ross massage his cramped foot. Red stretched full length in the leaves and watched approvingly. Danny glanced reproachfully at him.

"I'm sure glad you came, Pappy," he said. "I thought you might be home, and tried to send that fool dog there. But he wouldn't go. Mebbe he ain't as much dog as I thought he was. Every time the leaves rustled, he ran towards 'em barkin' like all get out. A dog, scared in the dark! 'Tain't right."

For a moment Ross looked steadily at him. "I got that varmint," he said at last. "It's a big lynx."

"Yeah? I heard you shoot. How'd you get him, Pappy?"

"I kept the hounds on leashes, and slow-tracked him all day and all night," Ross said soberly. "When the trail freshened, I let the hounds go and they bayed him. Danny, that trail freshened within five hundred yards of where you're sittin' now, and there wasn't no low wind to rustle the leaves last night. That varmint was studyin' you, and the smell of the dog, and the smell of that dead buck, all night, and tryin' to figger if he was safe. It was him you heard, rustlin' the leaves when he came towards you. If it hadn't been for your dog . . . How you goin' to make it up to him, Danny?"

But just at that moment Red came forward, buried his nose in Danny's cupped hand, and closed his eyes blissfully while Danny scratched his ears.

There was nothing to make up.

ONE IN A MILLION

Timothy N. Davis

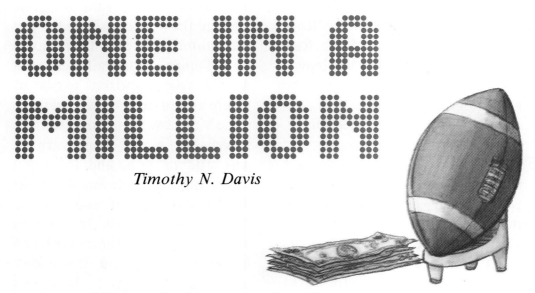

Of course the Mobsters were the best football team in the league. All of Boston was proud of them, and especially Coach Wilson. But one million dollars apiece? Nobody was worth that much, and the owner of the team knew it.

"We simply can't afford to pay them that much, Wilson. It's outrageous!" Mr. Libscomb, the owner, stood up behind his large desk. Then he turned and stared out the window. "They already make more than anybody else in the league."

Coach Wilson, sitting in Mr. Libscomb's office, heaved a long sigh. "It's just all gone to their heads," he said finally. "Those two undefeated seasons in a row—just went to their heads."

"I know, I know," said Mr. Libscomb. "But what are we going to do about it? The season starts in one week, and if we don't agree to their outrageous demands, they're all going on strike tomorrow!"

After a long pause, Coach Wilson replied, "Maybe we could take out a loan?"

Mr. Libscomb turned toward the coach with his teeth clenched. "A loan for forty million dollars?" he shouted. "Tell me, Wilson, who's going to pay it back? You?"

"Just kidding, Boss." Coach Wilson smiled weakly and wiped the perspiration from his face.

Mr. Libscomb bent over his desk and stared Coach Wilson right in the eye. "Listen, Wilson, we can't pay them that much. If they won't play, we'll get somebody else to play instead."

"B-but, Mr. Libscomb, sir, there's only one week left before the season starts," replied the coach. "We could never get a good team together in that time. Besides, the Mobster fans are so used to winning that they'd boo us off the field if we lost."

"Wilson!" Mr. Libscomb scowled and leaned even closer to the coach. "Everybody thinks you're a good coach. Now you get a team together, anyhow, anyway—and make them win! If you don't, you won't be a good coach. You won't even *be* a coach. Understand?"

Coach Wilson understood all right. After a long hard swallow, he politely excused himself and went home. Needless to say, he didn't sleep very well that night.

The next day disaster struck. All the sports pages proclaimed the bad news: "MOBSTERS GO ON STRIKE! Players Say No Season Without Million-Dollar Salaries."

Coach Wilson sat in his little office watching the news. As bad as the strike itself was for him, it was even worse when he saw a reporter interviewing some of his players.

Ace Spence, the quarterback, only bragged about how good he

was. However, Flex Bulk, the Mobsters' towering defenseman, really got everyone's attention.

Reporter: Flex, how about leaning down a little bit so both of our faces can be on the screen at once?

Flex: I don't think we need your face on the screen.

Reporter: Oh . . . uh . . . sure. So, Mr. Bulk, what do you think of the rumor that your team owner, Harry Libscomb, might hire players to replace you for this season?

Flex: I don't think that would be wise.

Reporter: Why is that, Flex?

Flex: Because anybody that signs up has a good chance of getting injured.

Reporter: Is that because he'll have so little time to get ready for the season?

Flex: No, that's not it.

Reporter: Why then?

Flex: Because I'll be paying him a visit.

"Oh, no," thought Coach Wilson, "now nobody will play for me. Everybody in Boston is afraid of Flex Bulk."

Coach Wilson felt very much discouraged. He was just about ready to turn off the TV and start typing his resignation when a news story came on about the city zoo. Looking at the bulky rhinos, the swift gazelles, and the agile monkeys, Coach Wilson came up with an idea. It was a crazy idea—even outrageous—but maybe it would work.

"Animals on a football team!" Mr. Libscomb couldn't believe his ears.

"I think it's our best shot, Mr. Libscomb," answered Coach Wilson. "I've read the league's rules thoroughly and it's completely legal."

"But animals?"

"Yes sir."

"But, Wilson, they don't even know how to play the game," snorted Mr. Libscomb. "And the season's only one week away!"

"I'll be working closely with some of the zoo's animal trainers, sir," replied the coach. "They're willing to cooperate with us fully."

"But animals?"

"I know it will take a while, sir, but just think of the potential!" A smile crept onto Wilson's face. "How would *you* like to tackle a rhinoceros?"

"Well, I . . . uh . . . but—animals, Wilson? It's outrageous!"

"The zoo is only asking for a reasonable contribution to improve the grounds—one *half* of what we paid in salaries *last* year, sir."

With that remark, Mr. Libscomb quieted down. "Yes." He smiled. "Heh heh. Yes, Wilson, you're a genius. Let's do it!"

The next morning all the animals and a couple of trainers were delivered to the stadium for Coach Wilson to start his one-week training camp. Everyone got along well. The animals seemed to take a special liking to their new coach. He was delighted to find out that many of the animals had already been trained to respond to a number of hand and voice signals.

Throughout the day Coach Wilson tested the animals' abilities in passing, running, blocking, and kicking. He was exceptionally pleased. And many of the animals seemed to be really enjoying themselves.

The rhinoceros seemed especially to enjoy charging toward the ball—or toward whoever had the ball, for that matter. "I can't wait to see him on defense," thought Coach Wilson.

The ostrich was particularly excited about running around the field with the football in his mouth. In fact, it was rather difficult to get it away from him. He was quite unpredictable. "A star if I ever saw one," thought the coach.

Then there was the orangutan. What an arm! And the gazelle made a terrific receiver! It seemed as though he could catch almost anything between his horns.

Actually it took several minutes to pry the football loose if the orangutan threw it too hard.

Coach Wilson was so excited he was jumping around on the field like a cheerleader.

"What a team!" he thought, "if only. . . ." Then his smile faded a little. "If only they can learn the rules."

The next day Coach Wilson tried to teach the animals some plays. Before long he had a terrible headache. It wasn't that they couldn't perform. But almost every play was offside, illegal procedure, illegal this or illegal that. Sometimes they even ran in the wrong direction!

"It's going to take time," Coach Wilson reminded himself. "Too bad the season starts this Saturday."

In just a few more days he would find out whether his outrageous idea would really work. If it did, it would be one in a million.

Saturday arrived. The whole team sat in the locker room. Each animal wore his own custom-made jersey. There was an uneasy silence in the air. Coach Wilson and the trainers stepped out of the office.

"I've never seen these animals so quiet," whispered one of the trainers.

"It's just a case of pre-game jitters," remarked the coach. "They'll get over it. . . . I hope."

"Let's go!" he yelled suddenly, running out to the hallway leading to the stadium. He led the stampede of enthusiastic animals onto the field.

Amidst the cheers of the crowd, Coach Wilson detected several screams. Apparently some people hadn't believed the reports that *real* animals would be playing. There were also some loud "boo's" coming from one particular section. It was the *old* Mobster team. Ace, Flex, and many others were hissing and booing as loudly as they could. The coach tried to ignore them. He also ignored the chuckles of the opposing coach and his team, the San Francisco Golden Gators.

The Mobsters got the ball first. On the very first play they were called offside: a penalty. (The giraffe had leaned his neck over the line.) The next play was a penalty similar to the first. Then on their third play, the ostrich got the ball. He dodged right. He dodged left. He hopped right over another defender. Before the San Francisco players knew what was happening, the ostrich was running straight toward the end zone.

"He's going to score!" yelled Coach Wilson, jumping up and down. But then something went wrong. The ostrich suddenly dodged right—right off the field! Right up into the stands!

Up and up he went to the top row. Then he ran around the top edge of the stadium. As you might guess, it took several minutes to catch him, and the Mobsters were penalized for delaying the game.

When the other team got the ball, things didn't go much better. The Mobsters gave up so many

yards in penalties that San Francisco had to gain only one yard on their own. The score became Gators 7, Mobsters 0. By half time it was Gators 21, Mobsters 3. The Mobsters' only score had come when the giraffe stumbled and accidentally kicked the ball through the goalposts. Coach Wilson was not discouraged, though. Each time the Mobsters made a play, they did it a little bit better.

In the second half it was the San Francisco coach's turn to get uneasy. Not only were the Mobsters playing better but they were also catching up! The gazelle made a leaping catch in the end zone for one touchdown. Having had his fling for the day, the ostrich ran straight for the end zone for the Mobsters' second touchdown. The score stood at Gators 21, Mobsters 17 with only two minutes left in the game.

The Gators had the ball. They wanted to hold on to it for only two minutes to finish the game and win. Now they were afraid of the Mobsters' defense. No longer was Coach Wilson's team making silly mistakes and being penalized. Now they were charging and tackling like—well, like animals!

On the next play, the hippo opened his mouth and let out a

tremendous roar just as the gators snapped the ball. It startled the San Francisco quarterback so much that he dropped the ball. It bounced on the grass. About half the players on both teams tried to jump on it at once.

The pile of men, gorilla, hippo, and baboons collided with a mighty "THUD!" The ball shot high up into the air. Down, down it came, right down on the rhino's horn.

"Go, rhino, go!" shouted Coach Wilson above the wildly cheering crowd. And the rhino did go—as fast as he could toward the end zone. Three—four—five San Francisco players tried to bring him down. He dragged them all into the end zone with him.

"Touchdown!" yelled the referee, just as the gun sounded to end the game. The crowd went crazy. The Mobsters had won, 24 to 21.

Each Saturday following that first game, the Mobsters seemed to get better and better. They beat Rochester, 31 to 14. Pittsburgh was defeated, 44 to 3, and Tallahassee lost by 52 points. And that was only the beginning.

Nowadays not many people can remember the names of the old Boston Mobster players. But the fans at Wilson Stadium do know one thing for sure. The team they have now is one in a million.

A Spear for Omar

Heddy Rado

Omar knelt at the bottom of the small dugout canoe and let his hand drift in the balmy water of the Red Sea. He loved this hour of the day, heading homeward with the keel of the canoe deep in the water, heavy with a day's catch of fish. It usually made him feel peaceful to watch the sun sink slowly behind the jagged mountains that lined the dry, hot desert.

Today, however, there was no peace in Omar for he had failed again. As if in answer to his shame came his father's soothing voice, "Do not worry too much, my Son. Tomorrow you will be able to hold your breath underwater longer than you did today."

Omar's father was known to be the best spearfisherman from Suez all the way down to Port Sudan. He was a big man with strong muscles rippling underneath his tanned skin. Clad only in a loincloth, he squatted in the canoe and paddled homeward with even, powerful strokes.

Omar's brother Gomez, who knelt in the stern of the canoe, cleaning and drying his underwater goggles with the tail of his galabia shirt, started to laugh. "Tomorrow Omar will be bobbing up for air every few seconds just like he did today," Gomez mocked. "How can he ever be a spearfisherman if he is afraid he might drown as soon as he is underwater for more than a few seconds?"

"Tomorrow I will stay underwater for hours, you will see!" cried Omar. Deep inside he was thoroughly ashamed of his fear of drowning.

With an angry motion Omar's father jarred the paddle against the canoe. "There will be no more fighting between you two," he said. "And as for you," he added, turning around to Gomez, "it would not harm you to exercise some more caution. It is not well to show fear, but also it is not wise to disregard danger altogether as you so often do. The sea is full of danger for the reckless spearfisherman." After that he took up his paddle, and no one spoke again.

Omar sighed and looked with deep longing at the spears at the bottom of the canoe. His father had promised him a spear of his own as soon as he had conquered his fear. The spears were slender, long shafts of smooth wood with metal points that gleamed dark red in the last rays of the sinking sun. To Omar the spears looked beautiful and well worth the effort he silently promised to make.

The next morning Omar's father announced that he would stay behind. "I want you two to go to sea alone today," he said. "Gomez is well able to do some spear fishing alone, providing he will be careful. And as for you, Omar," he continued. "I expect you to keep your promise and do some real diving today."

Omar respected his father too much to argue, although he did not want to go without him. Silently he nodded, and then the two boys went on their way.

Gomez smirked at Omar and said, "Let's go. I'll race you to the beach."

The minute the two brothers jumped into the crystal-clear water Omar forgot his disappointment that his brother had won the race over the burning sand. As much as Omar resented his brother's teasing, he felt great admiration for him. Now he admired the way Gomez gripped the heavy spear and shot downward with the ease and grace of a dolphin. It took only a few seconds until he bobbed up again with his first catch. He threw the fish into the canoe and grinned at Omar.

"How about coming down yourself?" he asked.

Omar held onto the canoe, "I will, I will," he said hastily. "But Gomez, please don't take any chances and stay down too long. You know that father warned you yesterday."

"You worry about yourself," Gomez called. Then he flipped back his hair, took a few deep breaths, and down he went again.

Now came the big moment for Omar to dive himself, and he was determined to dive well today. He let go of the canoe and submerged quickly.

A few feet below the surface the very water seemed to be alive with fish. The trembling rays of the sun penetrated the clear water and illuminated the colorful fish in a soft, mysterious light. Yet the whole scene seemed almost unreal because no sound broke the deep silence.

By now Omar's breath began to give out and he felt like darting to the surface. However, he forced himself to overcome his panic and swam deeper toward the pink coral reef. It was covered with flaming red sponges and the curiously nodding heads of purple worms. Scattered over the coral like precious diamonds were thousands and thousands of sparkling sea gems.

But the sight of numerous clams half hidden in the reef dampened Omar's enthusiasm a little. With their wide-open jaws they seemed to be just waiting for Omar. If he swam too near, they would close their shells as quick as a flash over a finger or an arm. Omar kept well away from the gaping jaws of the clams, swimming with smooth, careful strokes.

When he finally came to the surface he was very happy. His father would be proud of him when he heard how well Omar had dived today.

Gomez emerged a few feet away with another catch. He was panting for air but nevertheless didn't linger long. After treading water for a few moments, he took a deep breath and went down again.

A slight breeze had come up and sent gusts of hot air from across the desert. The water, however, was still as cool and smooth as flowing silk.

Omar turned on his back and paddled slowly to the canoe. He held on to the crudely carved wood which gave him a funny, tickling feeling in his palms. Then as he hung on to the canoe he suddenly went limp all over. The water around him became cold as ice.

Before Omar even saw the motionless shadow he knew that a shark must be near. With a quick glance he scanned the water below him and saw that most of the fish had disappeared into the countless alcoves of the reef. That was all he needed to know. In one smooth motion he slipped into the canoe.

The shark slowly emerged from the deep water and started circling the boat. He had a huge, silvery, streamlined body, small, murderous eyes, and a set of teeth that made Omar shudder. The boy leaned over the side of the canoe and looked frantically for his brother. The water was almost deserted. Only a few herring fish darted about.

There was no sign of Gomez.

Omar scanned the water from the other side of the boat. About fifteen feet below, half hidden by the protruding ridge of a deep alcove in the reef, he saw his brother.

Omar's hand went to his mouth to stifle a cry. He saw that his brother's hand had been caught in one of the many clams and he was desperately trying to free himself. But he was already weakened by lack of air and seemed unable to pry his hand loose.

"Oh, how could he have been so careless," moaned Omar. He knew that he had only a few precious seconds in which to save his brother.

There was a slim chance that the shark might not attack if Omar could disregard him completely. He felt his mouth go dry as he lowered himself into the water. He did not turn his head when the shark moved in closer. Without any outward sign of his deadly fear, he went straight down.

Never before had Omar dived as deep as that, and he felt as if his lungs would burst. For a second everything went black before his eyes.

But then he saw his brother in front of him. His body was swaying, helpless from the terrible lack of air. His hand was caught in the closed jaws of the clam. If he had not stayed underwater until there was hardly any breath left in him, he might have been able to free himself somehow. The cocky expression Gomez usually wore was gone. He looked at Omar with horror in his eyes.

Omar acted quickly. With deft fingers he pried the clam loose from the coral. He left it attached to Gomez's hand because he didn't want to waste precious time. He could attend to the clam when they were safe in the canoe, if they ever reached it.

The shark, whose giant shadow had been hovering above their heads, swam toward them. Omar tried to ignore the shark as he grabbed Gomez by the armpits and started upward. Suddenly the shark seemed to look directly at Omar with his murderous, yellow eyes. He came in closer, almost brushing against him with his powerful, fanlike fins. Omar's fingers began to loosen their grip on his brother, and they started to sink. The water around them had grown murky with waves churned by the shark.

If it was true that a shark might not attack if his victim showed no sign of fear, then Omar knew what he had to do. He tightened his fingers around his brother's arm until he could feel his nails sinking into the soft flesh. Then he turned his back on the shark and began to swim upward in calm, slow motions.

The effort took all Omar's strength and courage. Only a few feet more and they would be safe. A few feet more was all they needed.

When their heads broke the surface the shark came in for attack. He made a sharp turn and shot directly at Omar through the boiling waves. For a split second they were face to face, the shark a dreadful sight with his huge set of razor-sharp teeth.

In desperation, Omar took the last measure his father had taught him in an emergency like this. He let go of Gomez, raised his right arm and slapped the shark across its pointed nose. Then he struck again and again and again.

For a long moment the shark seemed stunned and motionless. Then he churned about, brushing against Omar's face with his rough fins as he turned toward the deep water.

Omar grabbed Gomez and pulled him into the canoe. Gomez sank to the floor, too exhausted to move, while Omar fell forward on his knees. His breath came in painful gasps and his eyes felt as if they would burst from their sockets. For a moment he gave way to the wave of faintness that washed over him, and supported his head against his arms on the seat in the boat's stern.

But only for a moment. Then he felt for his brother's arm. He took a knife and with its strong handle chipped away part of the shell. Although Gomez winced with pain, Omar worked fast until he could press the knife in and pry the clam open.

"It's only a flesh wound and will heal fast," Omar said after he had examined the wrist. He wrapped his dry shirt around it to stop the bleeding.

His brother opened his eyes weakly. He smiled at Omar and his smile was full of love and admiration. "Thank you, my brother," he said, "thank you."

Omar gave the makeshift bandage a last tug. "Shhh," he said, "do not speak now. You must rest."

Suddenly he felt very weary. His whole body ached and his right hand was bruised from fighting off the shark. However, it was not time for him to rest yet. Slowly he took the paddle and brought the boat in safely to the dock.

The next morning when Omar awoke he found a spear next to his sleeping mat. His father stood looking down at him, warm approval in his eyes. Omar jumped to his feet, gripping the spear tightly in his hand.

"You will be a fine spear-fisherman, my Son," his father said, and Omar lowered his head, a great surge of happiness rushing through him.

The Monkey, the Mirror, and the Red Paint

Paul White

Daudi held a great mirror before him. Those who came to the camp-fire crowded round to see themselves in it.

"Mirrors are things of wisdom," said Yohanna, who had just finished carving a small wooden dog.

M'gogo looked from the little large-eyed puppy at his feet to the wooden miniature in Yohanna's hand.

"There is another mirror which makes it possible for you to see inside your skin. The four-legged ones of the jungle will help you to understand it."

'Vumbe was a tan-coloured monkey who was interested in everything and who spent much of his time both in mischief and in rummaging in the rubbish-heap near the Jungle Hospital.

One morning he found an object that gave him no little joy. It was a nearly empty pot of red paint.

He sped through the thorn-bush, clutching his treasure and chuckling with glee.

Twiga the giraffe saw it all and thought thoughts of alarm. He bent his neck gently as 'Vumbe chattered importantly. Monkey wisdom and his strong curiosity urged him to wrench off the lid and investigate.

Giraffe knew the worst had happened when he saw 'Vumbe's head disappear into the pot as far as his ears.

Slowly, an oddly decorated monkey face appeared. 'Vumbe could smell oil, but no matter how he rolled his eyes he could not see his face.

Twiga coughed a gentle cough and with difficulty kept laughter from entering his neck.

"*'Vumbe,*" he said huskily, "your face will cause your family no amusement. You yourself will have no joy in the hard work of your uncle's paw in the way you know so well."

The corners of 'Vumbe's mouth moved up and down and a tear ran uncomfortably down his nose. He dropped the pot.

In a small voice he said, "What shall I do then?"

Giraffe nibbled at the thorn-tree shoots and thought deep thoughts. He turned to 'Vumbe:

"O ball of mischief, if you go carefully to the paw-paw tree at the hospital and look through the door you will see a small shining sort of window. Look into it and you will look back at yourself. This useful object is called 'mirror.' It is a thing of true wisdom. With it you will be able to see your trouble and remove it. That is the special and most valuable use of this shining thing."

Little monkey waited for no

more. He scuttled towards the hospital, going more cautiously as he came closer.

He peered through the fence, climbed it, looked this way and that. There was the paw-paw tree, there was the door, and there was the window of wisdom.

He took a deep breath, bolted through the door. There was the mirror, but before he could look into it, voices came from outside.

'Vumbe grabbed the mirror and scuttled through the window, up the pomegranate tree and on to the roof.

"Stop, thief!" someone shouted, and a large stone whizzed through the air.

Over the wall, through a hedge, round trees he rushed, till he stopped, panting, under a jifu bush.

He was about to look at himself when jackal passed. 'Vumbe was pleased to see the way hyaena's partner looked at the mirror under his arm. Even the wife of Simba the lion stopped and looked at him—a thing she had never done before. Monkey then made a tour of the larger buyu trees to impress both friends and relations. He felt warm in his inner monkey as he saw eyes turn towards him and mouths that moved behind hands.

'Vumbe made self-satisfied noises which stopped suddenly when he saw Twiga looking at him rather queerly.

"Have you looked at yourself, small monkey?"

'Vumbe shook his head, and in so doing he noticed something dancing along in front of him. As he moved the mirror to and fro he noticed how it threw a handful of bright light.

Curiosity welled up in his mind. He flicked the shining patch into the questioning eyes of Twiga who blinked and swung his neck sharply away.

'Vumbe somersaulted with monkey glee and dashed further into the jungle.

In the deep green coolness he saw Lwa-lwa the tortoise. The flying blob of light flashed blindingly in his beady eyes. Tortoise's head disappeared quickly under his shell and his voice came shrilly:

"Stop it at once, or I shall inform the senior members of your family tree."

'Vumbe swung by his tail and applauded his own sense of humour. He laughed till his ribs ached when he found that the light flashing in hippo's eyes made him sneeze in a way that reminded him of thunderstorms.

Twiga walked over to where mischievous monkey still swung by his tail and said very gently:

"Small one, you are so intent on mischief that you have forgotten the condition of your nose. A mirror is made to look in, not to play with. The light it reflects opens up the dark places. It helps you to see and avoid things of danger like pythons and leopards."

But 'Vumbe made a rude face and scuttled on to the top of an ant hill, where he saw Mbisi the hyaena winking at him.

'Vumbe came down to hyaena's level and heard his sinister whisper.

"O monkey, take no notice of giraffe. Do not look in that thing, or you will have fear."

'Vumbe shuddered and his mouth went dry.

"Wrap it in a banana leaf and hide it," advised Mbisi, slinking off towards the rubbish-heap.

Mischievous monkey decided to use it just once more when he saw his uncle Nyani comfortably and happily eating bananas.

The mirror moved in mischievous monkey's hand. Nyani blinked as the blinding light flickered into his face. He shaded his eyes and peered round to see what was producing the trouble.

Vaguely through the irritating glare he saw 'Vumbe with something dazzling in his hand.

Twiga saw that trouble was near and came closer.

Nyani continued to screw up his eyes and blink as the patch of light hovered round his face. Monkey words of horrid violence came through his clenched teeth, and threats that would turn monkey blood to water were directed towards gleeful little 'Vumbe.

With the skill of years, Nyani peeled an over-ripe banana, his hairy arms shot out and—*Wham!*—'Vumbe staggered back, tripped and fell, clutching the mirror over his head. His features were now decorated not only with red paint but with over-ripe banana.

Mbisi the hyaena laughed his evil laugh as he heard sounds of monkey misery mixed with the noise of hard paws striking with enthusiasm.

Twiga waited a suitable time and then came close to the tree where small monkey stood, for it was more comfortable that way, letting the cool wind from the jungle blow caressingly on his less comfortable portions.

Twiga said, "Small monkey, what is the use of a mirror unless you use it for its proper purposes? It is not a toy or an ornament or a charm."

But such are the ways of monkey wisdom that little mischievous monkey turned his back on giraffe, wrapped the mirror in a long strip of buyu bark and stuffed it in a convenient hollow in his family tree.

"The Bible is the Great Mirror," said Daudi. "Read it and you see yourself exactly as God sees you. It is to be read, not merely carried. A closed Bible on a shelf does little for its owner.

"To make light of the Bible, to misquote it, to twist its words to suit your convenience are certain ways of producing trouble.

"Its own words are, 'The man who looks into the perfect mirror of God's Law, the law of liberty, and makes a habit of so doing, is not the man who sees and forgets. He puts the Law into practice and wins true happiness.'"

Mijbil – Iraq to London

from The Otter's Tale
by Gavin Maxwell

Mijbil's story begins where the Tigris joins the Euphrates. A few years ago I traveled with Wilfred Thesiger, the explorer, to spend two months or so among the Marsh Arabs who live there. It had crossed my mind that I should like to keep an otter. I had mentioned this to Wilfred soon after the start of our journey, and he had replied that I had better get one in the Tigris marshes before I came home, for there they were as common as mosquitoes, and were often tamed by the Arabs.

I returned to the Consulate General, where I was living, late in the afternoon, having been out for several hours, to find that my mail had arrived. I carried it to my bedroom to read, and there squatting on the floor were two Marsh Arabs; beside them lay a sack that squirmed from time to time.

With the opening of that sack began a phase of my life that has not yet ended, and may, for all I know, not end before I do, because I can't any longer imagine being without an otter in the household.

The creature that emerged from this sack onto the tiled floor of the Consulate bedroom did not at that moment look like anything so much as a very small dragon. From the head to the tail he was coated with pointed scales of mud armor between whose tips you could see a soft velvet fur like that of a chocolate-brown mole. He shook himself, and I half expected a cloud of dust, but the mud stayed where it was, and in fact, it was not for another month that I managed to remove the last of it and see him, so to speak, in his true colors.

For the first twenty-four hours Mijbil was neither friendly nor unfriendly; he was simply aloof and indifferent, choosing to sleep on the floor as far from my bed as possible, and to accept food and water as though they were things that had appeared before him without human help. He ate small reddish fish from the Tigris, holding them upright between his forepaws, tail end uppermost, and eating them, always with five crunches of the left-hand side of the jaw alternating with five crunches on the right.

The second night Mijbil came on to my bed in the small hours and remained asleep in the crook of my knees until the servant brought tea in the morning, and during that day he began to lose his sulks and take a keen, much too keen, interest in his surroundings. I made a collar, or rather a body belt, for him and took him on a lead to the bathroom, where for half an hour he went wild with joy in the water, plunging and rolling in it, shooting up and down the length of the bath underwater, and making enough slosh and splash for a hippo. This, I was to learn, is what otters do; every drop of water must be spread about the place; a bowl must at once be upset, or, if it will not overturn, be sat in and splashed in until it overflows. Water must be kept on the move and made to do things.

It was only two days later that he escaped from my bedroom as I entered it, and I turned to see his tail disappearing around the bend of the corridor that led to the bathroom. By the time I had caught up with him, he was up on the end of the bath and fumbling at the chromium taps with his paws. I watched, amazed; in less than a minute he had turned the tap far enough to produce a dribble of water, and, after a moment or two, the full flow. (He had, in fact, been lucky to turn the tap the right way; later he would as often as not try with great violence to screw it up still tighter, chittering with annoyance and disappointment at his failure.)

After a few days he would follow me without a lead and come to me when I called his name. By the end of a week he had accepted me completely, and then he began to play. Very few species of animals play much after they are grown up; but otters are one of the exceptions to this rule; right through their lives they spend much of their time in play that does not even need a partner. In the wild state they will play alone for hours with some floating object in the water, pulling it down to let it bob up again, or throwing it with a jerk of the head so that it lands with a splash and becomes something to be chased. No doubt in their holts they lie on their backs and play too, as my otters have, with small objects

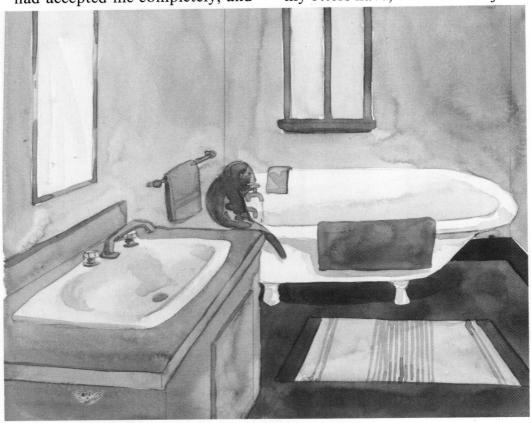

that they can roll between their paws and pass from palm to palm, for at Camusfeàrna all the sea holts contain small shells and round stones that can only have been carried in for toys.

Mij would spend hours shuffling a rubber ball around the room like a four-footed soccer player using all four feet to dribble the ball, and he could also throw it, with a powerful flick of the neck, to a surprising height and distance. These games he would play either by himself or with me, but the really steady play of an otter, the time-filling play born of a sense of well-being and a full stomach, seems to be when the otter lies on its back and juggles small objects between its paws. Marbles became Mij's favorite toys for this pastime, and he would lie on his back rolling two or more of them up and down his wide, flat belly without ever dropping one to the floor or, with forepaws upstretched, rolling them between his palms for minutes on end.

Even during those first two weeks in Basra I learned a lot of Mij's language. The sounds are widely different in range. The simplest is the call note, which has been much the same in all the otters I have come across; it is a

short, anxious mixture between a whistle and a chirp, and it can be heard for a long way. There is also a query, used at closer quarters; Mij would enter a room, for instance, and ask whether there was anyone in it by the word "Ha!" in a loud, harsh whisper. But it was the chirp, high or low, from a single note to a continuous flow of chitter, that was Mij's main means of talk.

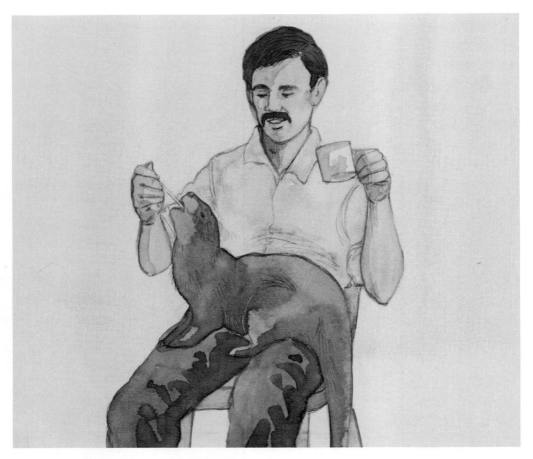

An otter's jaws are, of course, very strong, and those jaws have teeth meant to crunch into pulp fish heads that seem as hard as stone. Like a puppy that nibbles and gnaws one's hands, otters seem to find the use of their mouths the most natural thing; knowing as I do their enormous crushing power, I can see how hard my otters have tried to be gentle in play, but perhaps they think a human skin is as thick as an otter's. Mij used to look hurt and surprised when scolded for what must have seemed to him real gentleness, and though after a time he learned to be soft-mouthed with me, he remained all his life somewhat over-excitably good-humored with strangers.

The days passed peacefully at Basra, but I dreaded the prospect of transporting Mij to England. The airline insisted that Mij should be packed into a box of not more than eighteen inches square and that this box must be carried on the floor at my feet.

The box was delivered on the afternoon before my departure on a 9:15 P.M. flight. It was zinc lined, and it seemed to me as nearly ideal as could be.

Dinner was at eight, and I thought that it would be as well to put Mij into the box an hour before we left, so that he would become accustomed to it before the jolting of the journey began to upset him. I got him into it, not without difficulty, and he seemed peaceful when I left him in the dark for a hurried meal.

But when I came back, with only barely time for the Consulate car to reach the airport for flight, I saw an awful sight. There was complete silence from inside the box, but from its air holes and the chinks around the hinged lid blood had trickled and dried on the white wood. I whipped off the padlock and tore open the lid, and Mij, exhausted and blood-spattered, whimpered and tried to climb up my leg. He had torn the zinc lining to shreds, scratching his mouth, his nose, and his paws, and had left it jutting in spiky ribbons all around the walls and the floor of the box. When I had removed the last of it, so that there were no cutting edges left, it was just ten minutes until the time of the flight, and the airport was five miles distant. It was hard to bring myself to put the miserable Mij back into that box, that now

seemed to him a torture chamber, but I forced myself to do it, slamming the lid down on my fingers as I closed it before he could make his escape. Then began a journey the like of which I hope I shall never know again.

I sat in the back of the car with the box beside me as the Arab driver tore through the streets of Basra like a bullet. Donkeys reared, bicycles swerved wildly, out in the suburbs goats stampeded, and poultry found unguessed powers of flight. Mij cried in the box, and both of us were hurled to and fro and up and down. Exactly as we drew to a screeching stop before the airport entrance, I heard a splintering sound from the box beside me,

and saw Mij's nose force up the lid. He had summoned all the strength in his small body and torn one of the hinges clean out of the wood.

The aircraft was waiting to take off; as I was rushed through the customs by infuriated officials, I was trying all the time to hold down the lid of the box with one hand, and with the other to force back the screws into the splintered wood.

The seat booked for me was at the extreme front of the aircraft, so that I had a bulkhead before me instead of another seat.

The port engines roared, and then the starboard, and the aircraft trembled and teetered against the tug of her propellers, and then we were taxiing out to take off. Ten minutes later we were flying westward over the great marshes that had been Mij's home, and peering downward into the dark I could see the glint of their waters beneath the moon.

I had brought a briefcase full of old newspapers and a parcel of fish, and with these scant resources I prepared myself to withstand a siege.

I unlocked the padlock and opened the lid, and Mij was out like a flash. He dodged my fumbling hands with an eel-like

wriggle and disappeared at high speed down the aircraft. As I tried to get into the gangway I could follow his progress among the passengers by a wave of disturbance among them not unlike that caused by the passage of a weasel through a hen run. There were squawks and shrieks and a flapping of traveling coats, and halfway down the fuselage a woman stood up on her seat screaming out, "A rat! A rat!"

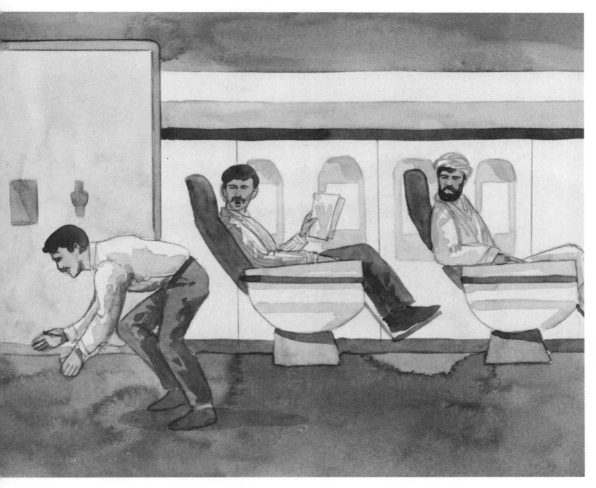

I ran down the gangway and, catching sight of Mij's tail disappearing beneath the legs of a portly white-turbaned Indian, I tried a flying tackle, landing flat on my face. I missed Mij's tail, but found myself grasping the sandaled foot of the Indian's companion; furthermore, my face was inexplicably covered in curry. I staggered up babbling apology, and the Indian gave me a long, silent stare. I was, however, glad to see that something, possibly the curry, had won over my fellow passengers, and that they were regarding me now as a harmless clown rather than as a dangerous lunatic. The stewardess stepped into the breach.

"Perhaps," she said with the most charming smile, "it would be better if you resumed your seat, and I will find the animal and bring it to you." I explained that Mij, being lost and frightened, might bite a stranger, but she did not think so. I returned to my seat.

I heard the ripple of flight and pursuit passing up and down the body of the aircraft behind me, but I could see little. I was craning my neck back over the seat trying to follow the hunt when suddenly I heard from my feet a distressed chitter of recognition and welcome, and Mij bounded onto my knee and began to nuzzle my face and neck. In all the strange world of the aircraft I was the only familiar thing to be found, and in that first return to me was sown the seed of the absolute trust he gave me for the rest of his life.

Otters are extremely bad at doing nothing. That is to say that they cannot, as a dog does, lie still and awake; they are either asleep or entirely absorbed in play. If there is no toy, or if they are bored, they will set about laying the land waste. There is, I am convinced, something positively provoking to an otter about order and tidiness in any form; and the greater the untidiness that they can make, the more contented they feel. A room does not seem right to them until they have turned everything upside down; cushions must be thrown to the floor from sofas, books pulled out

of bookcases, wastepaper baskets overturned, and the rubbish spread as widely as possible, drawers opened, and contents shoveled out and scattered. An otter must find out everything and have a hand in everything; but most of all he must know what lies inside any man-made container or beyond any man-made obstruction.

We had been flying for perhaps five hours, when one of these moods descended upon Mijbil. It opened fairly harmlessly, with an attack upon the newspapers spread carefully around my feet, and in a minute or two the place looked like a street upon which royalty has been given a ticker-tape welcome. Then he turned his attention to the box, where his sleeping compartment was filled with fine wood shavings. First he put his head and shoulders in and began to throw these out backward at enormous speed; then he got in bodily and lay on his back, using all four feet in a pedaling motion to hoist out the rest. I was doing my best to cope with the litter, but I was hopelessly behind in the race when he turned his attention to my neighbor's canvas TWA travel bag on the floor beside him. The zipper gave him pause for no more than seconds;

by chance, probably, he yanked it back and was in head first throwing out magazines, handkerchiefs, gloves, bottles of pills and tins of ear plugs. My neighbor was asleep; I managed, unobserved, to haul Mij out by the tail and cram the things back.

My troubles really began at Paris, a long time later. Mij had slept from time to time, but I had not closed an eye, and it was by now more than thirty-six hours since I had even dozed. I had to change airports, and since I knew that Mij could slip his body strap with the least struggle, there was nothing else to do but put him back in his box. In its present form, however, the box was useless, for one hinge was dangling unattached from the lid.

I explained my predicament to the stewardess. She went forward to the crew's quarters and returned after a few minutes saying that one of the crew would come and nail down the box and rope it for me. She warned me at the same time that Air France's rule differed from this of TWA's, and that from Paris onward the box would have to travel freight and not in the passenger portion of the aircraft.

Mij was sleeping on his back inside my jacket, and I had to steel myself to force him back into that hateful prison and listen to his pathetic cries as he was nailed in what now seems to me like a coffin.

It was the small hours of the morning when we reached London Airport at last. Mij, who had slept ever since the box was nailed up, was wide-awake once more by the time we reached my studio, and when I pried open the lid of the box, Mij clambered out into my arms to greet me with a frenzy of affection that I felt I had hardly deserved.

Man's Next-Best Friend

Michael Garrett Deas

Wouldn't it be fun to have a friend ready to play outdoors whenever you are? How about a friend that's outgoing, good looking, and loyal, besides being funny and talented? Any of us would like to meet someone like that—but few would think to look for such a likable personality in a river otter.

It may be that a dog is man's best friend, but the otter runs a close second. Even though he is the big brother to the weasel, an otter resembles a dachshund in quite a few ways. Both animals have sleek, dark brown fur, a whiskered muzzle, a long, low, "hot dog" body, and four short legs. Beyond that, the otter is also extremely friendly—even to approaching animals that are strangers to him. An otter, especially a young one, makes a great pet. He is easy to train, clean, smart, and faithful—almost *better* than having a dog!

But of course, you won't find many otters for sale in pet stores. This is because a river otter, as you can tell by the name, needs to live near fresh water. Although this remarkable swimmer is at home just about anywhere in the United States and Canada, the ideal habitat for him is a forest lake in the mountainous, midwestern regions. Plenty of coves and embankments around a lake suit the otter's need for "playground area." But more essential than these is the underbrush on the bank, for this is where the otter couple will build their den or holt. You can't spot the den from the outside. It is like a cave hollowed out deep within the thicket, comfortably lined with ferns and leaves. The only entrance to the den is a secret underwater tunnel, opening on the side of the lake.

This hidden passage keeps the otters from being seen coming and going and protects the otter-pups from predators.

The mother otter gives birth to as many as five pups. Once their eyes have opened, the family will dig out of the holt. They avoid the underwater passageway because young otters are not born knowing how to swim. The pups ride "piggy-back" on their mother and father until they overcome their fear of water and can swim on their own. Soon they learn not only to maneuver as gracefully as their parents but also to stay underwater for long periods of time. Can you imagine swimming the length of four football fields before coming up *once* for breath?

After about a year of close, affectionate family life, the young otters will travel on, abandoning their den and exploring new waters. But the mother and father usually remain intensely loyal to each other. In fact, when one mate dies, the other may seem to grieve for days, staying close by the body and mourning aloud. This ability to sense and express sorrow makes the otter seem almost human in his emotions.

Of course, there's much more work to family life than just learning and being together. For the otter, that work is usually keeping his family fed. He is mainly a fisherman, but instead of using hook and line, he chases and corners his prey in the water.

An otter can out-swim just about any fish in the lake—an amazing feat for a land animal. His "scuba gear" surpasses anything humans have ever invented. Two coats of hair cover everything but his eyes and nose. The outside coat, made of long, coarse, oily hairs, keeps him dry no matter how long he stays in the water. The inside coat of short, soft fur keeps him comfortable whether it's nine degrees or ninety outside. For his uncovered ear and nose holes, the otter has special membranes that seal water out. The skin between the five toes on his paws is called webbing, just like that on a duck's foot. Webbed paws allow him to steer underwater in any direction. To propel himself through the

water at speeds up to seven miles per hour, he swishes his muscular, foot-long tail.

The otter's sharp hearing, short-range vision, and good sense of balance help his hunting, but his real food-finding devices are his whiskers, which grow on his nose and—of all places—his elbows. Like television antennas picking up broadcast signals in the air, these fine-tuned whiskers tell the otter exactly where a fish or other likely prey is in the water. Breakfast for an otter may consist of turtles and eels, then snakes or crabs for lunch. He may snack in the afternoon on insects and snails and then possibly for supper try something really different, like frogs or birds. But dessert must be crayfish, the otter's favorite. All this he will catch himself by darting, circling, or jumping around his prey as if he enjoyed playing with his food before eating.

Most of the otter's time isn't spent in raising a family or in hunting food, but in playing. Unlike other animals, otters would rather have fun than do almost anything else. They excel in water sports, whether summer or winter. In summertime they do everything you love to do at the swimming pool—swim, dive, do belly-flops, splash and chase each other, play tag or tug-of-war, and frolic about. Otters even make their own slides. They clear a path down an embankment that leads to deep water. Then for hours they slip, slide, and roll down their slick pathway again and again. Wintertime doesn't stop any of their activities. The mud slide becomes a snow slide; but instead of splashing into water, they go skiing across the frozen lake. When they find a break in the ice, the otters dive in and continue their usual antics, not the least bit hindered by the cold. To catch a breath of air, they'll stick their flat noses into air pockets trapped beneath the ice. In this way they can keep on playing without having to rush back constantly to an ice-hole for air.

These special abilities of the otter make him seem not so much like a dog after all. He's not much like *any* other animal. But many qualities we admire in "man's best friend" are also in the otter. Add to this the otter's extraordinary playfulness, and you can see why he stands out from others in the animal kingdom. If you ever have an opportunity, get to know an otter at a river or lake in the woods. You may find yourself a next-best friend!

Skill Lesson:
Taking Notes

Doug's teacher wanted the class to write reports on the subject "Creatures." Even though most of the students picked certain types of dogs or cats to write about, Doug chose the topic of spiders. His teacher required that Doug tell the class what spiders eat and where they make their homes.

Doug checked an encyclopedia on the topic of spiders. He headed his paper with the first question he had to answer for the teacher.

What do spiders eat?

The encyclopedia article told him about different kinds of spiders and how spiders spin webs, but as he scanned the headings he found a paragraph entitled "The Spider's Diet." He carefully read the following paragraph.

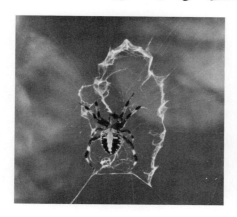

The Spider's Diet. Most spiders eat small insects, especially flies. But larger spiders will catch and eat insects bigger than themselves. Pirate spiders eat only other spiders. Fisher spiders live near water and eat small fish. Although most spiders are not considered harmful to animal life, the group of the biggest spiders, tarantulas, sometimes attack and eat rodents. One type of tarantula, the bird spider, lives in trees and eats small birds.

Under his heading of "What do spiders eat?" Doug made a short list from what he had read.

What do spiders eat?
large and small insects
other spiders
small fish
rodents
small birds

Then he decided that he might want to include some more facts, just in case some of his classmates didn't believe that a spider could eat a bird. He added the following:

○	*What do spiders eat?* *most spiders — large and small insects* *pirate spider — other spiders* *fisher spider — small fish* *tarantula — rodents*
○	*bird spider (a tarantula) — small birds*

Doug's system of getting information is simple, fast, and efficient. He knew what he wanted when he did his research, and that helped him to choose only the information he needed so that he didn't waste time on information the teacher didn't want.

Doug had learned to *take notes* from what he read. All students learn to take notes. They select the information they need and write it down as briefly as possible. Some people take notes on index cards, and some use regular-sized paper. The best way to take notes is to write down the heading as Doug did and make room for the notes to follow. Doug's two headings were "What do spiders eat?" and "Where do spiders live?" Headings for notes do not have to be in question form. Instead of questions, Doug could just as easily have written headings like "Food for spiders" and "Homes for spiders." As long as he captured the correct ideas for his headings, he could use them for making notes.

Moses and Joshua

Henry Becker

Everybody knew that Mrs. Morrison did the best job putting on plays of all the teachers at Riverside Christian School, even if she was kind of old. I had been in plays in the third grade and the fourth grade, but they weren't anything compared to being in Mrs. Morrison's fifth-grade class and trying out for the part of Joshua. Crossing the Jordan River and fighting the battle of Jericho—boy, oh boy!

It probably wasn't as exciting for the sixth graders since they'd gotten to be in a play the year before, but when you come right down to it, there wasn't a single sixth grader who said he'd rather not.

Everybody got a script to learn a part for tryouts. I figured I would probably get the main part. Most other people thought I would too. Just about everybody knew I was one of the best speakers. Some of the sixth grade boys said they thought I was too little, but I figured they were just jealous because they knew I could do a better job than they could.

When I got home that night I told Mom about the play. Mom said, "Oh, wonderful, honey!

Another main part!" I explained to her that this wasn't like those little kid plays I'd been in before; this was the fifth- and sixth-grade *Bible* play, directed by *Mrs. Morrison.* I started to tell her that I wasn't *positive* I was going to get the main part, but I decided not to. I ran up to my room to start learning my lines. I highlighted them with my yellow marker—fifty-seven of them!

I worked on my lines every spare minute for days. While I set the table I shouted, "Prepare food! For within three days you shall pass over this Jordan to possess the land that the Lord your God gives to you!" While I carried out the trash I said, "Go. View the land of Jericho. Tell us what sort of people inhabit this land and whether they stand in fear of our almighty God." While I mowed the lawn I yelled, "Listen to me! This is how you will know that the living God is among you. As soon as the priests' feet touch the edge of the mighty Jordan River, the waters shall part and stand up in a heap." My sisters even had to come ask me to be quiet one night because I was saying my lines in my sleep.

Mrs. Morrison heard me saying my lines on the playground one afternoon. She came up behind me and listened for a minute. I sort of pretended I didn't know she was there so I could show her what a good job I could do—before the tryouts actually came.

Finally she said, "That's a pretty important part you're rehearsing to yourself there."

I just said, "Yes, ma'am."

I guess she could tell I was happy, because she looked at me really seriously. Then she said, "You do a really good job with the part of Joshua, Mark." She thought for a second, and then she added, "I shouldn't say this because I don't have the final word in the matter, but I feel almost sure you'll get that part. I know you can do a good job with it. But if you do get it, you should be sure to be a good example before others while we prepare for this play. I know you can."

"Yes, ma'am," I said, grinning. I knew I could, too. That wasn't what mattered. "I know I'll do a good job," I said.

After two weeks, long enough for everybody to feel like he could say the part he wanted to try out for, we had tryouts. The principal and all the fifth- and sixth-grade teachers were there. When it was finally my turn, I saw Mrs.

Morrison lean over and say something to the principal, and I could see she was smiling. That made me stand up even taller and say my lines even louder. I knew she thought I was good. But then the principal started to frown a little, and he waved his hand around. That made it a little hard to concentrate. Mrs. Morrison looked worried, and she leaned back and whispered back to the principal. And he whispered to her again and pointed somewhere on stage, and she whispered to him again and looked even more worried. And I was starting to get a little nervous.

I had to leave before the last person tried out, but I kind of hung around Mrs. Morrison for a minute wondering if she would go ahead and tell me something terrible. But she was too busy taking notes on the tryouts. She just said, "Good-bye, Mark. I'll see you in class in the morning."

After school the next day Mrs. Morrison had all the people sitting in the reading circle who had tried out for anything. The reading circle was the most cramped it had ever been. First she said the little speech that the sixth graders remembered from

the year before. "You young folks are all so good that it was very hard for me to decide who would play which part. But, as always, some people will have more lines to say than others. Now I don't want you to think that just because you may have gotten a smaller part, you're not good. After all, every part in this play is important. Every one of you is important. There are no small parts, just small actors."

Well, everybody knew that there were *too* small parts, and if Joshua got sick it would be a whole lot worse than if one of the Israelites who just marches around the wall did. We were all kind of squirming in our seats waiting for her to assign the parts, but she kept on going. "Now one thing that we have to remember is that we have some unsaved parents who will be coming to see some of you in this play. All through our rehearsals and other preparations we have to remember to honor the Lord above all. Maybe some of them will see our testimonies and come to know the Lord."

Well, wouldn't you know it, she started with the smallest parts and worked up to assigning the big ones. I could tell that some people were happy and some were

disappointed. I guess it was always that way. But I was starting to get a little worried about *me*. Maybe I was losing my nerve, but suddenly I wasn't as sure of myself as I had been.

Finally, when she had assigned all the way up through Caleb and I still had not been named, she stopped for a long, long time. Everybody started to get nervous, and I think I might have been the most nervous of all. Then she said, "I'll be assigning the part of Joshua tomorrow. All of you who have your parts go home and learn them well so we can honor the Lord with this play!"

Everybody else was leaving and a bunch of them whispered to me that they thought I would get the part, but Mrs. Morrison asked me to stay and talk to her. I stood around until everybody else had left. Boy, were they curious!

As soon as the rest were all gone, Mrs. Morrison said, "Mark, I didn't get a lot of sleep last night—worrying and praying. More worrying than praying, I'm afraid."

Now I could hardly stand it. "Well, what is it?" I asked.

She stopped a little, and then she said, "I'm afraid you don't make a suitable Joshua—"

"You mean I don't do a good job?" I could hardly believe it.

"Oh, no, it isn't that. It's just that, I'm afraid . . . you're too small. Mr. Alexander and the other teachers and I all talked about it after tryouts last night. You are so much smaller than most of the other boys, and your voice is . . . well, quite a bit higher. . . ."

"Yes, ma'am." My eyes stung some, but I wasn't going to let her see me cry.

"Mr. Alexander and the other teachers decided that we should use Randy Ortega from the sixth grade—"

"Randy Ortega!" I said it so loudly I almost scared myself. "I never hear him say anything! He couldn't do a good job!"

"Well, apparently the principal thinks differently," she said in a quiet voice. "Randy is a big boy with a deeper voice, and I think he could do a good job with some help. I know he's shy, but this might be just what he needs."

"Well, but what about me?" I asked. "I mean, what part do I get now? Can I at least be Caleb or somebody like that?"

"Well . . ." she hesitated. "The principal said he would rather you be an understudy. And a coach. I wasn't sure Randy could do a good job of learning his lines without a coach—"

"I'll say," I said.

"Mark, I won't tolerate that kind of spirit."

"Yes, ma'am."

"And we thought you could do the job," she went on. "You can also be an Israelite. Since you'll be an understudy, you'll have to have a nonspeaking part."

"Mrs. Morrison, I can't," I said. "I just can't! I can't help Randy when he took my part away from me. Please don't ask me to do that."

"Well, Mark," she said slowly, "first of all, let me say that Randy didn't take your part away from you—that was a part you were never promised. I never should have spoken to you the way I did on the playground. And let me say furthermore that before you say you can't, you should ask the Lord if He wants you to. Because if He does, He will give you the strength to do it."

"Yes, ma'am." I looked down and left.

When I told Mom and Dad about it, they seemed a little upset too. I mean, at first. But then they both told me that this was what the Lord wanted for me and it was for the best and I would be the best Israelite around. You know, the typical Mom-and-Dad-type things to say. Maybe they didn't know how much I wanted that part. But how could they not know, as hard as I worked on these lines? It seems like they should have been on the phone in a minute, calling up Mrs. Morrison to tell her what they thought of her.

Well, I didn't pray about it. Not really. Everybody teased me at school the next day. A few people felt sorry for me, mostly girls, but some of the sixth-grade boys just told me I thought I was hot stuff and this was going to cool me off.

I put off helping Randy on purpose, and he was too shy to ask me. When the first rehearsal came, we hadn't gotten together even once. I sneaked into the back to see the first rehearsal. It was only for people with speaking parts. Randy was still reading his part from the paper. He didn't have any expression, and he couldn't pronounce a bunch of the words. He didn't even seem to know what he was saying. Mrs. Morrison was pretty patient with him, but I felt kind of glad, in a mad sort of way. They thought Randy would do a better job than I would.

The next day Mrs. Morrison called me up to her desk again. "I was hoping I wouldn't have to talk to you about the play again, Mark," she said. "I was hoping you would follow the leading of the Lord and serve Him with a willing heart. But it looks as if pride has gotten in the way. Did you even pray about helping Randy?"

I just looked down.

She sighed, but she still sounded patient and still kept her voice soft so the rest of the class couldn't hear what she was saying. "Maybe you *will* pray about it tonight. But before you do, read some verses—I'll find the reference and give it to you before you leave today."

I didn't much care anymore. I'd gotten plenty of verses in my life. She put a piece of paper on my desk later while she was checking homework. All it said was, "Read Deuteronomy 3:23-28 tonight." I stuck the paper away in my math book.

At supper I told Mom and Dad what Mrs. Morrison asked me to do, but I forgot about the verses. They didn't say much—I guess they knew it would be a hard thing for me to do. But I was just opening my math book to do my homework when Dad called us all for devotions. There was the paper with the note on it, so I grabbed it and took it with me.

"Can we read this for devotions tonight, Dad?" I asked. And I explained how Mrs. Morrison had said I should read that before I prayed for the Lord to tell me what to do about helping Randy.

So Dad read it in his quiet voice.

"And I besought the Lord at that time, saying, O Lord God, thou hast begun to shew thy servant thy greatness, and thy mighty hand: for what God is there in heaven or in earth, that can do according to thy works, and according to thy might? I pray thee, let me go over, and see the good land that is beyond Jordan,

that goodly mountain, and Lebanon. But the Lord was wroth with me for your sakes, and would not hear me: and the Lord said unto me, Let it suffice thee; speak no more unto me of this matter. Get thee up into the top of Pisgah, and lift up thine eyes westward, and northward, and southward, and eastward, and behold it with thine eyes: for thou shalt not go over this Jordan. But charge Joshua, and encourage him, and strengthen him: for he shall go over before this people, and he shall cause them to inherit the land which thou shalt see."

When he was done I said, "I don't get it. I mean, I know that

Moses is talking there, and I know that story about how Moses didn't get to go into the Promised Land, but I don't see why Mrs. Morrison wanted me to read that before I prayed about it. I mean, except that it has Joshua in it, and Randy's going to be Joshua now."

"I get it!" Sandy said. Sandy's my older sister. "Don't you see, Mark? Randy's Joshua, and *you're Moses.*"

"I think you're right, Sandy," Dad said. "Mrs. Morrison is trying to tell you something, Mark."

"Wait—maybe we'd better read it again," I said. "Maybe I can get it this time."

So Dad read it again all the way through.

"Now, Mark," Mom said, "if you think of yourself as Moses and Randy as Joshua, what does that passage mean to you?"

"I think I get it now," I said. "I don't get to be in the play, just like Moses didn't get to go into the Promised Land. But Moses had to help Joshua, and I'm supposed to help Randy."

"That may very well be it," Dad said. "We'll pray that the Lord will show you just what He wants you to do. We won't make this decision for you."

But even before we prayed I knew what the Lord wanted me to do.

It was pretty rough. Randy wasn't exactly what I would call a quick learner. It seemed like a million times that I had to say, "All right, say that line again." And he would say, just the same way, "Pass through the hosts—" and I would stop him. "No, Randy! Joshua is talking to all the officers, and he's excited. Say "PASS THROUGH THE HOSTS!!" And Randy would say, "PASS THROUGH THE HOSTS!!" And over and over again we did it. And he started to get a little better. We got to talk some after we worked, too, and he seemed to be a pretty nice guy, and not so shy when you got to know him. I found out he was

really funny sometimes. And he didn't try to act big and tough like a lot of the sixth-graders do. In fact, one time he said to me, "Mark, I know you were supposed to be Joshua." He hadn't ever said anything about it before. Then he said, "It was really nice of you to help me. I feel like I can do a lot better now. I was pretty scared when Mrs. Morrison told me she wanted me to be Joshua because I'd never done anything like that before in my life. But I figured I could learn. And you've really helped me."

I was about to say something like, "Well, I'm glad to do it," because I couldn't stand to think about what he would have sounded like if I *hadn't* helped him. But he interrupted me. He said, "A lot of the other guys made fun of me because a fifth-grader was going to help me learn my lines. But I told them to get lost, and they did." He laughed a little. "After all, I *am* the biggest boy in sixth grade."

Well, I'd never thought about it from his side of things. I didn't say what I was going to say.

Randy was a little better every day we worked together. I could tell he was really trying hard. And I tried hard to remember that I was Moses and he was Joshua,

and I wasn't going to get to be in the play because I would be dead—I mean, Moses didn't show up in the Jericho story, did he? But he did a lot of work behind the scenes. Just like Mark Whitmore.

I liked Mrs. Morrison better now than I had for a while, and sometimes she called me Moses, like a private joke.

Then dress rehearsal night came, and I got to dress up like an Israelite—big whoopee. I guess it was fun. I got to watch Randy the whole time, and he did a great job. He messed up only a couple of times. At the end I heard Mr. Alexander joke to Mrs. Morrison, "They say that if the dress rehearsal goes well, the performance night will be a flop."

But Mrs. Morrison said, "Pshaw. I don't believe in any of that superstitious nonsense. We've always had good dress rehearsals, and we've always had outstanding plays."

Her words reminded me of stories I'd heard, stories about opening nights of plays when one of the lead players got sick and the director had to find a stand-in at the last minute. That's what understudies are for.

I couldn't help thinking . . . what if Randy gets sick at the last minute and they need some-body . . . I'm the only other person who knows the lines. And Mr. Alexander would *have* to say yes then.

I thought about it a lot, and I know I shouldn't have. Especially because Randy didn't get sick, and he was right there ready to be Joshua on performance night. Just before Mrs. Morrison called us all together for prayer, he pulled me into a corner.

"Mark, it's great! I've been praying for this for months!" he said.

I wanted to say, "What? You want me to be Joshua after all?" But I just waited.

He said, "My mother is *here*, Mark! She came! She isn't a Christian, and she would never come to anything at this school. She never would really say whether she was going to come to this play, even though I was going to be Joshua. So I prayed and prayed, and tonight she came! I just peeked out and saw her sitting in the second row!"

I was really glad, but I didn't get a chance to say anything, because Mrs. Morrison was calling us together. "I know we have some parents here who are lost," she said. "Let's especially pray that they will see the Lord in our performance tonight."

Randy really did do a great job being Joshua. I mean, he really sounded like he was Joshua! I did a pretty good job of being an Israelite too. Whenever I got a chance, I peeked out into the second row and tried to figure out who Randy's mother was. I finally decided she was the lady with the tall hair who kept smiling a lot and couldn't stop looking at Randy.

When it was all over, everybody especially applauded for Randy. I couldn't help thinking how if I had been where he was, they would have been applauding for me. But I had helped behind the scenes, so maybe they *were* applauding for me a little bit, without knowing

it. And besides, what difference did it make? Helping Randy had pleased the Lord, and I guess that's what mattered most.

Everybody's family came backstage to congratulate all of us, and of course my family told me that I was the best Israelite of all. But when Randy got a chance he ran over to me and whispered, "Thanks, Moses."

I was pretty surprised. "How did you know about that?" I asked. "I never told you."

"No, but Mrs. Morrison did." His face was all lit up like I had never seen it. "Have you seen a program?" I hadn't yet, and he handed it to me. Right there at the bottom of the first page it said, "Director: Linda Morrison. Assistant Director: Mark Whitmore." "Wow!" I shouted. That was almost as good as getting a speaking part! But Randy was pulling on my arm. "Come on, Moses," he said. "I want you to meet my mother."

David's Endeavor

David and Goliath
I Samuel 17:1-54

1 Now the Philistines gathered together their armies to battle. . . .

2 And Saul and the men of Israel were gathered together . . . and set the battle in array against the Philistines.

3 And the Philistines stood on a mountain on the one side, and Israel stood on a mountain on the other side: and there was a valley between them.

4 And there went out a champion out of the camp of the Philistines, named Goliath, of Gath, whose height was six cubits and a span.

5 And he had an helmet of brass upon his head, and he was armed with a coat of mail; and the weight of the coat was five thousand shekels of brass.

6 And he had greaves of brass upon his legs, and a target of brass between his shoulders.

7 And the staff of his spear was like a weaver's beam; and his spear's head weighed six hundred shekels of iron: and one bearing a shield went before him.

8 And he stood and cried unto the armies of Israel, and said unto them, Why are ye come out to set your battle in array? am not I a Philistine, and ye servants to Saul? choose you a man for you, and let him come down to me.

9 If he be able to fight with me, and to kill me, then will we be your servants: but if I prevail against him, and kill him, then shall ye be our servants, and serve us.

10 And the Philistine said, I defy the armies of Israel this day; give me a man, that we may fight together.

11 When Saul and all Israel heard those words of the Philistine, they were dismayed, and greatly afraid.

12 Now David was the son of that Ephrathite of Bethlehem-judah, whose name was Jesse; and he had eight sons: and the man went among men for an old man in the days of Saul.

13 And the three eldest sons of Jesse went and followed Saul to the battle: and the names of his three sons that went to the battle were Eliab the firstborn, and next unto him Abinadab, and the third Shammah.

14 And David was the youngest: and the three eldest followed Saul.

15 But David went and returned from Saul to feed his father's sheep at Bethlehem.

16 And the Philistine drew near morning and evening, and presented himself forty days.

17 And Jesse said unto David his son, Take now for thy brethren an ephah of this parched corn, and these ten loaves, and run to the camp to thy brethren;

18 And carry these ten cheeses unto the captain of their thousand, and look how thy brethren fare, and take their pledge.

19 Now Saul, and they, and all the men of Israel, were in the valley of Elah, fighting with the Philistines.

20 And David rose up early in the morning, and left the sheep with a keeper, and took, and went, as Jesse had commanded him; and he came to the trench, as the host was going forth to the fight, and shouted for the battle.

21 For Israel and the Philistines had put the battle in array, army against army.

22 And David left his carriage in the hand of the keeper of the carriage, and ran into the army, and came and saluted his brethren.

23 And as he talked with them, behold, there came up the champion, the Philistine of Gath,

Goliath by name, out of the armies of the Philistines, and spake according to the same words: and David heard them.

24 And all the men of Israel, when they saw the man, fled from him, and were sore afraid.

25 And the men of Israel said, Have ye seen this man that is come up? surely to defy Israel is he come up: and it shall be, that the man who killeth him, the king will enrich him with great riches, and will give him his daughter, and make his father's house free in Israel.

26 And David spake to the men that stood by him, saying, What shall be done to the man that killeth this Philistine, and taketh away the reproach from Israel? for who is this uncircumcised Philistine, that he should defy the armies of the living God?

27 And the people answered him after this manner, saying, So shall it be done to the man that killeth him.

28 And Eliab his eldest brother heard when he spake unto the men; and Eliab's anger was kindled against David, and he said, Why camest thou down hither? and with whom hast thou left those few sheep in the wilderness? I know thy pride, and the naughtiness of thine heart; for

thou art come down that thou mightest see the battle.

29 And David said, What have I now done? Is there not a cause?

30. And he turned from him toward another, and spake after the same manner: and the people answered him again after the former manner.

31 And when the words were heard which David spake, they rehearsed them before Saul: and he sent for him.

32 And David said to Saul, Let no man's heart fail because of him; thy servant will go and fight with this Philistine.

33 And Saul said to David, Thou art not able to go against this Philistine to fight with him: for thou art but a youth, and he a man of war from his youth.

34 And David said unto Saul, Thy servant kept his father's sheep, and there came a lion, and a bear, and took a lamb out of the flock:

35 And I went out after him, and smote him, and delivered it out of his mouth: and when he arose against me, I caught him by his beard, and smote him, and slew him.

36 Thy servant slew both the lion and the bear: and this uncircumcised Philistine shall be as one of them, seeing he hath defied the armies of the living God.

37 David said moreover, The Lord that delivered me out of the paw of the lion, and out of the paw of the bear, he will deliver me out of the hand of this Philistine. And Saul said unto David, Go, and the Lord be with thee.

38 And Saul armed David with his armour, and he put an helmet of brass upon his head; also he armed him with a coat of mail.

39 And David girded his sword upon his armour, and he assayed to go; for he had not proved it. And David said unto

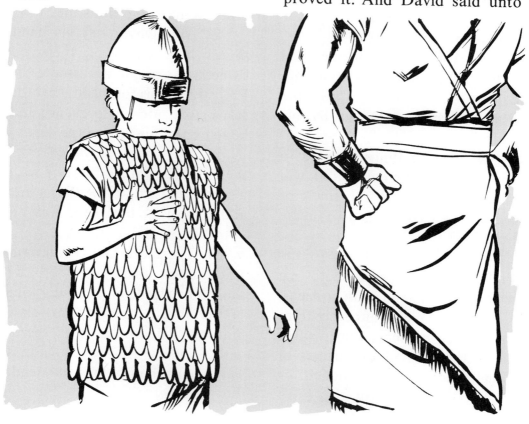

Saul, I cannot go with these; for I have not proved them. And David put them off him.

40 And he took his staff in his hand, and chose him five smooth stones out of the brook, and put them in a shepherd's bag which he had, even in a scrip; and his sling was in his hand: and he drew near to the Philistine.

41 And the Philistine came on and drew near unto David; and the man that bare the shield went before him.

42 And when the Philistine looked about, and saw David, he disdained him: for he was but a youth, and ruddy, and of a fair countenance.

43 And the Philistine said unto David, Am I a dog, that thou comest to me with staves? And the Philistine cursed David by his gods.

44 And the Philistine said to David, Come to me, and I will give thy flesh unto the fowls of the air, and to the beasts of the field.

45 Then said David to the Philistine, Thou comest to me with a sword, and with a spear, and with a shield: but I come to thee in the name of the Lord of hosts, the God of the armies of Israel, whom thou hast defied.

46 This day will the Lord deliver thee into mine hand; and I will smite thee, and take thine head from thee; and I will give the carcases of the host of the Philistines this day unto the fowls of the air, and to the wild beasts of the earth; that all the earth may know that there is a God in Israel.

47 And all this assembly shall know that the Lord saveth not with sword and spear: for the battle is the Lord's, and he will give you into our hands.

48 And it came to pass, when the Philistine arose, and came and drew nigh to meet David, that David hasted, and ran toward the army to meet the Philistine.

49 And David put his hand in his bag, and took thence a stone, and slang it, and smote the Philistine in his forehead, that the stone sunk into his forehead; and he fell upon his face to the earth.

50 So David prevailed over the Philistine with a sling and with a stone, and smote the Philistine, and slew him; but there was no sword in the hand of David.

51 Therefore David ran, and stood upon the Philistine, and took his sword, and drew it out of the sheath thereof, and slew him, and cut off his head therewith. And when the Philistines saw their champion was dead, they fled.

52 And the men of Israel and of Judah arose, and shouted, and pursued the Philistines, until thou come to the valley, and to the gates of Ekron. And the wounded of the Philistines fell down by the way to Shaaraim, even unto Gath, and unto Ekron.

53 And the children of Israel returned from chasing after the Philistines, and they spoiled their tents.

54 And David took the head of the Philistine, and brought it to Jerusalem; but he put his armour in his tent.

Prayer and Bible reading are the sources of a Christian's daily strength. God speaks to the Christian through His Word. Reading the Bible through book by book is one good way to study your Bible. You can also study your Bible by *topics*. It's not hard to do a topical study once you understand how to use some easy Bible study tools. God promises that His Word will always accomplish His purposes.

Skill Lesson: Bible Study

Cross-References

Look at the sample Bible page on the next page. The verses given in tiny print in the middle column are called cross-references. Each cross-reference directs you from one word on the page to another place in the Bible where the word appears again. Cross-references can show you the first place where a specific word is mentioned, or they can take you to another passage that explains who someone is.

Sometimes when a cross-reference takes you to the same word somewhere else in Scripture, you will find a second cross-reference on the same word. For instance, in I Samuel 17:4 the word *Goliath* has a cross-reference *b* to chapter 21:9. When you turn to I Samuel 21:9, you might find another cross-reference to chapter 22:10, where the word *Goliath* appears again. The cross-references will lead you through every place that Goliath is mentioned.

4 And there went out a ^achampion out of the camp of the Philistines, named ^bGoliath, of Gath, whose height *was* six cubits and a span.

5 And *he had* an helmet of brass upon his head, and he was armed with a coat of mail; and the weight of the coat *was* five thousand shekels of brass.

6 And *he had* greaves of brass upon his legs, and a target of brass between his shoulders.

7 And the staff of his spear *was* like a weaver's beam; and his spear's head *weighed* six hundred shekels of iron: and one bearing a shield went before him.

8 And he stood and cried unto the armies of Israel, and said unto them, Why are ye come out to set *your* battle in array? *am* not I a Philistine, and ye servants to Saul? choose you a man for you, and let him come down to me.

9 If he be able to fight with me, and to kill me, then will

a I Samuel 17:51

b I Samuel 21:9

c I Samuel 16:21-23

d Genesis 37:13-14

15 ^cBut David went and returned from Saul to feed his father's sheep at Bethlehem.

16 And the Philistine drew near morning and evening, and presented himself forty days.

17 And Jesse said unto David his son, Take now for thy brethren an ephah of this parched *corn,* and these ten loaves, and run to the camp to thy brethren;

18 And carry these ten cheeses unto the captain of *their* thousand, ^dand look how thy brethren fare, and take their pledge.

19 Now Saul, and they, and all the men of Israel, *were* in the valley of Elah, fighting with the Philistines.

20 And David rose up early in the morning, and left the sheep with a keeper, and took, and went, as Jesse had commanded him; and he came to the trench, as the host was going forth to the fight, and shouted for the battle.

Concordances

In addition to cross references, many Bibles contain a *concordance* in the back. Like a dictionary, a concordance contains words listed in alphabetical order. But the concordance's main purpose is to help the reader find as many references to one subject as possible.

A person who has read the story of David and Goliath might be curious to find out if there were any more giants mentioned in the Old Testament. He would look for the key word *giant* in his concordance. Look at the sample concordance below and find the word *giant*.

Gethsemane—*A garden in which Jesus prayed shortly before His death*
    Matthew 26:36 Then cometh Jesus . . . unto a place called G.
    Mark 14:32 they came to a place which was named G.

Geuel—*A man whose name means 'God of Salvation'*
    Numbers 13:15 Geuel, the son of Machi

Gezrites—*inhabitants of Gezer*
    I Samuel 27:8 David . . . invaded . . . the G.

giant—*fearful one*
    Deuteronomy 2:11 Which also were accounted gi.
    Joshua 12:4 Og . . . of the remnant of the giants
      18:16 in the valley of the giants on the north
    II Samuel 21:16 gi., . . . thought to have slain David
    I Chronicles 20:4 Sippai, . . . of the children of the g.
      20:6 he . . . was the son of the giant
      20:8 These were born unto the gia.

Gideon—*One of the judges of Israel*
    Judges 6:11 his son Gideon threshed wheat
      7:1 Gideon and all the people . . . rose up early
      8:4 G. came to Jordan *and* passed over
      8:35 shewed they kindness to . . . Jerubbaal, namely, Gi.

gin—*A snare*
    Job 18:9 The g. shall take *him* by the heel
    Psalm 140:5 they have set gins for me
      141:9 the gins of the workers of iniquity
    Isaiah 8:14 for a gin . . . to the inhabitants
    Amos 3:5 Can a bird fall . . where no g. *is* for him?

Topical Study

You will notice that sometimes the concordance abbreviates the key word *giant* if the line is long. It's easier to glance at a reference if it is on only one line; so most editors of concordances provide just a few words from the verse. They often abbreviate the key word to fit everything on one line.

The books of Joshua and I Chronicles contain several references to the word *giant*, but the titles *Joshua* and *I Chronicles* appear only once under the entry word. Each title is followed by a list of the chapter and verse numbers that belong to it. This also is done to make finding verses easier. It provides spacing between several of the book titles so that they are easier to find.

Once you know how to use a concordance, you will find out how valuable it is. A concordance can help you study the Bible *topically*. Looking up the word *giant* throughout the Bible would be a topical study. Some people enjoy doing topical studies on words such as *mercy* or *salvation*. A topical study can give you a full picture of one idea. For instance, in doing a topical study on the word *giant*, you would find out that giants had been worrying Israel ever since the Israelites journeyed to the Promised Land. You would also find out that late in David's life he was almost killed by one when he and his best soldiers battled some giants. But David's men won and destroyed the giants.

The best way to study the Bible is to read it for yourself. Using a concordance will help you in your private study of God's Word.

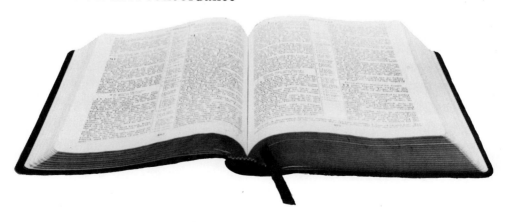

Today's Swordsmen

Andy Thomson

A gleaming sword dances in and out. It flashes under the lights. Two armed men leap back and forth at each other. A crowd looks on in respectful silence. The air is charged with tense expectation.

Perhaps this scene reminds you of the three musketeers or the famous swashbucklers from another century. But it could describe one form of sword fighting that is still practiced today—the sport of fencing.

We usually think of sword fighters as men who fearlessly swung their swords while hanging from chandeliers or striding across tabletops. But today fencing matches are limited to narrow, taped-off lanes called fencing strips. Contests are supervised by four judges and a director. The challenge of fencing is no longer in brute strength. Good fencers rely on skill and the ability to make decisions quickly.

The Uniform

Although fencing comes from an age when men solved their problems with sharp swords, today it is a sport carried out with much concern for personal safety. Fencers wear regulation helmets made of a heavy but finely woven wire mesh. The fencing jacket is padded. The jacket's collar and a heavy canvas bib attached to the mask protect the fencer's neck. A heavy glove covers the fencer's sword hand.

The fencing sword is usually a long, thin weapon called a *foil*. It weighs a little more than one pound. From end to end it is a little over three and a half feet long. A curving handguard protects the handgrip. The blade itself is sturdy and stiff above the handguard. It tapers to a flexible point. A heavy plastic coating, usually red, covers the blunted tip.

A fencing foil cannot pierce the sturdy jacket of a fencer, but it can still inflict a nasty bruise if it is driven too hard into its target. Fencers usually try to avoid hurting each other with the foil. Since the goal of fencing lies in speed and skill, "muscling" a foil into an opponent is poor sportsmanship.

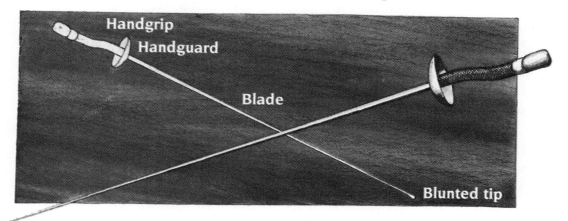

Handgrip
Handguard
Blade
Blunted tip

Competition

Fencers observe many rules of etiquette while competing. Opponents salute each other by standing at attention with their heels at right angles. The fencer's front foot and eyes face his opponent. He points his foil down to the floor. Then he snaps it up straight so that the handguard is level with his chin. With the same brisk motion he returns the foil to its original position.

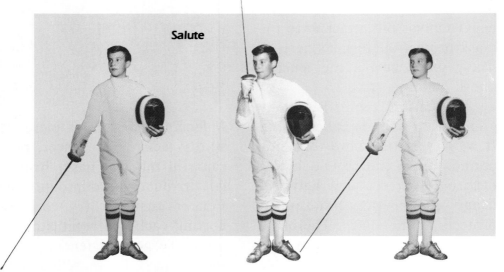

Salute

After a match, fencers remove their masks and shake hands. Fencers always shake hands with the hand that is not holding the foil. That means that a right-handed fencer will hold his foil in his right hand and shake hands with the left.

The fencer's stance is low. His feet are almost two shoulder widths apart. He holds his back arm high, with the wrist and hand relaxed. Every step takes coordination and poise, but the fencer can use his stance to gain enormous distance and power. He advances by stepping forward first with the front foot and then the back. He retreats by moving the back foot first and following it with the front foot. The fencer lunges by leaping forward with the front foot and keeping the back foot planted firmly. A good fencer's lunge will cover almost his own body's length, and he will be able to pull back quickly to retreat.

Lunge

Fencers also observe strict etiquette to score during the fencing match. A fencer must claim his "right of attack." He does this by being the first one to make a threatening action. Usually he will simply thrust his foil forward. This shows that he is claiming the right of attack. He follows the thrust with several complicated techniques. His opponent must first parry the attack or demonstrate a clean evasion. The opponent can then *riposte*, or counterattack. Then the first person must parry or evade. This back-and-forth type of attacking and defending continues until both persons draw back or one of them scores a point.

Thrust

Parry

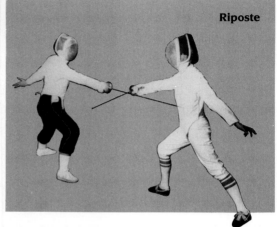

Riposte

It may seem confusing at first, but a fencing match can be compared with a conversation. In conversation one person speaks, and the other replies. In fencing one person attacks and the other parries and counter-attacks. It is impolite to interrupt one person's attack with another attack. Instead, the defender parries, ending the attack, and then has the chance to counterattack.

Fencing matches are conducted with four judges. The judges form a square around the fencers. They follow the fencers up and down the fencing strip. A fifth person, called the director or president, governs the match. When a judge sees a point, he will call it, and the director recognizes him and consults the other judges. It may sound as though a fencing match would take a long time, but judges and directors know the sport so well that they can decide points in seconds. In recent years electronic equipment has been used in some matches, replacing the four judges and leaving only the director to decide on points. Electronic equipment is more accurate than human observers, but it is also more expensive.

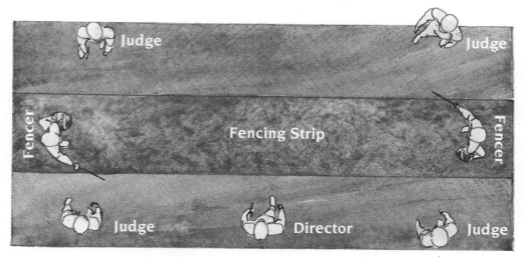

Judge · Judge · Fencer · Fencing Strip · Fencer · Judge · Director · Judge

Although skill is the key to good fencing, the fencer can use his strength in some attacking techniques. He can *beat* his opponent's foil with a single sharp blow to the blade. This will knock it away and allow for a strike. Or he can execute a *press*. He forces his opponent's blade down or away. When he feels his opponent pushing back, he releases suddenly. The opponent usually jerks his foil too far the other way, and opens himself up for a strike. A strong fencer can also use the *glide,* pushing so hard against his opponent's blade that he forces it down and then slides his own blade across it to score a point.

Occasionally one fencer will try to block another fencer's glide by strength alone. When this happens, their foils will slide up against each other all the way to the handguards. The result is that they stand pushing against each other at the handguards, using all their leverage and strength. Such an encounter is called a *corps-à-corps*. It literally means "body-to-body." Although it certainly looks dramatic, a *corps-à-corps* sometimes means that one or both opponents are using strength as a substitute for skill.

Corps-à-corps

Other basic techniques include the thrust, the parry, and the *disengage.* In a disengage, a fencer quickly circles his blade *under* his opponent's blade. Often a fencer uses a disengage when he thinks that his opponent will use a press or a glide. A disengage can prevent a contest of strength. The fencer can also use a *cutover,* in which he circles his blade *over* the blade of his opponent. Although mod-

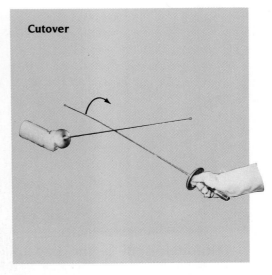

Cutover

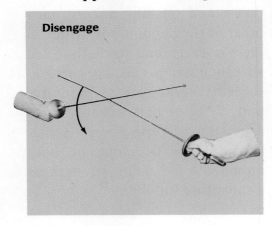

Disengage

ern fencing does require strength, it is designed so that a person cannot win by strength alone but must develop speed, coordination, and strategy. As is true in any sport, fencers develop their skills with practice and hard work.

Corps-à-Corps

Jeri Massi

"Six . . . four . . . six—four—six!"

We thrust our foils back and forth, repeating the parries at Mr. LeBlanc's commands.

"Aha! Sloppy defense! Rest!"

Perspiring, we dropped our arms and stood up straight while he corrected Robert. "The power is here!" he exclaimed, straightening Robert's gloved wrist. "Don't bend it so!" He clapped his hands. "Come, come!"

We all lined up before him like soldiers. "Ah, Jack, you will preside. My four judges will be Bruce, Rick, Harry, Sid. Ah, now, let me see. . . ." He deliberately ran his eyes up and down the line of us. "You, Patrick." He pointed at me and then at Robert. "And you, Robert."

Inside, I groaned. Robert! Yes, he held his wrist wrong, but that didn't matter. He outweighed me by at least thirty pounds. I had never beaten him. Nobody had ever beaten him.

He took his position, the light fencing foil pointed down to the ground as he prepared for the salute.

I took my position; we saluted smartly. Yes, that one dramatic part of the game—the snapping of the foil straight up and then snapping it back down—he had mastered that. We slipped our masks on.

"Are you ready?" Jack asked him. Robert grunted. I sensed his excitement. Another victory for him.

"Are you ready?" Jack asked me.

"Yes," I replied.

"Commence!"

I sprang from my place with a leap. He hesitated. I feinted to his outside, slipped the point under his blade, and neatly scored against him, tapping him in the chest.

All four judges agreed to the score, and Jack nodded. For once I was winning, but I knew it wouldn't last long.

He slapped his foil against mine, beating the blade. The blow knocked my foil aside. Effortlessly, he pressed his blade against my foil and slid it straight across until the red protective button nipped me in the chest. The judges called it.

Beating and pressing the blade were Robert's techniques. He could overpower anybody in the class. He quickly scored on me three more times.

It went on until my right hand could barely grip the hilt. He made me retreat, and I gave ground as far as I could, even

beyond the white warning line on the fencing strip.

Once when he executed a straight lunge, I ducked low, bending at the waist and dropping my back leg as though in a split. The point went over my head. As he retreated, trying to pull out of too deep a stance, I pushed myself forward and caught him again, square in the chest. But the judges argued over my move. In fencing a man must have the right of attack. They were accustomed to somebody's parrying a thrust before counterattacking. They argued about my ducking, for they had never seen anybody avoid a hit in that way.

I knew that behind his mask Robert was sneering, for he already had four points on me, and the match was nearly over.

For once, Mr. LeBlanc interfered with the boys in a class match.

"The technique was masterful. Award the point, Jack."

"Yes, sir."

"The time is up," he said. "I want to get another match in."

Grateful to my teacher, I slipped the mask off and went up to shake hands with Robert. He gripped my hand and ground my knuckles together. I gasped and winced. "Masterful!" he ex-

claimed sarcastically and strode away.

Holding my left hand in my right, I walked off the strip.

"Ah, masterful!" Mr. LeBlanc exclaimed much later to my parents. Mom smiled, and Dad glanced over at me.

"Next month is your first tournament, Patrick," Mom said.

Mr. LeBlanc rubbed his hands together. "What a day that will be! There will be spectators there from the Olympic Committee—" He stopped short. "Pardon me, Julio," he said to my father.

Dad waved it away. He glanced down at his bad leg a little wistfully but without pain in his eyes. "Once it hurt to think of it, but not any more." He glanced at me fondly. "Not with Patrick here. Come here, Son."

I came and sat on the arm of his chair. Before my birth my father had been diagnosed with bone cancer, and the doctors had amputated his right leg just above the knee. No longer could he fence back and forth on the strip, high on the balls of his feet, ready to leap or lunge. In his prime he had been an Olympic contender, but now he was just my father, Dad instead of Poppa, for he and my mother wanted me to grow up thoroughly American.

But I had seen film clips of him, and ever since I had been able to walk he had shown me his foils and equipment. Fencing, I had always thought, was the finest sport in the world.

"Mr. LeBlanc, do you think I can win next month?" I asked.

"Of course I do!"

"But Robert—"

"But Robert! But Robert!" LeBlanc threw his hands into the air. "He has strength, but no style. Look what you did to him tonight!"

"I lost to him tonight."

"Yes, but the way you scored!" He turned to my parents. "The big boy comes in, so—" He imitated Robert's powerful lunge. "What does the little one do—" He imitated the way I had ducked. To my surprise it did look graceful. Mom and Dad looked pleased. "And then so—he comes up and thrusts the boy right on the chest." Mr. LeBlanc demonstrated the lunge, a little bit of sweat gleaming in his silver hair. "Where have I seen such technique?" he asked, smiling at my father. He had been my father's coach.

"Where indeed?" Dad asked, laughing.

Mr. LeBlanc stood up to leave. Dad gripped a crutch and stood

up, shaking hands with him. "Good night, good night, LeBlanc. Thank you."

"Good night, Julio, and you, Marie. Good night, Patrick."

"Good night, sir. Thank you."

That night I lay awake in bed, watching the triangles of light from the highway play across the roof of my narrow room. Our house bordered the highway, but the traffic had become my lullaby. I went to sleep thinking of the tournament, of Robert, of Mr. LeBlanc. Masterful, they had said, but what was it to be a master? What good are thinking and practice and style if, with one strong blow from his blade, Robert could sweep away my defense?

At breakfast I was still sleepy.

"Patrick, you are dragging. Your mind is on the tournament, eh?" Dad asked, smiling. For the first time I noticed how his eyes crinkled up when he smiled. He was a handsome man. "But for now you have to eat and think about schoolwork, right?" He rubbed his big rough hand over my hair. I tried to smile.

"I must go," he said. "The boys will be here soon." He drained his coffee, pulled himself up, and stumped away to get his briefcase. During the mornings my father worked as a law clerk. In the afternoons and at night he went to law school. He would not be dependent, he said. Ever since I could remember, Dad had been in school, but soon, I knew, he would be taking his bar examinations.

"I must go, too," Mom said. "Finish, Patrick. Will you do the dishes this afternoon?"

"Yes."

"Mrs. Strand will drop in to check on you and put the roast in."

We hurriedly cleared up breakfast in the cramped kitchen and then left. Mom usually drove me to school.

"Are you nervous about the tournament?" she asked me as we pulled out.

"Robert is undefeated in the class. Mr. LeBlanc did not tell you that."

"Hmm." She frowned at the road. "Mr. LeBlanc says only what he thinks is important," she replied at last. "So he must not think that Robert's strength is that important."

"Mr. LeBlanc doesn't get beaten by Robert every week."

She smiled. "Strength alone guarantees nothing, Patrick. If this Robert boy has no style, then it is only a matter of time until you defeat him."

I shrugged.

"I will help you," she said at last. "Yes." She nodded, suddenly resolute. "I will help you."

Then she said no more. That afternoon I came home and did the breakfast dishes, and Mrs. Strand came and helped start dinner, then left. At 5:00 Mom came in. "Ah, what's this?" she asked. "Put on your gear, quickly. We only have an hour!"

"But Mom—"

"Do it, Patrick! Hurry down!"

I ran upstairs and put on my gear. When I came down, she had pulled most of the furniture out of the living room and into the dining room and the small hallway.

"This is not a big room," she said. I saw to my astonishment that she was wearing a fencing outfit. "But it is almost regulation

length. We shall practice as best as we can."

"You fenced?"

"The jacket is mine. The rest is your father's. Yes, for a while I fenced. But more important, I watched your father when he fenced, and I can judge you correctly and test your strength."

We slipped our helmets on and saluted each other. Hesitant, I took the offensive and lunged at her. She parried with a clack of foil against foil and tapped me on the chest.

"We cannot fence nonstop for an hour," she said. "You will let me attack. Defend as best as you can."

"All right."

She beat my blade and knocked it away just enough so that she slipped in and hit me again. "Ah! That is where you are weak. Hold your foil closer. Do not extend the arm so much. Better," she said as she tried it again. "Be ready, Patrick, to slip under my foil with your own if you see that I am about to beat my blade against yours. Avoid it if you cannot parry."

She thrust at me again and again, varying her attacks, sometimes beating, sometimes pressing or gliding on my foil. We sparred until my hand was numb. Only a half-hour had gone by.

"Wait," I gasped, pulling off my mask. She pulled off her mask and collapsed into one of the chairs that she had pulled to the side. "Perhaps," she said, puffing, "a half-hour is enough for the first day, eh?"

Dad came home a little later. He had just enough time to eat and talk a little, and then it was back to class until nine o'clock.

"You seem tired out, Son," he said.

"Patrick and I have been practicing for the tournament," Mom said.

"Ah!" he raised his eyebrows at her. "And how does your

mother fence, Son?" he asked without looking at me.

"Very well, Dad."

He glanced at me. "If you don't want to be in the tournament, Patrick, you should tell us," he said sternly.

"Dad!" I exclaimed.

"Julio!" Mother exclaimed.

He looked a little ashamed. "It's just that—you know—fencing meant so much to me, Son. I don't want you to think that you must fence to please me."

"I want to fence," I said.

"For now, anyway." He nodded. "Well, then, back to class for me. I will be home later."

The next day I went to class, but I did not fence with Robert. On Saturday Mom and I practiced for an hour while Dad studied upstairs at his desk in their tiny bedroom.

Again on Monday we practiced. Tuesday night at class I fenced with Robert, and he beat me, 5-1.

"You are tired," Mr. LeBlanc told me as he drove me home. "But I see new things in your defense. You are practicing at home?"

"Yes."

"Good. You will improve."

I doubted him that night, but then on Thursday when I fenced with Robert, I began to feel more confident. I saw that when he struck at my blade he would pull his hand up a little, barely an inch. But it was enough warning for me to drop my blade. Once when I did it, he missed it entirely, and I thrust at him. Twice he still struck my blade, but not where he intended to, not as strongly, and I kept him from gliding up or pressing.

Yet I was not perfect. He scored three times on me, and I scored only once on him—I was still wearing myself out against his strength. The other boys congratulated me on holding him off so well. But next time, I thought, he will be ready for my defenses. He will know what to do to wear me out more quickly.

Mom and I worked with each other every day. Sometimes Dad came home and asked me to put on my gear. Then Mom and I worked together in front of him, with all the furniture pulled back except one tiny chair where he sat and directed us.

For two weeks Mr. LeBlanc kept Robert and me apart. The other boys I defeated easily enough, for they never practiced in their spare time.

At last I again met Robert on the strip. He had not forgotten our

last match, and he was not ignorant of my latest victories.

He fenced carefully at first, and I began to think that he had been polishing his style. But then when I lunged at him, he suddenly drove his foil straight into me. The red button drilled into my chest as I met it full force, unable to stop myself. I gasped as I saw the foil bend and then snap in two, and I was thrown back a pace on the strip. My own foil dropped to the ground, and I clutched my right shoulder and chest.

"Leave the floor! Leave the floor!" Mr. LeBlanc barked. I looked up, thinking he was talking to me. But no. Red-faced, Robert was walking toward the dressing room, his eyes bitter. So he had not fooled Mr. LeBlanc. "Help that boy up," Mr. LeBlanc said.

Jack and Bruce pulled me up and helped me out of the fencing jacket. I could barely move my right arm. The other boys were arguing over whether Robert had done it purposely or not. Simultaneous attacks happen in fencing, and I have known of men to snap their foils in half while they were fencing. Yet I was sure that Robert had deliberately broken the rules and attacked me before defending himself, knowing that my attack had been declared first by my out-thrust blade.

There was a black bruise with a red spot in the middle on my chest. It glistened as though it weren't a bruise at all but a puddle of ink somebody had spilled on me. The sight turned my stomach. Mr. LeBlanc was in the dressing room, and I could hear him shouting. I sank down onto a bench against the wall. The other boys crowded around, curious and awed. Nobody had ever been hurt before in class.

Mr. LeBlanc suspended Robert until the tournament. He dismissed the class early and drove me home. In the car I saw that his hands were shaking as he gripped the wheel.

"Never! Never!" he kept murmuring. "Never in my class! What possessed the boy? Never has this happened—not with two Olympic trainees! Never before!"

Dad looked shocked when Mr. LeBlanc told him. With some difficulty I showed him the bruise. Mom only set her teeth.

"Get into your pajamas, Patrick. Come down and I will put something on it for you," she said.

As I went upstairs, I heard Dad's voice. "I will not let him fence in the tournament, LeBlanc. Why did you not suspend that other boy from competing?"

"What, and protect a champion? Should I add that insult to Patrick's injury?" Mr. LeBlanc replied.

Mom put hot compresses on the bruise. "They will draw the blood and you will heal more quickly," she said. "Let your right arm rest."

Mr. LeBlanc looked at me gravely. "Your father does not want you to compete next week," he said.

"Fencing is not sword fighting," Dad added. "You do not have to be a swashbuckler, though that other boy is."

"You told me yourself that we win by style, not by brute strength," I replied. "If that is true, then I can beat him."

"The boy is right," Mr. LeBlanc said. "You know he is right, Julio."

"You have to grow yet, Son," Dad said. "You can fence Robert again later."

"It will be worse than losing a match to him if I allow him to frighten me away."

He hesitated, then nodded. "I would not have you think of yourself as a coward. I will not forbid you to fence him if you think that your heart is ready for such a contest."

"A champion at heart can never be defeated. When a fencer has his courage, he is a champion," Mr. LeBlanc added. "Patrick will yet defeat Robert."

"I will compete," I said, and Dad nodded gravely.

As the days ran out, Mom made me build up more strength in my right arm. Sometimes in the evenings when Dad came home, he would let me arm-wrestle with him. We were in dead earnest when we did it. He never budged his great muscular forearm, and I would push and push against it for twenty seconds at a time— never moving it, but building my own muscle against it. Then twenty seconds of rest, and then I would start pushing again while he encouraged me or said nothing, only watching me steadily.

At last the Saturday of the tournament came. We had steak for breakfast. Mom ate silently while Dad told me to relax and chew carefully.

There was little conversation as we drove to the gym. I was already registered, so I went into the dressing rooms while they found seats.

The pledge was over quickly, the salutes exchanged. Several schools had come to compete, so for several bouts I did not fence with anybody I knew.

Mr. LeBlanc was beside himself with pride, and I was surprised at myself. It seemed so easy—ridiculously easy. "Was this what I had been so nervous about?" I thought. Again and again I fenced, and again and again I won.

"You are doing splendidly!" Mom exclaimed during a break.

"Marie!" Dad retorted. He looked at me. "You win so easily, Son, because these are the first eliminations. These are the boys who do not practice. It gets harder in the second eliminations. Do not get overconfident."

He was right. As the judges filled in the double elimination chart and my name went lower and lower, the matches became harder. Fewer of us were competing, and the judges conducted the matches one at a time.

I examined the chart and saw that Robert also was undefeated. Yes, his huge size and unusual strength were coming to his aid. Perhaps he had even been practicing during his suspension. Mr. LeBlanc had been careful to keep us scheduled apart, perhaps

hoping that somehow Robert would be eliminated by somebody else.

But no. The clusters of names around his name grew smaller and smaller, as did the cluster of names around mine. Several of the spectators strolled over to my parents and shook hands with my father. They looked at ease in the gym. Perhaps they were from the Committee. They pulled up folding chairs and sat by my parents while I fenced again.

Again I won, and the judges called a ten-minute recess, and I checked the chart again. Robert and I were the only ones left. We would have to fence each other at least twice because we were both undefeated.

"Give me your hand," Dad said. He pulled off my fencing glove and massaged the tendons and knuckles of my hand with hard short rubs. "Do not play his game, Patrick. Take the offensive. Use speed and style. You must rely on evasion. I have been watching him, and he is quite strong."

The judges called my name, and I felt afraid.

I slipped on the mask, saluted Robert, and went to work.

Dad had been right. When he took the offensive, he beat my blade or tried to glide on it, using

his strength. I evaded him and quickly gained the lead on him by two points, but I was tired. At last he thrust aside my foil long enough to score on me. Then I scored on him, so that he had three points against him. Two more, I thought, and I would win.

I thrust out, and he quickly swept his foil up, catching my blade as it came in. Next thing I knew he was almost on top of me, with our foils locked. I leaped back, and he scored on me. Somehow when he came in again, we were locked in a *corps-à-corps* position; only this time he bore down on me with his foil, and I resisted with mine the best I could. But he was too strong. He was pushing me back, the handguard of his foil pushing on the handguard of mine, for our blades were crossed right at their bases.

He has been practicing, I said to myself quite calmly. I managed to break away, but he scored on me again.

My hand was numb. While the judges discussed the point, I quickly rubbed it with my other hand.

He defeated me in our first match. As the president declared him the winner of the bout, I returned to my parents.

"What can I do?" I asked my father while he rubbed out the cramps in my right hand. "Every time we lock together he gets a point."

"Watch his blade!" Mr. LeBlanc exclaimed. "You are taking your eyes off his blade!"

"When I watch his blade he uses his feet."

"You must try," Dad said.

"You think I will lose!" I exclaimed.

"Perfection of style will come with time. But if you let him defeat your heart—if you quit, then you are truly defeated. I have always believed that, and I feared that you were too young for such a contest."

I had tears in my eyes, and I rubbed them on the back of my hand.

"For some, the contest comes in fencing," he said. "For others, the fight lasts all their lives to keep their hearts from defeat." He looked down at his leg and then

back up at me. And then I understood. "Now this contest has come to you, and you must fight. There is more at stake here than a fencing match."

The president called my name, and I went back to the strip.

I saluted Robert and leaped to the attack, taking the first point as usual. But my hand would not obey me. It was too tired. I saw him come in to beat my blade, to press on it, to glide on it, yet my reactions were clumsy. I evaded him too slowly, and he scored on me. He had worn me out in the last match.

Again he took the offensive. Something savage surged through me. I discarded style and poise and smashed his foil close to the tip, where the blade is most flexible. It knocked his attack aside, and I lunged in, scoring on the riposte.

Again we clashed, and again he slid his blade up mine until we met hilt to hilt and chest to chest, one knee straight and one bent as we strained against each other. His mask hid his face completely under the gym lights, but I felt his gasping breath as he pushed against me.

I pushed and resisted until I heard myself grunting, but still he was more powerful. My hand

quickly grew numb, and the numbness started up my wrist. We broke apart, and he scored on me.

After the judges conferred, he smashed his blade against mine, and this time the foil flew out of my hand.

One of the judges retrieved it for me. Even in that brief space some feeling had returned to my fingers. I grasped the hilt and tried to take the offensive, but again found myself locked into a *corps-à-corps* with him.

I grunted and gritted my teeth as I pushed against him. Tears rolled out of the corners of my eyes, but when I lifted my eyes to that faceless mask, the tears stopped. Perhaps he would defeat me. Perhaps he would knock me right off the strip, but I would never stop resisting him. I had fenced him for months and never won, but each time I got better, and suddenly I knew—as my father knew—that his time of victory was limited. Let him win this match—there would always be another, and another beyond that. I would never stop trying. That was the reason he had disliked me so much. He had known all along that someday I would defeat him.

The thoughts gave me courage, and I pushed against him more heartily than before, but then the buzzer went off, and the match was over.

I pulled off the mask with my left hand and suddenly found myself in my dad's arms with Mr. LeBlanc and the visitors and the boys from the school all around me, pounding me on the back and congratulating me. The silver medal was thrust into my hands, and I saw that Dad was crying and one crutch was thrown down on the floor as he hugged me. I looked from him to the medal, and I realized that, when the contest goes beyond fencing, a silver medal can be better than a gold.

RACE

Millicent Vincent Ward

Wet wind, dark wind pushing through the trees,
Tall grass, cold grass, quick against my knees,
Wild night, black night, catch me if you can!
And I dashed down the hillside, and ran, and ran,
  and ran.

But the tree bent fiercely after,
And the long wind blew,
And the clouds piled faster, faster,
And the sharp grass grew,
And I stumbled through the hollows
As I raced, the panting night
Close at my heels,
Till we crashed into the light,
And I leaped up the stairs,
Two steps at a stride,
And banged the door behind me,
Safe inside.

THE ALL=AMERICAN GAME

Henry Becker

Although there are many team sports that Americans enjoy, there is only one official team game that can trace its roots back to no other country but America. This is the story of the invention of that game, which took place in 1891.

"OOOF! Dr. Naismith, did you see that last soccer ball? It almost knocked me out!"

"Yes, and the one before that just about smashed a window. Another inch and we would've been collecting broken glass."

"I know, I know, boys." James Naismith shook his head sadly. "I guess soccer is just too rough a game to try to play inside a gymnasium. But so is Rugby and so is football. And baseball would be impossible! What other team games are there?"

No one had an answer. The young men slowly gathered their belongings and trooped out of the YMCA. James Naismith shook his head and trudged back to his office. The YMCA had given the coaches two weeks to invent a new indoor game—one that would not cost so much in broken windows as indoor soccer did. The time limit was almost up, and Dr. Naismith had been determined to submit the best idea. But so far none of his ideas had been practical. Somehow he still had to find an answer.

He sat down at his desk and mulled over the problem again. The young men had several wonderful rough-and-tumble games to play outside when the weather was pretty. But in the wintertime they had to stay inside the gymnasium, so all there was to do was calisthenics, marching, and weightlifting. But the fellows didn't want this routine day after day. They needed the teamwork and excitement of *competition*. They just didn't see any point to any of those activities. It was obvious that what they needed was a *game*.

But it seemed that none of the games the men were familiar with could be modified for playing inside. What in the world could

he do? Once more he racked his brain, trying to think of some game that could be modified. But the problem with all those games was that they were just too rough! He had to find a different game, one that would require more skill than brute strength. But there simply wasn't one.

"Well!" Dr. Naismith whispered to himself. "Why, how foolish I've been! All along I've been trying to modify a game when what I really need to do is *invent* one." He grabbed a piece of paper and began to scribble furiously.

"Now," he muttered while he scribbled, "we want it to be simple so all the young men can understand it easily. We want the ball to be big enough to maneuver with the hands instead of some other instrument—too dangerous to be swinging bats or mallets in a gymnasium. We don't want the young men to have to tackle each other, because that's too rough. But they could get the ball away from the other team a different way—instead of running with the ball, they could pass it to each other. That would give everyone a sporting chance.

"And what about a goal? If we had a goal as big as a soccer goal, they'd just throw the ball and possibly break out a window. Hmm, that's what almost happened today. Well, why not have a small goal, like a box? And why not put it up high so they have to have even more skill? Yes, a box mounted up on a post—they pass the ball to their teammates and shoot for the box. That's it! That's our new game!"

Dr. Naismith couldn't wait to try out his new invention. He asked the janitor to nail up a couple of boxes at either end of the gymnasium. As it happened, the janitor couldn't find any boxes and used two peach baskets instead.

Once again the young men gathered in the gymnasium. They were a little discouraged by now, because none of Dr. Naismith's experiments had worked so far. But when they saw the baskets nailed up and heard the rumor that they were going to try out a brand-new game, their interest perked up.

Dr. Naismith read the thirteen simple rules to the young men and watched them grow more and more excited as they listened. This sounded like a game that could really work! A game of skill that even the smaller and skinnier young men could play as well as the big brawny ones.

The young men grabbed the Rugby ball, the ball they used for this new game, and went at it.

"Here, throw it here, Jim!"

"I can get it in the basket!"

"No, you missed! Ha!"

"Wait, there goes William!"

"William did it! He got it in the basket! YEA!"

And William Chase scored the one and only point of the first historic game. Teammates cheered as one person ran up to the balcony to get the ball out of the basket. Even the opposing team had to admit that here was a pretty good game.

"Hey, Dr. Naismith, what do you call this game?" one boy hollered.

"Well, I haven't got a name for it yet. What do you boys suggest?"

"I know," one offered. "Why don't we call it *basketball?*"

"Well, we have a basket and a ball," Dr. Naismith said with a grin. "Basketball seems as good a name as any!"

So basketball it was. It soon became a favorite sport at the YMCA.

Basketball was fifteen years old before someone finally got the idea to use a basket with no bottom so that the ball could fall through easily. The game went on to become popular all over the nation. The rules changed again and again until they were finalized at last in the mid-1900s. Dr. Naismith lived to see the game he invented become the most popular indoor sport in the world.

To Open Their Eyes

Kristi Wetzel

Mary Baker, a short, dark-haired, energetic lady, checked her list to make sure she hadn't forgotten anything. She was preparing for an evangelistic trip to villages along the border of Chad, Africa. Her Christian Chadian helper was loading up the back of her truck with supplies. From an open window in Miss Baker's living room, Cathy could hear Miss Baker's clear, authoritative voice instructing Elijah as the truck was being loaded.

"Elijah," she said, "please push that barrel of filtered water over there in that corner. We need to make room for all these cots we're bringing."

"Are those missionary children coming on this trip, Miss Baker?"

"Yes, Dr. Jones's two daughters, Cathy and Margaret, are coming along," she answered as she picked up the girls' one suitcase and swung it over the side of the truck. Then she added, "Here's Cathy's accordion case. Watch out! This accordion has to be treated carefully."

Elijah climbed down to get the accordion. He looked at Miss Baker with a puzzled expression and asked, "What's an accordion?"

"Oh, Elijah, you're in for a real treat! It's a big box that has many buttons and black and white keys on it, and it makes pretty music! You'll see."

Miss Baker pushed her glasses back up on the bridge of her nose and said, "Looks like we finished this job in record time." She checked the items on her list with a stubby yellow pencil. "We packed the mosquito nets, the cots, the pots and pans, my trunk of canned food, the filtered water, our suitcases, two spare tires, a tool box, my camera, some salvation tracts, French Bibles, the first-aid kit, and . . . ," she paused to catch her breath, "well, that's everything, except for the girls."

"We're coming," Margaret called. She turned to her big sister. "They've got the truck loaded. Are you ready?"

"Here I come." Cathy was tucking her diary into her carry-on book bag.

The girls hurried out of Miss Baker's house with their father behind them. "It's 2:30, and you need to arrive in N'dacoria before dark!" he said.

The little group gathered around the loaded truck, and Dr. Jones prayed for a safe trip. "Dear Heavenly Father, we ask You to take care of Miss Baker and my girls as they travel out to the bush country to tell people about You. We know that there are many lost souls out there. Open their eyes and convict them to turn from the darkness of their sins to the light of Your Word. I pray that You'll protect these missionaries as they drive on those unpredictable dirt roads. Bring them back safely to us. In Jesus' name I pray, Amen."

The truck was crowded by the time everyone got on it. Cathy and Margaret rode in the cab with Miss Baker. They let Margaret sit on the window side so she could see better. Elijah and Joseph Bogal, a Bible school student, climbed into the back with all the supplies.

With a roar Miss Baker started the old truck. They moved out with a lurch as she shifted gears.

"Miss Baker," Cathy had to talk loudly over the noise of the engine. "Do you know any of the people in the villages we're going to visit?"

"Oh, yes, Honey! Tomorrow you'll meet a Christian friend of mine who is the chief of the Lito village. He has been wanting me to come and have meetings in his area for a long time. He's very concerned for his people. Many of them are animists."

Margaret leaned forward and balanced herself against the dashboard as the truck lurched along. "I've heard Dad use that word—what's an animist?" Miss Baker swerved the truck to miss a bump in the road, and Margaret almost landed in Cathy's lap.

"Animists worship ordinary sticks, stones, and plants. When we get to his village, you'll see some of these sticks and plants stuck in the ground all around the outside walls of their mud-brick huts."

Cathy looked at Miss Baker in disbelief. "You mean they worship just plain old sticks?"

Margaret leaned forward again to join in. "I thought idols were carved out of gold or silver."

"It's hard to believe, but Satan has blinded these people's minds. Their religion seems ridiculous to us, but it seems right to them. It shows you how powerful Satan

can be." Cathy could see a big tear form and roll down Miss Baker's right cheek. Cathy knew that the chief was not the only person concerned for the Africans' souls.

After a minute's pause, Miss Baker cleared her throat and continued, "These people are very superstitious. In addition to their idols, the people buy animal-teeth necklaces called fetishes. Their witch doctor sells them and tells the people that they will keep evil spirits away."

Suddenly Miss Baker jerked the truck to the left as she veered around a young goat. Margaret squealed, "We moved just in time!" Unconcerned, the small goat was nibbling a bit of brown grass in the middle of the dirt road.

"Daddy sure was right when he said these dirt roads were bad," exclaimed Cathy. "If it isn't potholes we're avoiding, it's goats!"

Miss Baker grinned with a twinkle in her eye and said, "That goat came pretty close to being in somebody's stew tonight! By the way, have you two had any goat meat yet?"

"Yes," Cathy said unenthusiastically. "It's not the *worst* food I've ever eaten, but almost! I'm not eager to try it again."

"Why is that?" asked Miss Baker.

Margaret started giggling. Cathy poked her in the side and said, "You're just laughing because it didn't happen to you. If it had, you wouldn't think it was so funny. Now let me tell her what happened."

"Several months ago Margaret and I were invited to a birthday party for an African girl, and they served some fried goat meat. As I reached into the pan of meat, I remembered that several missionaries had warned me to pick something that had a bone attached to it. You know how the Chadians like to cook every part, including the intestines. So I took a piece with a big bone on it. Then I realized I got a hoof! I managed to be polite and ate some of the meat, but I'll never forget that party!"

Miss Baker's hearty laughter filled the truck. She laughed so hard that tears of happiness spilled down her cheeks. In her own time she had eaten fried grasshoppers and Bobo ants, and she knew how shocking it was for Americans to try African specialties for the first time.

As the truck made its way around a sharp bend in the road,

an African sunset filled the sky. Shades of red, purple, and golden yellow streaked across the horizon. A group of round brick huts stood silhouetted in front of the colorful sunset like quiet sentinels.

"Miss Baker, is that the village?" asked Margaret.

"That is N'dacoria ahead of us. We've made good time. We'll be able to have a meeting tonight yet."

"But you won't need to have us help this first time, will you?" Cathy was suddenly apprehensive.

"I'll be counting on you to play that accordion, Cathy. These people have never heard anything like it, so I'm sure we'll get plenty of attention if you start our meeting with a few songs."

Margaret put her hand on her sister's arm. "You'll do all right; this is why we came along to help."

Before Cathy could say another word, Miss Baker pulled the truck up to the side of a big hut and stopped. The men in the back had already jumped out and were greeting their friends. Miss Baker, Cathy, and Margaret could hardly open the doors to

get out because so many people were crowding around the truck to greet them. The people finally formed a crooked line beside the truck so the missionaries could shake their hands. "I told you they'd be friendly," Miss Baker whispered as they moved along the line of people. Many Africans thought Margaret and Cathy looked like twins. They had to explain over and over that they were just sisters. Although the girls were a full two years apart, the natives were so impressed with their long brown hair and white skin that they didn't notice the difference in age.

Elijah and Joseph wasted no time in unloading the truck; however, they were unloading everything right out in the dusty road. When Margaret asked why they were putting all the things in the middle of the village, Miss Baker answered, "They're doing just what I told them to do. We're going to be sleeping right out here under God's shining stars."

"What!" gasped Margaret, "You mean we're going to be out in the open? I've never slept outside before."

"Margaret, you needn't be afraid," Miss Baker reminded her. "I've slept outside over here many

times on these trips, and God has always taken care of me. Elijah and Joseph will make a fire out here to burn all night, and they're going to take turns guarding us."

Margaret remained a bit worried, but soon both girls were busy helping to prepare supper. During supper a large crowd of African children gathered around the missionaries.

"Miss Baker, it seems strange to sit here on our cots and eat spaghetti while all the children stand around and stare at us. Do you think they've had any supper yet?" asked Margaret.

Miss Baker replied sadly, "I don't know. They usually get only one meal a day, sometimes not even that often if their crops didn't do well. I've got a big bag of peanuts that I'm going to give to the pastor here to distribute to them later."

They finished eating their supper quickly because it would soon be time to start their meeting. Miss Baker wanted to take some time to pray before the service began. Margaret talked to the children for a few minutes while Cathy got her diary and wrote.

March 24th, Friday
It was extremely hot today—120 degrees at least. I can't wait for a shower when we get back home. In the meanwhile, a bucket of water is about the closest thing we have. Right now, Elijah and Joseph are tying our mosquito nets up on some tall sticks they stuck in the ground at each end of our cots. Margaret is a little scared about sleeping out here. I would be afraid to sleep outside if I didn't have my mosquito net. It keeps out not only the mosquitos, but other creeping things like snakes and lizards. I'm more frightened about the idea of playing my accordion.

In just a few minutes, we'll be having our first meeting, and I'll be playing by flashlight! Miss Baker said not to worry if I make mistakes. The main thing is that people get saved during the meeting.

The first meeting went well. Many people came, especially when they heard the accordion music. Although Cathy's hands trembled on the keys and she kept having to take deep breaths to try to relax the tight muscles in her arms, she got through her songs. After she finished, her heart did not stop pounding until Joseph started to preach. Two people got saved at the meeting, and Miss Baker, and her helpers went to bed

thankful and thrilled that two people had responded to God.

At the sound of a rooster crowing early the next morning, Cathy thought, "That means 'wake up' in any language." She looked at her watch and groaned. "It's only five in the morning. Go back to bed, you silly rooster!" she called. In her cot Margaret started giggling.

Despite the early hour, the group had to get moving. The next village was over two hours away and there was much to do. After breakfast, Cathy asked, "Where can we go brush our teeth?"

"You can go over behind that hut," answered Miss Baker, "I don't think anyone will mind."

Cathy and Margaret were in the middle of brushing their teeth when they heard some giggles. They turned around, and there stood several small children, laughing at them. Margaret looked at Cathy, and with her mouth full of bubbles, she said, "I don't think they've ever seen anyone do this before!"

They both started laughing, and soon there were bubbles dripping down their chins and plopping to the ground. Before it was all over, the girls were surrounded by many noisy, laughing children.

"I think we'd better get back to the truck before everyone wants to try this!" said Cathy.

"The name of this town is Lito," said Miss Baker. The truck pulled up at 9:00 in the morning. "Hop out quickly; here comes my friend the chief."

Again, they all got out to shake hands. The chief, a small wiry man with a big toothy grin, welcomed his missionary friend. He presented her with a gift—a live chicken. In this land of poverty it was a sacrifice for anyone, even a chief, to give away a chicken. Miss Baker thanked him and handed it to Elijah to cook. She decided that they would all share it for lunch.

Then the chief directed them to a hut that was larger than the others. It even had a tall grass fence around it. "This is where you ladies are going to stay," he said, eager to be a good host.

That night Cathy put the kerosene lamp on a rickety table. "It sure has been a long, busy day," she thought. Pulling up a little bench, she sat down to recount the day's events in her diary.

March 25th, Saturday
At first I thought it unusual for the chief here to be so friendly, but then I realized

how lonely he must be. He's almost the only Christian in his whole village! Other villages are at least a day's journey on foot. It's sad to think of him living every day surrounded by idol worship. But he's the most cheerful man I know. I hope the Lord will save some of the other villagers tonight. It would be a wonderful answer to prayer.

We spent most of the morning unpacking the truck and organizing our things inside the hut. After eating fried chicken for lunch, Miss Baker said that we would be taking the chief and his son to visit some of their relatives in the next village. It was too hot to travel near noon, so we took a long siesta and left at 2:30.

It was a good thing Miss Baker kept some spare tires and tools in the trunk. Too bad she didn't keep a mechanic too! Two miles from the other village, a sharp rock poked a hole in a tire. It was funny to hear Miss Baker try to explain to the chief about working the jack and unscrewing the nuts that held the tire on. Margaret and I played ticktacktoe in the dust in the little bit of shade we found under a scraggly little tree. The repair job seemed to take forever. Finally, we got going again and made it to the village. We had to cut the visit short to get back to Lito for an evening service.

Cathy put away her diary and started preparing for bed. As she reached over to grab her towel off the cot, she jerked back with fright. Petrified, she whispered, "Margaret! Did you hear that rustling noise?"

Annoyed at her big sister's fright, Margaret said, "Your imagination is running wild. There's nothing in here. Now go to sleep."

But when Miss Baker came to the hut a few minutes later, the tune she was humming turned into a scream. "Margaret! There's a huge rat under your cot!"

All three women shot out the door. A band of African men quickly rushed in with machetes. They searched every inch of the hut but could not find the rat. Much later the nervous girls re-entered the hut. For a long time they sat up talking. Cathy wrote a long paragraph in her diary about the rat and the natives with their machetes. They finally did get to sleep, but it would have been much easier if the natives had found the rat.

The next morning, in the shade of a huge mango tree, Miss Baker spoke to a crowd of people. Joseph translated her French message into the tribal language. After Miss Baker's testimony, Cathy played her accordion and Margaret sang. Soon some African teen-agers joined the group to listen. Then Joseph preached a simple salvation message. While he gave an invitation, Miss Baker and the girls prayed. Several teen-agers, some women, and an old blind man came to Christ.

After the service was over, Joseph came rejoicing. "Did you see that little old blind man that came forward? He's the village witch doctor! He said that he wants to have all his idols and fetishes destroyed because he is going to serve the true God from now on."

Miss Baker looked at the girls in amazement. She explained that witch doctors rarely get saved. The girls were thrilled to see how God's Word could open the sinful heart of a man who had been blinded by Satan for many years.

Almost the entire village gathered for the idol-burning. The witch doctor had so many idols that it took two men to carry

them. What a strange collection they made! Ordinary sticks and scrawny plants were soon piled into a three-foot heap. Among the various idols were three six-inch sticks carved exactly the same. Miss Baker was curious why the man had three of the same carved sticks. When she asked Joseph, he told her, "Why, they represent the father, the son, and the spirit in his pagan religion!"

The blind witch doctor smiled as he stood near the fire. He felt the heat from the burning idols. Though he was physically blind, for the first time he could now see God's truth.

March 26th, Sunday

This was the best day of all. I'm not afraid to play my accordion anymore, and the rats I wrote about last night don't seem as bad anymore either. After Miss Baker's testimony and Joseph Bogal's preaching, three teen-agers and some other people got saved. Tonight we watched a blind witch doctor burn all the things he used in his pagan religion. He loves the Lord now. But Miss Baker and Joseph will have to come here often to read the Bible to him.

"Heavenly Father, You used me today with my accordion, and I know You answered our prayers during the service. When I'm older and I'm through school, I'd be willing to do just what Miss Baker does and come back here to be a witness to people like the blind witch doctor, the teen-agers, and the women, so that You can open their eyes. In Jesus' name, Amen."

Sissa and the Troublesome Trifles

an East Indian folktale
retold by I.G. Edmonds

Now it happened in the old days that King Balahait was ruler of a province in India. One day he called for his adviser, Sissa.

"Sissa," the king shouted angrily, "it is not possible for a king to do everything himself. He must have advisers to do his work."

"That is true, O Greatest of Kings," Sissa said mildly.

"My other advisers take care of important problems for me," the king went on, his temper growing hotter. "Why don't you do the same?"

"O King, live a thousand years," Sissa said. " I work hard."

"O King, live *two* thousand years," spoke up Rhadama, another of the King's advisers and a man most jealous of Sissa. "Surely Sissa works *hard,* but he never does anything when he works!"

"O King, live *three* thousand years," said Devatta, still another adviser. "Yesterday I inspected the army for you. Rhadama counted your treasure. Indra collected your taxes. But when Sissa was supposed to repair your garden, he wasted his time listening to the complaint of an old beggar woman!"

"O King, live *four* thousand years!" spoke up Indra. "The day before yesterday, Sissa wasted time looking for a lost child!"

"O King, live *five* thousand years!" Rhadama said. "Sissa is forever wasting time with trifles such as this when he should be worrying about the king's problems."

The king looked at Sissa. "What should I do with you?" he asked, his voice heavy with rage.

"O King, live *six* thousand years," Sissa said. "I do not know

456

what you should do with me."

"What should I do with him?" the king asked the others.

They hesitated. Although they hated Sissa themselves, they knew that the king loved the old man for all his faults. They were afraid to seem too harsh.

"O King, live *seven* thousand years," Indra began slyly. "Why not give Sissa another chance? Then if he fails this last chance, he must be banished."

"That is good advice," the king said. "Rhadama, give Sissa a task to do for me. Let it be something of importance."

"O King, live *eight* thousand years!" the evil adviser said, smothering his glee. "Now it is known that our great king is a lover of peace, but other kings are always fighting him. Let Sissa find a way for all men to live and fight the wars which they must fight without killing anyone!"

"Is that possible?" the king asked. "Oh, I wish it were. I am tired of killings."

"Oh, it must be possible!" the three enemies of Sissa cried together. "We are sure Sissa can do it."

"Fine," the king said. "Sissa, this is your last chance to serve me. Solve this problem, and you shall be my Grand Vizier. Fail and I must banish you forever. Since I cannot permit one to leave who knows the palace secrets, I will have no choice but to chop off your head."

The three evil men smiled, for they thought Sissa would not be able to solve the problem. "O King, live *forever!*" they cried.

"O King, live forever and a day," Sissa said. "I will go to the mountains and return in a month with the solution."

"O King, live forever and *two* days," Indra said. "I—"

"Oh, be quiet!" the king snapped. "I am sick of this live so long business. Rest assured I will live as long as I can. And I don't think your silly wishes will help me at all. Go, Sissa. I expect you back in one month."

Now within a week the evil men reported to the king that their spies claimed that Sissa was not working on the problem at all. Instead the old man was sitting in the shade of a tree, carving little men and animals from ivory while he listened to trifling complaints brought to him by the villagers.

This saddened the king, for he really loved his old adviser. How-

ever, he had given a king's word that Sissa would be killed if he failed. This could not be changed although the king regretted now that in his anger he had made the promise.

Finally, it was the end of the month. Sissa came back to court. He brought with him the toys he had carved during his stay in the mountains. Gravely he set a checkered board in front of the ruler. Then he placed the little figures upon it. There were tiny castles, war elephants, grand viziers, soldiers, and two kings and two queens. All together they made two armies. One was white ivory. The other was ivory stained black.

"Lord of all the lands!" Sissa said. "Live as long as you wish. On this board, which I have named the Royal Game of Chess, men can make war against each other without killing. The rules of chess are the same as the rules of war. A leader must play it the same as he would plan his strategy on the battlefield."

"O King!" cried Rhadama. "No game can take the place of real fighting. Sissa is trying to trick us. He has not solved the problem at all. He must be banished. The king has given his royal word."

"I suppose you are right," the king said thoughtfully, looking at the chessboard with interest. "But I would like to try the game myself."

"O King," Sissa said. "I do hear tell that the King of the South is talking of war against our kingdom. Why not try the game with him?"

The king agreed and sent a challenge to the rival king to meet him on the battlefield of chess.

And it was arranged. The two kings fought across the checkered board for days. They plotted like generals leading armies. They attacked with their foot soldiers.

They smashed lines with their elephants. They made sly thrusts with their viziers. And they sent their knights charging against the enemy.

But neither could win. Their great battle was a draw. When the rival king saw how closely each was matched with the other in his knowledge of the arts of war, he decided that it would not be wise to attack King Balahait with a real army. The war was called off.

The king was both amazed and overjoyed. He called his advisers and told them how Sissa's game had indeed permitted them to fight without killing anyone.

Sissa's enemies glowered with rage as the king asked the old man to name his reward.

"Just some rice, O King," Sissa said. "And let it be measured by the chessboard which I have invented. Place one grain of rice on the first of the sixty-four squares of the board. Then place two grains on the second square. Four on the third, doubling each amount until the sixty-four squares are covered."

"Sissa!" the king cried. "How can any man be so wise as to invent chess and so stupid as to ask for such a trifling reward? You have been this way all your life. It was the same when you wasted time from my big problems to listen to the villagers' small ones."

"O King, this is the reward I ask," Sissa said stubbornly.

"Then let it be so," the king said. "I thought you had learned to be wise. I see I was wrong."

Sissa only smiled as the rice was brought. One grain was placed on the first square and swept into a bag for Sissa. Two grains were placed on the second, four on the third, and eight on the fourth. By the time they came to the tenth square, it was necessary to measure out 512 grains. This was doubled to 1,024 for the eleventh square. By the time they got to the twentieth square, the amount was over a half million grains.

The king looked uneasy and looked searchingly at Sissa, who only smiled.

Soon rice filled all the sacks, covered the floor, and ran out the windows.

"How much rice is it going to take to double the amount sixty-four times?" the alarmed king asked.

"I cannot speak so great a figure," Sissa said, "but I will write it down."

And on the marble wall he wrote:

"18,466,744,073,709,551,615."

The king gasped. "There isn't that much rice in the world! How can such a little thing add up to so much?"

"It is the same with small troubles, O King," Sissa said gently. "All together they are very large, even though each may be small in itself. Then they are so great that they can crush a kingdom."

"I see," the king said slowly. "I also see now why you spent so much time listening to the small troubles of my people. You have proven to me that I was wrong."

"The king is very wise," Sissa said.

"Now you may ask for another reward for teaching me the value of small things," the king said, "but please, Sissa! Make it a *big* one, for rich as I am, I cannot afford another of your *small* rewards!"

"For my other reward I ask only that this rice be given to the poor of the country," the old man said.

"So let it be," the king said. "And as an additional reward, I appoint you my Grand Vizier to see after all the little problems of the people of my kingdom. You are to see that they do not add up like your doubled grains of rice until they become so big they crush our kingdom."

And it is written that Sissa took the job and did very wisely at it.

THE PILGRIM'S PROGRESS

John Bunyan

City of Destruction

Morality

Slough of Despond

Vanity Fair

Clear

By-Path Meadow

Doubting Castle

Caution

Error

Delectable Mountains

By-Way to Hell

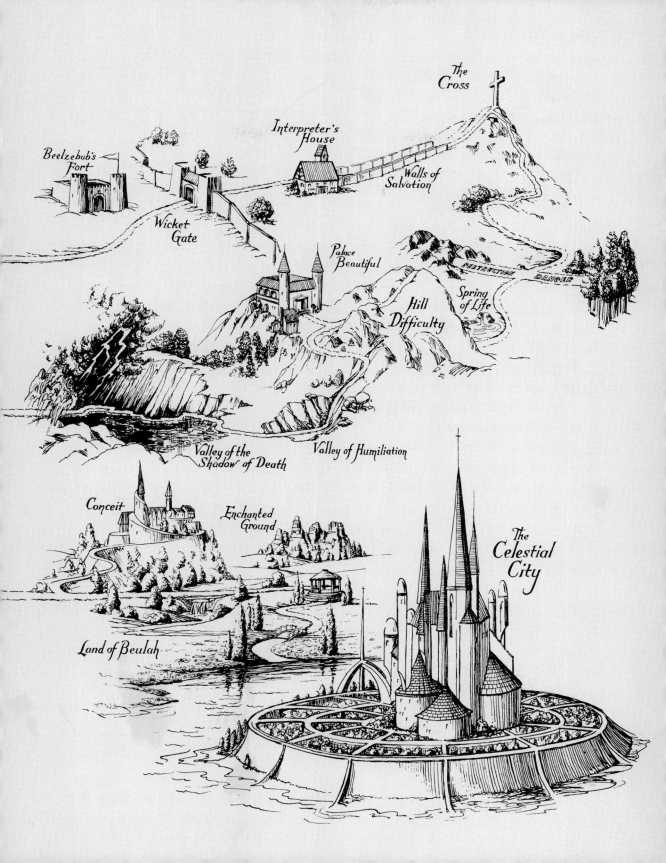

BUNYAN'S DREAM

Karen Duncan

John Bunyan tells the story of *The Pilgrim's Progress* as if it were a dream he had in prison. He opens the book with these words:

"As I walked through the wilderness of this world, I lighted on a certain place, where was a den; and I laid me down in that place to sleep: and as I slept I dreamed a dream."

In the beginning of his dream he saw a man standing outside a city. The man wore a heavy burden tied to his back. In one hand he had a book that he had been reading. All his clothes were rags, and he stood alone, afraid of what he had read in the book, afraid to go back to his city, and afraid to venture out anywhere else.

At last he turned back to his city, the City of Destruction, and went home. He told his family and friends of his fears, but they thought he was insane. The miserable days of loneliness lingered while the man, weighed down more than ever by his burden, read his book. The book told him to flee from the wrath to come, but he did not know where to flee.

And he was sure that his burden would sink him to the grave eventually.

At last a man named Evangelist found him and told him that to be loosed from his burden, he must follow the light on a distant hill to the Wicket Gate. At the Wicket Gate he would be directed further.

The burdened man started out. He passed through many dangers, and many times his heavy burden put him in more danger. When he sank into a bog called the Slough of Despond, his burden weighed him down, and he almost drowned. Later in his journey he was tricked into leaving the path to the Wicket Gate, but Evangelist found him and brought him back.

At last when he arrived at the Gate, he thought he would be turned away. But the gate-keeper, Mr. Good-Will, insisted that all are welcome and none who knock are cast out. So the man came in, and after learning more about his burden of sin and how it could be removed, he started up a straight and narrow path. Although there were many wide turnoffs, his path was always straight and narrow. He stayed on the straight path, his burden weighing him down all the time.

At last he saw that the narrow path was fenced with Walls called Salvation. The path climbed up a small hill, and the man walked on. He passed an open tomb at the foot of the hill but did not stop to look at it.

He came to the top of the hill, and there he found the Cross. The moment he saw it, the burden sprang from his back. It tumbled over and over down the hill, back the way the man had come, until finally it rolled into the open tomb and was never seen again.

The man, whose name was Christian, stared in awe at the Cross, amazed that it had so much power to free him. Tears came to his eyes when he realized all that had been done upon that Cross for his sake. While he stood crying for joy, three Shining Ones came to him. They took away his rags and dressed him in clothes given by the King of the Celestial City. They put a mark on his forehead to show that he now belonged to that King, and they gave him a scroll to take on his way. Now his feet were on the King's Highway, and he would travel it to its end at the Celestial City.

Christian traveled through danger and trouble on his way. He met many people, such as Formal and Hypocrisy, who tried to persuade him or trick him into leaving the King's Highway. But he also met friends who helped him. He found rest at one house, and the people there gave him armor for his journey. The armor proved to be a good thing.

The next day as Christian journeyed on, he saw some kind of monster stalking him through a field ahead. The beast was so tall that he could straddle the roadway with his feet, and he was covered with scales. He had dragon wings, and he breathed fire. His feet and hands had powerful claws like bear's feet, and his mouth, like a lion's mouth, had a snout, strong jaws, and sharp teeth.

This dreadful monster was Apollyon, the king of that world and lord of Christian's home city, the City of Destruction.

At first sight of him, Christian was afraid and wanted to run the other way, but he had no armor for his back. He decided it would be better to face Apollyon with armor than to turn his unprotected back to the beast. So Christian went on and met him.

Apollyon was gruff and haughty at first, but when he saw how sternly Christian set his face to go on to the Celestial City, the monster decided to coax him. He bribed Christian with the promise of good wages, but Christian knew that the wages of Apollyon's work is death. Then Apollyon accused Christian's new King. He said that the King of the Celestial City offered no better wages and that He often forsook His people when they needed Him most. But Christian would not believe him. Apollyon reminded Christian how other pilgrims had died on the Way to the Celestial City, but Christian answered and said that these were now delivered to the Celestial City.

So at last Apollyon accused Christian of all his sins, those past and present, and reminded him that he was utterly sinful and undeserving of the King of Glory. But Christian knew that he had been pardoned, and he was so convinced of the love and mercy of his new King that he would not turn back.

Then Apollyon attacked him and flung his fiery darts at Christian. Christian used his shield well, yet some of the darts wounded him. When he became weak from bleeding, Apollyon rushed and threw him to the ground so hard that Christian's sword was flung away. The monster fell on top of him to crush him, but Christian freed one hand

and reached his sword in time. He dealt Apollyon such a blow that the monster staggered off him. Christian leaped up to strike again, but Apollyon spread his dragon wings and flew away.

Even after Christian tended his wounds, he faced a grim journey, for then he had to walk through the Valley of the Shadow of Death, and night was falling. But he could not stop and wait. The territory was dangerous, and he must move on.

He went forward with sword in hand. The highway had become a narrow path barely wide enough for him to put one foot in front of the other. On the one side was a deep ditch with horrible things lurking in the bottom. On the other side there was a quagmire. Above him, dark clouds had covered the night sky so that not even the starlight could seep through.

Cautiously he picked his way along, but as he walked he realized that his danger was even more terrible than he had guessed. Goblins and nameless creatures raced across the path in the gloom, seeking to trip him. They babbled at him as he passed by, and they howled from the darkness. He could not see them, but he often felt them close enough to reach out and touch. The path wound its way through flames and smoke, and the sad and horrible howling increased. Yet Christian forced his way on until at last morning came, and he saw ahead of him another pilgrim.

Coming out of the Valley, he met the pilgrim whose name was Faithful. They talked of their past adventures and quickly became good friends. Daily they walked on and had many adventures together. At last they came to Vanity Fair. They stayed there longer than they had intended and saw some grim times. Afterwards, Christian and Faithful had to part ways. Christian traveled the Highway with a new friend named Hopeful. As for Faithful, he went on to the Celestial City before them.

Christian and Hopeful also became friends, but Hopeful was the younger man. Often on the path Christian had to watch out for him and warn him of danger. But Hopeful always listened willingly, and he loved Christian as a brother.

Though Christian tried to guide Hopeful, he did lead him out of the Highway once by carelessness. Then they were caught trespassing by a giant and put into a dungeon. After many days of suffering and horror they did escape. They resolved to stay on the Highway no matter what.

To their joy, they saw that they were coming closer to the Celestial City. Several times friends along the way took them to high mountains where they could see their destination. Yet as they came closer, the perils that they faced became subtler and more dangerous. Now enemies of the King dressed as His own Shining Ones to lead the pilgrims away. More and more frequently they saw handsome travelers who tried to persuade them of new ways to reach the City.

But there were watchers on duty, and these servants of the King helped or rescued the travelers when they were in trouble. At last through all their difficulties, they came to a deep river. It was the last step of their journey, and then they would be safe in the City, which they could see from the riverbank.

But there was no bridge on this river and no ferry. A man had to cross it by going through it, and it was deep or shallow according to a man's faith in the King. As they stepped in, Christian sank and called for help. He could feel no bottom, and he was afraid of the cold waters of the river.

But Hopeful, the younger and weaker of the two, held on to Christian to help him. "I feel the bottom and it is good," he urged Christian, trying to keep his friend's head up out of the water. But all his life Christian had been afraid of this river, and now such a horror fell on him that he even forgot how his sins had been forgiven, how he had overcome Apollyon, and how he had walked through the terrible Valley of the Shadow of Death.

"Brother, I see the Gate and men standing by to receive us," Hopeful called to him, but Christian only answered, " 'Tis you, 'tis you they wait for." He would have forgotten everything, but suddenly Christian's heart was revived. He remembered the promises of the King, and he took

courage again. "I see Him again!" he exclaimed, "And He tells me, 'When thou passest through the waters, I will be with thee.' "

Then Christian's feet felt the bottom, and he and Hopeful walked on and were received into the City with trumpets and joy. There they rejoined their friends who had come before them, and they were given the rewards of all their journeying, suffering, and mourning. Yet for their sins they were pardoned and fully recovered, for they were given shining clothes, and they would never sin again. So they lived happily in the presence of their King from that day forward.

Thus ends the story of Christian. "So I awoke," Bunyan wrote, "and behold, it was a dream."

VANITY FAIR

John Bunyan, adapted by Karen Duncan

(Christian and Faithful are traveling together on their way to the Celestial City.)

Then I saw in my dream that they saw a town before them. The name of that town is Vanity, and at the town there is a fair called Vanity Fair. It is called Vanity Fair because all that is sold there and all who come there are worthless and empty.

This fair is no new business, but an ancient thing. Almost five thousand years ago, pilgrims began walking to the Celestial City. Beelzebub, Apollyon, and Legion saw that the pilgrims' road led through this town of Vanity. The evil ones decided to set up a fair there. At that fair would be sold all sorts of vanities, everything empty and worthless. That is why these things are found at this fair: houses, lands, businesses, silver, gold, privileges, countries, kingdoms, honors, lusts, pleasures, cheats, and all delights that belong only to this world. Here one can see also, for no extra charge, many thefts, murders, and terrible lies. Indeed, this fair has people from all the countries of the world, and the goods that belong to them are arranged in rows on its streets.

Now, as I said, the way to the Celestial City lies just through this town where the fair is kept. The Prince of princes himself passed through this town on the way to His own country. Beelzebub, the chief lord of the fair, invited Him to buy of the vanities. He took Him from street to street and showed Him all the kingdoms of the world in a little time, hoping to tempt the Blessed One to cheapen Himself and buy some of the worthless things. The Prince did not want what Beelzebub had to sell, and left the town without buying a single vanity. As you can see, this fair is an ancient thing.

Now Christian and Faithful had to travel through this fair. Well, so they did; but even as they entered the fair, all the people there and in the town itself were thrown into a hubbub for these three reasons:

First, the pilgrims dressed differently from any who did business at the fair. (They still wore the armor that their Lord had given them for the journey.) The people therefore stared at them, and some said that they were fools or madmen or strangers from some other country.

Second, few of the people there could understand what they said. The pilgrims spoke the language of the Promised Land, but the merchants at the fair were men of this present world. From one end of the fair to the other, they sounded like foreigners to the merchants.

Third, these pilgrims paid very little attention to the things that were for sale. They would not even look at them. If a shopkeeper called to them to buy, they would put their fingers in their ears and say, "Turn away mine eyes from beholding vanity." Then they would look upward to show that their business was in heaven.

One citizen who was mocking them happened to say, "Come,

will you buy nothing?" But they answered him seriously, "We buy the truth." This made the people hate them even more. At last almost everyone was mocking and ridiculing and speaking cruelly and calling on others to beat the pilgrims. The entire fair fell into confusion.

Soon the master of the fair sent some of his most trusted friends to find these men who had almost turned the fair upside down. So they questioned the pilgrims, and when they found out who they were and where they were going, they would not believe them. They thought they must be

madmen or troublemakers. Therefore, they took the two travelers and beat them and smeared them with dirt and then put them into a cage so that all men of the fair could come and stare at them.

There the two men stayed for some time. Anyone who passed could make fun of them or hurt them as he wished. The master of the fair only laughed at anything that happened to them. But the pilgrims were patient and did not give back evil for evil. Instead they gave good words for cruel ones and returned kindness for injuries.

Some of the men there who were more fair-minded watched them carefully. After a while, these men tried to stop the others from treating the prisoners so cruelly. This interference made the abusers angry. "You are as bad as the men in the cage," they cried. "You are plotting with them and you should have the same treatment."

The others replied, "For all we can see, the men were quiet and sober and meant nobody any harm. There are many who do business in the fair who deserve punishment more than these you have abused."

After they had argued for some time, they began to fight among themselves and hurt one another. Then, even though the pilgrims had behaved wisely and quietly through it all, they were blamed for the new trouble at the fair. The citizens of Vanity Fair beat them and put chains on them. Then they led them up and down the streets to warn other people from joining them.

But Christian and Faithful took all this treatment with so much meekness and patience that it won to their side several more men of the fair. This threw the cruel men into a rage.

"You two shall die for what you have done," they shouted. "Neither a cage nor chains will do. You will die for deceiving the men of Vanity Fair!"

The pilgrims then were sent back to the cage again to wait with their feet fastened in the stocks. They were not afraid to suffer but put themselves in the care of the all-wise God who rules all things.

When the time came for the trial, they were brought before their enemies and charged with their crimes. The judge's name was Lord Hategood, and here is the charge he read against them:

"They are enemies to the fair and disturbers of trade. They have caused unrest and rioting in the town, and have won other people to their dangerous ideas. This is all against the law of our king."

Then Faithful answered, "I spoke only against those who oppose the God Most High. And I made no disturbance, for I am a man of peace. The men who joined us were won by seeing our truth and innocence. And as for the king you talk of, since he is Beelzebub, the enemy of our Lord, I defy him and all his angels."

When he had finished, the judge called for any who wanted to give evidence to step forward. Three witnesses came: Envy, Superstition, and Pickthank.

Envy spoke first, and said, "My Lord Judge, this man is one of the worst men in our country. He does not obey any of our laws or customs. Instead he tries to persuade all men with his evil notions, which he calls principles of holiness and faith."

"And I myself once heard him claim that Christianity and the customs of our fine town were exactly opposite, and that they never could agree. By saying that, my Lord, he condemns all our good efforts and us as well."

Then the judge said to him, "Have you any more to say?"

"My Lord," he said, "I do not wish to bore the court. Yet if the court needs more evidence to convict him, I will think of more to say."

Then they called Superstition, and asked him what he had to say against the prisoner.

"My Lord Judge," he began, "I do not know this man well, and I do not wish to know him better. However, this I do know: he is a very bothersome fellow. I heard him say that our religion was nothing, and that a man could not please God with it. When he says this, my Lord Judge, he means that we worship in vain, we are still in our sins, and shall finally die without hope. That is what I have to say."

Then Pickthank was brought to testify.

"My Lord Judge," said he, "I have heard this fellow speak things that should not be said. He has scorned our noble prince Beelzebub and all the rest of our important men. He has said, besides, that none of these men live according to the truth. He has not been afraid to call even you, his judge, an ungodly villain. I have told my tale."

When Pickthank finished, the judge spoke to Faithful, saying, "You renegade, heretic, and traitor—have you heard what these honest men have witnessed against you?"

"May I speak a few words in my own defense?" asked Faithful.

"You deserve to be killed this moment," answered the judge. "But so that all men may see our kindness to you, we will hear what you have to say."

Faithful began to speak. "I say only this to them: The worship of God requires faith and must agree with the Word of God. Any law or custom or rule that is against the Word of God, or is added to the Word of God, is error; it cannot lead to eternal life. As for the prince Beelzebub and his gentlemen, they are more fit to live in hell than in this country. The Lord have mercy upon me."

Then the judge called to the jury (who had heard and seen all this): "Gentlemen of the jury, you see this man who has made such an uproar in this town. You have also heard what these gentlemen have witnessed against him. Also you have heard his reply and confession. Now it is up to you to hang him or save his life.

"Remember our ancient laws," he continued, "the same laws by which Pharaoh killed the Hebrew male children and Nebuchadnezzar threw the faithful men into the fiery furnace. By the same laws of our land, Darius cast Daniel into the lions' den. This rebel has broken these laws in both word and deed. For the treason he has confessed, he deserves to die the death."

Then the jury went out to discuss the verdict, even though each of them had already decided for himself to condemn him.

Mr. Blind Man, who was in charge, said, "I see clearly that this man is a heretic."

Then said Mr. No-good, "Away with such a fellow from the earth."

"Ay," said Mr. Hurtful, "for I hate the very sight of him."

"Hang him, hang him," said Mr. Headstrong.

"Hanging is too good for him," said Mr. Cruelty.

Then said Mr. Unforgiving, "If the whole world were given to me, I could not stand to have him live. Let us find him guilty and condemn him to death."

All the others spoke in the same way, and so they did find him guilty. Then was Faithful condemned to the most cruel death that could be invented.

When they brought him out to carry out his sentence, first they scourged him, then they struck him, and then they cut him with knives. After that they stoned him with stones and stabbed him with swords. Finally, they burned him to ashes at the stake.

Now I saw that there was nearby a chariot and a pair of horses waiting for Faithful. As soon as his enemies had killed him, he was taken up into the chariot, and carried up through the clouds with the sound of a trumpet. He went by the shortest way to the Celestial City.

But Christian was sent back to prison instead of killed. There he stayed for a time; but He who rules all things gave Christian a way to escape. He went on his way singing, thankful that Faithful was still alive and with God.

Now I saw in my dream that Christian did not leave the town alone. A man named Hopeful, who had seen the testimony of Christian and Faithful at the fair, joined him on his journey. Thus one died to bear testimony of the truth, and another came as a result to walk with Christian on the King's highway. Even more, in the time to come, would follow in the way because of them.

DOUBTING CASTLE

*John Bunyan,
adapted by Karen Duncan*

I saw then that Christian and Hopeful came to a pleasant river. David the king had called this river "the river of God"; but John, "the river of the water of life."

Here the King's highway went along the bank of the river. Christian and his companion walked along it with great delight. They also drank the water from the river, which was pleasant and lifted their weary spirits. Besides this, on the banks of this river were green trees that bore all sorts of fruit and also leaves that were good for medicine. They were delighted with the fruit of these trees, and they ate the leaves to prevent illnesses. On either side of the river there was a meadow beautifully carpeted with lilies. It stayed green all year long.

478

In this meadow they lay down and slept, for they knew they would be safe in this place. When they awoke, they gathered more fruit from the trees and drank more water from the river, and then lay down again to sleep. This they did several days and nights. They felt so happy and comfortable that they sang songs in praise of the sweet crystal water and pleasant fruit.

At last they knew they must continue on their way. They ate again a meal of the fruit and drank from the river, and started down the road.

They had not journeyed far when their path led away from the river. They were sorry to leave the pleasant bank, but they dared not leave the road that they were traveling. Now the road away from the river was rough, and their feet were already tender from walking so far on their journey. As they went on, they wished for an easier way, and began to be much discouraged.

Now a little before them, they saw on the left side of the road a meadow, and a stile to go over the wall into it. Christian and Hopeful did not know it, but that meadow is called the By-path meadow.

Then said Christian to his friend, "If this meadow goes alongside our road, let us cross over and walk there." He went to the stile to see and found a path lying along the way on the other side of the fence.

"It is as I hoped," said Christian. "Here is an easier way to walk. Come, good Hopeful, and let us go over the stile."

"But what if this path should take us the wrong way?" asked Hopeful.

"That is not likely," said the other. "Look, does it not follow the highway?"

So Hopeful, being persuaded by his companion, followed him over the stile. The path on the other side was very easy for their feet, and they began to enjoy their walk. Suddenly the night came on and it grew very dark. When they could no more see the path before them, Hopeful stopped and said, "Where are we now?" But Christian was silent, because he feared that he had led them in the wrong way.

Now it began to rain and thunder, and lightning flashed around them, and the water in the river rose and rushed against the banks.

Then Hopeful groaned, "Oh, I wish that I had kept on the King's highway!"

Christian answered, "Who could have thought that this path would lead us out of the way?"

"I was afraid of it at the very first," said Hopeful. "But you are older than I, and I thought that you would know best."

"Good brother, I am sorry I have led you out of the way, and that I have brought you into this place of danger. Please, my brother, forgive me; I meant to do no evil to you."

"Be comforted my brother, I forgive you," Hopeful replied, "and believe that this shall work out for our good."

Then said Christian, "I am thankful for your kindness, brother; but we must not stay here. Let's try to go back to the right way again."

By this time the waters were high and made the way back by the river dangerous. (You know that it is easier going out of the right way when we are in it, than going back when we are out.) Still, they tried to go back, but the night was so dark, and the water was so high that they probably would have been drowned nine or ten times before they reached the highway.

Try as they might, they could not reach the stile that night. At last they found a sheltered spot beside some trees. They sat down to wait for day to break, but were too weary and fell asleep.

Now there was nearby a castle called Doubting Castle, which was owned by Giant Despair. It was on his property that the pilgrims now were sleeping. The Giant, getting up early in the morning, went walking in his fields and caught Christian and Hopeful there asleep. Then with a grim, loud voice he told them to awake, and asked them where they came from and what they were doing in that place. They, trembling, told him that they were pilgrims and that they had lost their way.

Then said the giant, "You have this night trespassed on my property, and therefore you must come with me."

They were forced to go because he was stronger than they were, and besides, they knew that they were in the wrong. The Giant took them then into his castle and put them into a dark dungeon, nasty and stinking to their spirits. There they lay from Wednesday morning until Saturday night, without one bit of bread or drop of drink or any light, and far from friends or anyone who knew them. Christian was doubly sorry, because he knew his eagerness for

the easy way had brought them to this trouble.

Now Giant Despair had a wife, and her name was Distrust. That night the Giant told his wife what he had done, and asked her what else he should do with them now. She counseled him that he should beat them the next morning without mercy.

So when he arose, he found a heavy crab-tree club and went down into the dungeon where the pilgrims were. He first began to scold them as if they were dogs, although they never said a word to offend him. Then he beat them fearfully with the club until they were not able even to turn over on the floor. This done, Giant Despair left them there to comfort each other and to mourn about their distress.

So all that day the pilgrims did nothing but sigh and lament. The next night Distrust and her husband talked further of the prisoners and decided he would counsel them to end their own lives.

When morning came he went to the dungeon and saw that they were sore from their beating the day before. He told them that since they would never leave that place, their only hope was to end their own lives quickly, either with knife or poison, or by hanging themselves. "For why," said he, "should you choose life, seeing

that living is so painful?"

Still they begged him to let them go. That angered him, and he rushed at them to kill them. But at that moment he fell into one of his fits. (Sometimes sunshiny weather made him lose the use of his hands or legs for a time.) Since he could not hurt them at that time, he left them again to consider what to do.

"Brother," said Christian, "what shall we do? The life that we now live is miserable. I know not whether it is best to live this way or simply to die. The grave would be more easy for me than this dungeon. Shall we live and be ruled by the giant?"

"Indeed," answered Hopeful, "death would be far more welcome to me than to live for ever in this place. But consider this: the Lord of the country we seek hath said, 'Thou shalt do no murder.' If we are not to murder others, we are much more forbidden to obey Despair and kill ourselves. And remember, too, that all the power does not belong to Giant Despair. Others, I think, have escaped from him before. Who knows? God who made the world may cause Giant Despair to die, or at some time the Giant may forget to lock us in. He may soon have another of his fits and altogether lose the use of his limbs. And if ever that should happen again, I am resolved to try my utmost to get away from him. My brother, let us be patient and endure a while. The time may come when we can get away. Let us not be our own murderers."

With these words Hopeful comforted the mind of his brother.

Well, toward evening the Giant went down into the dungeon again to see whether his prisoners had done what he said. He found them alive; and truly, alive was all. For now, from hunger and thirst and the wounds he had given them, they could do little but breathe. Even so, finding them alive sent him into a terrible rage.

"Since you will not do what I say," he howled, "you'll wish you had never been born, you will!" And he slammed the bars behind him.

At this they trembled greatly, and began to talk about the Giant's order. Christian again seemed to be for doing it.

"My brother," said Hopeful, "do you not remember how brave you have been until now? That evil giant Apollyon could not crush you, nor could all the things you heard, or saw, or felt in the Valley of the Shadow of Death. I am a far weaker man than you are, yet I am in the dungeon with you, and also wounded and hungry and thirsty, and like you I mourn without the light. But let us be a little more patient. Remember how brave you were at Vanity Fair, and were afraid of neither chains nor cage, nor even of death. Therefore let us be patient as well as we can."

That night, Distrust asked her husband if the prisoners still lived. He replied, "They are sturdy rogues. They choose to bear all hardship rather than to kill themselves."

Then said she, "Take them into the castle yard tomorrow, and show them the bones and skulls of those that you have already destroyed, and make them believe that you will tear them in pieces also before the week comes to an end."

So when the morning came, the Giant went to them again, and took them into the castle yard, and showed them the bones, as his wife had told him to.

"These," said he, "were pilgrims once, and they trespassed in my grounds, as you have done. When I saw fit, I tore them in pieces, and within ten days I will do the same with you. Go, get down to your dungeon." With that he beat them all the way there. They lay all day Saturday recovering from their wounds.

Now when night came, Mrs. Distrust and her husband the giant began to talk again about their prisoners. The old giant wondered why he could not bring them to an end.

With that his wife replied, "I fear that they live in hope that some help will come, or that they have with them some means of escape."

"Think you so, my dear?" said the Giant. "I will search them in the morning."

Well, on Saturday about midnight the two pilgrims began to pray, and continued in prayer till almost daybreak.

Then suddenly Christian jumped to his feet and shouted aloud. "What a fool am I," said he, "to lie in a stinking dungeon when I can easily have liberty! I was given a key called Promise. It will, I am certain, open any lock in Doubting Castle."

"That is good news, good brother," said Hopeful. "Take it out quickly and try."

Then Christian pulled out the key and began to try the lock on the dungeon door. The bolt shot

back, the door flew open, and Christian and Hopeful hurried out. They opened yet another door and came to the iron gate. Although the lock was terribly stiff, the key did open it. But that gate, as they pushed on it, made such a creaking that it woke Giant Despair. He jumped up to go after his prisoners, but one of his fits came upon him, and he fell down helpless in the sunshine. Christian and Hopeful went on until they came to the King's highway. There at last they were safe from the Giant.

Now when they had climbed back over the stile, they began to plan what they should do to prevent others from falling into the hands of Giant Despair. So they made there a stone marker, and wrote upon the side of it this sentence: "Over this stile is the way to Doubting Castle, which belongs to Giant Despair. He hates the King of heaven and tries to kill His holy pilgrims." (Many who came later read the warning and escaped the danger.)

When they had finished, the two pilgrims began to sing, and went on their way to the Celestial City.

John Bunyan: Prisoner with a Pen

Bea Ward

"Mommy, Mommy! Help me! He's going to get me! Come quickly!"

For the third night in a row, little John's cries pierced the quiet night. His mother quickly lighted a candle, slid on her slippers, and hurried to comfort the fitful sleeper.

"John, John, wake up." She gently shook him as she sat on the edge of his bed. "It's only a dream, son, wake up," she said, kissing his forehead.

"Mommy," he panted, wide-eyed and frightened, "the jugglers were chasing me, and the puppets were laughing because I couldn't run fast enough!"

"John Bunyan," his mother said sternly, "I knew I shouldn't have taken you to the fair. Too

much excitement always stirs up your imagination."

Truly the Stourbridge Fair was the most exciting event of the year. Those living in the small village of Elstow looked forward to it all year long. For three weeks in September, merchants and entertainers from all over England—and from other countries as well—set up stalls to sell goods of every kind.

Farmers and their wives bought tools, furniture, cloth, and other household items. But children had the best time watching jugglers, puppet shows, performing animals, and musicians. For a ha'penny they could buy delicious sweets like gingerbread and peppermint drops. Children with extra money

could choose from a delightful array of toys such as dolls, drums, hobbyhorses, popguns, kites, hoops, shuttlecocks, and much more.

An imaginative child like John Bunyan would always remember the sights and sounds of the fair.

Except for his visits to the fair, John's boyhood was uneventful. He lived in a small village in the countryside and learned to read and write at a school for poor farmers' children. When he was still young, he left school to become a tinker like his father, repairing pots and pans and other metal utensils.

Though John didn't have much schooling, he heard and read many tales and saw plays of medieval romance. These experiences filled his mind with visions of knights, dragons, and giants. He also heard many sermons and read the Bible. But the Bible reading in the Bunyan family did not indicate that the family had a saving faith in Jesus Christ. The Bunyans were religious people, members of the Church of England. But John was not saved during his boyhood in the church his family attended.

In 1644 when John was sixteen, his secure and happy

home life came to an end. In June his mother died, in July his younger sister Margaret died, and in November he was mustered—that is, drafted—into the army of Lord Oliver Cromwell.

For two years England had been fighting a civil war. The English Parliament (like our Congress) had many disagreements with the king, Charles I. They wanted the king to change many things in government. Parliament usually argued with the king about money—harsh taxes and foolish spending. Many members of Parliament were also concerned with the religious condition of the country.

One member, Oliver Cromwell, was a leader of the Puritans (those who wanted to purify the Church of England). He especially wanted freedom for personal religion in England. The Church of England controlled every church in the land and the ways in which the worship services were conducted. Cromwell believed that groups of Christians should be able to follow their own methods of worship. In 1642 the House of Commons, one of the houses of Parliament, appointed Oliver Cromwell to help command an army to fight the king.

When John Bunyan came into Cromwell's army, he had many new experiences. Besides gathering his soldiers around campfires at night for prayer meetings, Cromwell made sure his army had good treatment and regular pay, but he exercised strict discipline.

A soldier who swore had to pay a fine. A soldier who got drunk was put in stocks. If he deserted, he was whipped. All this discipline made good soldiers, and Cromwell was able to win many battles, ultimately defeating the king.

Although John Bunyan didn't become a Christian in the army, the prayers and actions of Christian soldiers greatly impressed him. One particular event made a lasting impression on him. One day John was pulled out of his regular troop and ordered to fight at a nearby town. While he was away, a friend who took his place was shot and killed. Later when John became a preacher, he gave God the glory for sparing his life.

After leaving the army, John married a girl whose name we do not know. She was an orphan, and she and John were so poor that they didn't have one dish or spoon between them. But his wife did bring to their little home two Christian books, which they read together over and over.

John had not been a particularly naughty boy or a wicked young man, but he had been lively and sometimes mischievous, and his imagination often ran away with him. As he became a man, John was confused and restless in his search for God. The people of Elstow knew him as a carefree fellow who spent Sundays with rowdy friends and whose main vice was his constant swearing. But since he was pleasant and hard working, most folks liked him.

However, in his soul John was tormented with doubts and guilt. He thought that God was a terrible Judge who would send him to hell for all his frivolous ways. He had nightmares, just as he had experienced as a boy, dreaming he was in everlasting fire. Often, though, to shake off these fears, he became even rowdier in his attempts to forget about God.

One day John was walking to the town of Bedford on business. It was a beautiful day—gardens and orchards in bloom, a little river flowing under stone bridges. As he walked past the churches, stores, and thatched-roof cottages, he saw a group of women, their housework done, sitting in the sun spinning and talking. They weren't talking about families or neighbors but about religion.

"I'll join them," John thought, "for I like a good conversation, and I know something of religion too."

Yet when he listened for a moment, he heard them speaking

of a joyous Christian life, of a loving God, and of Jesus as their friend! John's casual friendliness turned to deep interest and concern.

"Please," he begged them, "how can I know this great happiness that you have? My religion fills me only with dread and terror." Explaining that they knew little of theology, the good women urged him to speak to their pastor, John Gifford, at St. John's Church.

He left directly to find this man they called pastor, the leader of a little church, not part of the Church of England. But knowing himself to be only an ignorant tinker, he hesitated to speak to so godly a gentleman. "Sir," he said after having introduced himself, "can God save so wretched a sinner as I?"

"As you?" the preacher smiled. "Let me tell you what I was before God saved me. Then you'll worry no more about your own sins." And he told John Bunyan of his years in the army.

"I served with King Charles's army and was taken prisoner in battle and condemned to die. The night before I was to be hanged, my sister came to bid me farewell. Believe it or not, she found all the guards asleep and all my fellow prisoners in a drunken stupor. Only I was awake, for I had wanted to talk to my sister. So she whispered to me, 'Now's your chance to escape. Get as far away as you can.' So, like St. Peter, I escaped from my jailers.

"For three days I hid in a ditch until the search for me died down; then I went to friends in London. Finally, I came here to Bedford, where no one knew me. Since I'd had some training in medicine, I set up as a doctor.

"You would think I would have been grateful to God for my escape, but I was not. I was not even a good doctor, for I spent all my time drinking, gambling, and swearing. One day I read a little book. The message of the writer spoke to my soul and made me consider my sinful ways and turn to Jesus Christ as my Saviour. How surprised my neighbors were to see their wicked doctor so soon changed into a God-fearing preacher!"

John Bunyan was amazed to hear a story so similar to that of his own life. Then and there he found a friend and counselor in this fervent preacher. John moved his family to Bedford, partly to gain more work in a larger town and partly to join Mr. Gifford's congregation. With good Bible preaching and counseling, Bunyan turned from his sins and put his trust in Jesus Christ. Soon he too was eager to tell friends and neighbors of this wonderful Saviour. John Bunyan was a fine preacher, and many townspeople came to hear about Jesus from him.

Not long after he became a Christian, trouble came to John Bunyan. His wife became sick and died, leaving him with four small children, the oldest a blind daughter. Not long afterward his good friend John Gifford also died, leaving the congregation in Bedford without a pastor.

Then in 1658 Oliver Cromwell died. Two years later King Charles II was invited to rule England, but when he came to the throne, he no longer allowed religious freedom for the people. All Englishmen had to return to the Church of England, even those in the little Bedford congregation, or be punished.

By this time John Bunyan was a leader of the Bedford church. One cold night, November 12, 1660, a group of men and women, their dark cloaks wrapped tightly about them, quietly but quickly walked in small groups to a large farm house. They carried no lanterns, for they did not want the king's soldiers to know of their meeting. Once inside, they nervously whispered to each other, waiting for one other member to arrive.

Finally, John Bunyan's broad shoulders appeared in the doorway, "Peace to you, brethren," he greeted them warmly.

"Brother Bunyan," said one who stepped quickly toward him, closing the door, "we have bad news. We think you should not preach tonight."

"What's that? What have you heard?"

"The Magistrates know you have been preaching. They are sending men here to arrest you tonight. Please flee to safety!"

Everyone in the crowded room looked at John Bunyan, wondering what he would do. They had come to love this tinker-preacher and did not want him in jail.

After a long silence Bunyan spoke cheerfully, "Come, let us have our meeting. I will preach. Nothing can happen to me unless it is God's will. First, let us pray."

So these poor country folks, many who could not read but who could recite from memory long passages of Scripture, settled onto chairs or benches or stood about the room to pray and then listen to their bold preacher.

Then came a heavy tramping on the doorstep and a rough voice called, "Open, in the king's name!" Two men pushed to the front of the quiet room, "John Bunyan, tinker?"

"I am John Bunyan."

"You are under arrest for preaching unlawfully. Come with us."

So it was that he left the care of his family to his little congregation and to his new wife, Elizabeth.

Bunyan had not been in prison many months before his pious ways and joyous attitude won the respect and confidence of his jailer. Talking kindly to his fellow prisoners, praying with them, and teaching them the Bible, he soon had an influence over them as well. So when a member of Bunyan's congregation was on her deathbed asking for him, the jailer let him out to see her, only warning, "Be back before night." By and by the jailer allowed Bunyan some freedom to go away to preach and to visit his family.

One day, however, a man on horseback rode to the jail to speak to his friend, the jailer. "Ho, friend," he called out. "I hope all your prisoners are safe in their rooms. You are to have visitors this afternoon."

"What? What's this you say?" he asked in alarm.

"Someone has been telling

tales of you to the Magistrates, and they are coming to check on John Bunyan."

"Oh, I am ruined then!"

"Do you not know where he is to send for him?"

"Yes, I know. But he is in London to preach and not due back until tomorrow."

"My dear friend, then you are in trouble. The Magistrates will surely lock you in your own jail."

The jailer dropped his head to his hands, thinking all was lost, when John Bunyan stepped around the corner. "What's the trouble, my good man?"

"John Bunyan!" the jailer cried, his arms outstretched, a smile on his face. "What brings you home a day early?"

"I'm not sure," Bunyan answered, "but I just felt I must come back."

"Then up to your room quickly. And you're welcome to leave whenever you please, for you know better than I when to come back."

But after that, the Magistrates had Bunyan watched closely, and he could not leave nearly as often.

For twelve long years Bunyan stayed in prison. Often he had the

comfort of visits from his family and friends. Often he kept busy writing or making shoelaces to support his family. Sometimes, though, he was unhappy; sometimes he doubted God's love and promises. He would sometimes brood over his sins for days and wonder if such a sinner could really be right with God. But God was faithful and comforted Bunyan when he got discouraged. And Bunyan learned to love the promises of God in Scripture.

Eventually his faith in God's ability to save him and keep him became stronger as he studied these promises and claimed them for himself.

When he was finally freed from prison, the congregation at Bedford voted to have him as their pastor, and Bunyan was happy to be home with his family.

He was put in prison later for a short time. At that time he thought about all the experiences he had had as a Christian.

He remembered how miserable he had been before he trusted Jesus as his Saviour, and he wrote about a man named Christian who also carried a great burden until it rolled off him at the cross.

He remembered the Stourbridge Fair that had both excited and terrified him as a child, and he wrote about Vanity Fair, where the worldly townspeople could not understand a Christian who did not crave all the pleasures and temptations of the world.

He remembered the doubts he had suffered in prison before and wrote about Doubting Castle and the Giant Despair.

Many more experiences he thought about and described so that every Christian could recognize his own journey to the Celestial City, heaven.

As soon as it was published, *Pilgrim's Progress*, as he named the book, became popular. People, rich and poor, saw themselves as Christian and enjoyed reading the story of his journey. Before long nearly every home in England had a copy of John Bunyan's *Pilgrim's Progress*. In many homes it could be found alongside a well-worn Bible.

Soon Bunyan wrote other books. Remembering his experiences as a soldier in Cromwell's army, he wrote *The Holy War*, about troops of the Devil trying to capture the town of Mansoul.

When his wife and children became curious about the family of the pilgrim Christian, Bunyan wrote a second part to *Pilgrim's Progress*. It tells the story of Christian's wife, Christiana, and their children on their way to the Celestial City.

As John Bunyan grew old, he spent his time preaching and writing. He was well known in England and well loved.

One evening when Bunyan was nearly sixty years old, a young man came to see him. Bunyan recognized the caller as the son of an old acquaintance.

"Mr. Bunyan, I wish to ask a great favor of you, please."

"Certainly. I'm always glad to be of help."

"My father and I have quarreled," the young man began. "I know it was my fault, and since he is old, I wish to apologize, but he refuses to see me."

"What would you like me to do?"

"Mr. Bunyan," he pleaded, "I know my father lives a long way off, but he greatly respects you. If you would kindly see him and talk to him, I know he would soon forgive me."

"I'll be glad to do what I can. I leave tomorrow to preach, and your father's house is not too far out of my way."

"Thank you, Mr. Bunyan, and Godspeed to you."

When the young man had left, Mrs. Bunyan looked up from her mending and said to her husband, "John, why must you go there? You are not well, and you could easily write a letter to the man."

"No, I know the boy's father. He must have a visit. But don't worry about me; I am in God's care."

The next day John Bunyan saddled his horse, kissed his good wife, and set off on his journey.

What he said to the angry father we do not know, but soon the man and his son were reconciled.

He went on to visit friends and to preach, but as he rode through the rainy countryside, he caught a chill. After several days he became too ill to preach and knew that he too was about to enter the Celestial City.

"I'll be glad to go," he told his friends gathered at his bedside. "My affairs on earth are in order, and I shall be with my Lord."

Thus, like the Christian he wrote of, John Bunyan entered the gate to hear the Shining Ones say, "Enter thou into the joy of thy Lord."

Literature Lesson:
Biography

John Bunyan had a great ability to understand the sorrows and joys of other people. He understood the Christian's fight against the world to know God. His understanding enabled him to write a book that Christians would read through four hundred years of change. Even though our world today is much different from Bunyan's world, we can still see ourselves in *"The Pilgrim's Progress."*

Bunyan's ability to understand people was a gift from God. Today we have an opportunity that he didn't have to understand other people. Biographies can help us understand exactly how people in the past encountered some of the same problems and enjoyed some of the same pleasures that we enjoy today.

A biography is the story of a real person's life. Most biographies are written about people who lived in the past. Authors write about people whose fame or accomplishments will attract readers.

Enjoying Biographies

If you've ever wondered what it was like to be the first president of the United States, then perhaps you've read a biography of George Washington. Or if you've wondered how the man who ended slavery felt, then you may have decided to read about Abraham Lincoln. People read biographies out of curiosity. They also read them to understand a certain time in history or the meaning behind one person's accomplishments.

Consider John Bunyan. It may have been interesting to read selections from *The Pilgrim's Progress,* but the book becomes more important when you realize that he wrote it from prison, trying to comfort the members of his church who themselves were in danger of going to prison. We know that Bunyan was suffering for his beliefs. This knowledge helps us to see that his book was a statement of his enduring faith. We also can understand how he used his own long periods of doubt and despair to write the episode about Doubting Castle. When we see how Bunyan overcame his struggles, we can know the meaning of his book better. This is one way that his biography helps us.

Biography helps us to understand history better. It may seem dull to learn that Cromwell died in 1658 and that Charles II replaced him and took away religious liberty. But it isn't dull to read that armed soldiers of the king broke into a small church and that they took John Bunyan to jail for his religious beliefs.

The Range of Biographies

A biography should be based on fact. Some biographies are completely factual. They are made up of quotations from diaries and other documents, along with the author's comments and explanations. Other biographies, such as the biography of John Bunyan in this book, are written in story form. The author researched a person's life, found out as many exact details as possible, and then made it easier to understand by writing it as a story. The difference between these two types of biography can be compared to the difference between a photograph and a portrait. The first captures the exact details of a person, and the second tries to bring out the personality and character of the person to make others interested in him.

But biography, whether in report form or story form, should always be true to facts. Authors of biographies have to know their facts. They have to be willing to admit that the people they write about had faults as well as virtues. It would not be honest for the author of the biographical story on John Bunyan to have the reader think that Bunyan never felt depressed while imprisoned. The author let us know that Bunyan was often in despair while in prison. Bunyan sometimes wondered if God had deserted him. Despair and doubt were the greatest problems in Bunyan's life. If the author had never told us about these problems, Bunyan would have seemed too perfect and too different from his readers. Readers have to know they have something in common with the people they read about.

Not every biography you might read will be about a Christian. And not every biography will have a Christian author. Some authors might think that the actions of one person are good, even though you know that the same actions are contrary to Scripture. It's important to remember, especially while reading biography, that some authors may use facts to serve their own purposes. The reader has to think about what he is reading and decide whether all the facts are being presented fairly in a biography. Using good judgment is part of a reader's job.

The
STAKEOUT

Milly Howard

Jonathan Conley was as normal as any other ten-year-old boy. In all respects, that is, except one. His mother insisted that he was born with more than his share of imagination. At the age of three, he carried an imaginary alligator everywhere he went. When an amused adult asked if the "alligator" might run away, Jonathan had considered the question, then answered gravely, "He's on a leash."

The alligator gave way to "Davey," an imaginary friend. "Davey" remained for a long time. By the time Jonathan was six, Mrs. Conley began to worry about both Jonathan and "Davey." But when Jonathan started to school, "Davey" went along and didn't return. According to Jonathan, "Davey" had decided to live in the school library.

It was only the combined efforts of Mr. and Mrs. Conley

that prevented Jonathan from packing his sleeping bag and joining "Davey." As it was, Jonathan spent most of his spare time reading. He read everything—funny stories, historical stories, stories about animals, people, and faraway lands. Not content just to *read* stories, Jonathan responded to them in various ways. When he read about Daniel Boone, he memorized the tracks of every animal around the small town of Sweetbriar. After he encountered an annoyed skunk, his mother confined his activities to the neighborhood. When Jonathan read about medieval times, the teacher called to complain about the organized jousts at recess. When he read about space flight, he constructed a rocket that was the envy of every child in Sweetbriar. However, he made the mistake of asking his friends to offer a pet to occupy the nose cone. Two days before the rocket was scheduled to be launched, every pet within two blocks of the Conley house disappeared behind locked doors. Jonathan had to be content with an unsuspecting cricket as his passenger.

Through careful supervision, most of Jonathan's activities ended without mishap. Then on his eleventh birthday one of his aunts sent him a popular detective novel. When he finished the book, Jonathan hurried to the library to check out more. After the fourteenth detective story, Jonathan no longer ran cheerfully in and out of the house. Instead, he slunk. Eyes scanning quickly from left to right, he turned up his collar, adjusted his dark glasses, and dashed from tree to bush to door before slinking inside.

"I tell you," Mrs. Conley told her husband, "this is too much. He thinks he is a detective! He's even got his friends doing the same thing."

"Better a detective than a crook." Mr. Conley chuckled, pleased with his joke. He picked up the newspaper, adding, "Let him pretend a little. Remember, you're a child only once."

"All right," Jonathan's mother said. Smiling, she went back into the kitchen to put the dishes away. More than once she had suspected that Jonathan had inherited his imagination and adventurous spirit from his father.

The newspaper rustled as Mr. Conley unfolded it. He read the first page, then turned the page. On page two he stopped, his attention caught by a headline. "Hmmmm," he said thoughtfully. Standing, he went to the kitchen door. "Better make sure the doors are locked tonight," he told his wife. "Iona Appleman told reporters that she saw a burglar in this area the other night. Probably nonsense, of course.

The last person Sheriff Hadley had to arrest in Sweetbriar was charged with jaywalking. Has Jonathan come in yet?"

"He's upstairs in his room," Mrs. Conley replied nervously. "A burglar, you say!"

"The article's on page two," Mr. Conley said, handing her the newspaper. "I'll go check on Jonathan."

A few minutes later he came downstairs. "He's asleep, lying across his bed," he told his wife in a puzzled voice. "I tucked him in, but—Jonathan, asleep at six o'clock?"

"He's been tired lately," Mrs. Conley replied in a worried voice. "I'll make an appointment to take

him to the doctor. He may be getting sick."

"Might be a good idea," Mr. Conley agreed. "He should have more energy than he has shown the last few days; that's for sure. Boys should be up and raring to go during summer vacations."

Late that night after the house was still and dark, a sound came from Jonathan's room. Sleepily, Jonathan reached out a hand and stopped the vibrating clock. He slowly crawled out of bed and dressed. Then, yawning, he opened the door to the hall. His sneakered feet made no sound as he tiptoed down the carpeted stairs. He found the key ring on the memo rack next to the refrigerator. After the door was unlocked, it swung silently on its hinges. Jonathan closed it gently and stood looking at the moonlit street. A light breeze lifted the leaves of the hibiscus bush beside the door, causing deep shadows on the lawn to shift. Jonathan frowned. "Too much light," he thought, "but it can't be helped. We'll just have to stay in the shadows."

Choosing his way carefully, he edged over to the house behind his own. He crept around the wide front porch, using the honey-suckle bushes as cover, and reached the back of the house. Corey's bedroom was on the bottom floor. Jonathan scratched lightly on the window screen, then stopped to listen. The only sound was the scraping of crickets in the bushes behind him. He tried again, a little louder this time.

A hand reached out of the darkness and touched him on the shoulder. Jonathan whirled, choking back a scream. The moonlight glinted off Corey's braces as he beamed.

"I decided to wait outside. I'm getting better at being quiet. You never even heard me," he whispered triumphantly.

"You nearly scared the life out of me," Jonathan hissed. "Give me a warning next time!"

Corey's smile disappeared. "Okay," he said, crestfallen.

Jonathan took a deep breath. "Yes, you're much better. I doubt if even Danny can walk quieter than you can. Now, come on."

Corey's braces glinted again. He followed Jonathan soundlessly down the street to Danny's house. Getting Danny out of the house was going to be much harder. His bedroom was upstairs, and Danny was a sound sleeper. Without much hope, they tried bouncing pebbles off his window.

There was no response. Jonathan sighed. "I'll have to climb up again," he whispered to Corey. "You stay here."

He put one foot on the rose trellis and began to climb. Corey waited, listening. A cloud drifted across the moon, darkening the night. Far away a dog howled. The only other sounds were the slight scraping of the trellis as it swayed under Jonathan's weight and the muffled exclamations Jonathan made when he caught hold of a thorn. Just before Jonathan reached the window, the screen slid open. A leg swung over the sill, and Danny's head and shoulders appeared in the opening. Feeling blindly for the first rung, he stepped down.

One of Jonathan's muffled exclamations turned into an agonized shriek. "Get off my hand!"

For a moment Danny froze. Then the trellis swayed as he scrambled back over the sill. The window slammed shut.

The cloud sailed off the face of the moon, and once again the lawn was flooded with light. Corey caught a glimpse of Danny's white face at the window just before Jonathan's flailing body crashed down the trellis and slammed into him. A light went on two windows away from Danny's.

Jonathan rolled off Corey as the window went up, and Mr. Allen's head appeared. The boys scrambled awkwardly on their hands and knees into the shadow of an oak tree. They huddled, motionless, as Mr. Allen inspected the yard. After a moment he withdrew his head, muttering, "Nothing out there, Grace. Nothing at all. You're hearing things again."

The window closed, shutting off Mrs. Allen's indignant reply.

"You okay, Corey?" Jonathan asked quietly.

"Uh," Corey wheezed, still bent over. Jonathan looked at him uncertainly and moved back into the moonlight. He made an impatient gesture toward Danny's window. It opened cautiously. Danny whispered softly, "That you, Jon?"

"Yes!" Jonathan whispered back fiercely.

He turned up his collar, then stuffed his hands in his pockets as he watched Danny climb down. By the time Danny reached the ground, Jonathan was back in control. "Okay, Crimebusters, let's go," he said quietly. "We've got a job to do."

The three boys made their way down Larkspur Lane, keeping under the shadow of the trees. Near the corner they cut across the Dalrimples' lot, running through the crab apple orchard. They turned into the alley and again crept carefully along, staying in the shadow of the board fence that edged Mrs. Appleman's yard. Nearly ninety, she had trouble sleeping and often sat on her back porch, rocking and talking to her big, battle-scarred cat, Aristotle.

One night last week the cat had been scavenging in the trash cans on the alley side of the fence. Corey had brushed against the cans, knocking one of them over. It was the can Aristotle was dining in. The trash can rolled down the alley, sending Aristotle rattling end over end. To make matters worse, in his efforts to stop the can, Corey had stepped on Aristotle's tail as he emerged, shaken, from the can. The offended cat had let out a horrible screech, bringing an excited Mr. Appleman hobbling to the fence. The boys ran. From that night on Aristotle had disliked the boys. Even in broad daylight he spat at them. At night they used the alley with extreme caution. Tonight, exercising every skulking skill

they had learned from Jonathan's books, the boys passed through without incident.

Crossing Abbey Street, they skirted the old church and took the shortcut through the cemetery. Savoring the tingles that ran down their spines at the night noises, they opened the creaky back gate and crossed a wide expanse of lawn to their destination—the huge live oak that bordered both the cemetery and yard of old Judge Trevor's boarding house.

At the trunk of the big tree, Jonathan signaled the other two to wait. Thrusting his arm deep into a hole in the trunk, he pulled out a canvas-wrapped parcel. Holding it carefully, he began to climb, followed by Danny and Corey. At his appointed place, Jonathan settled himself and unwrapped the parcel. He took out a battered notebook, a pencil stub, and a penlight. Using the faint glow from the penlight, he licked the end of the pencil and carefully entered the date and time into the notebook. The stakeout had begun.

Even Jonathan didn't know exactly why he had chosen this particular spot for his first stakeout. It probably had something to do with the heart-thumping

nearness of the cemetery, the marvelous twisted old live oak, or even the mysterious old moon-silvered boarding house behind them. In any case, Jonathan had been just as surprised as the other two boys when the first furtive meeting took place under the live oak.

From that meeting they had heard enough to guess that Judge Trevor was involved in a real estate swindle. The Judge's family had lived in Sweetbriar since the early 1800s. Until the last few decades, the family had been the wealthiest in town. The stock-market crash of the 1920s had stripped the Judge of his fortune, forcing him to rely on his own income. But that hadn't been enough to cover the cost of operating a huge house. In order to save the family mansion, the Judge had opened it to the public as a boarding house. Perhaps in another town he might have made ends meet. But Sweetbriar was a small town, surrounded by other small towns. Even in the booming growth of the fifties, Sweetbriar slept on, content with the quiet and peace of tree-shaded streets and old neighborhoods. The Judge never recovered his fortune, and the Trevor mansion remained a boarding house, graying slightly with the years.

Two beams of light swept around the corner. Jonathan tensed and signaled the boys. They watched silently as a long car eased down the street and parked next to a huge bank of shaggy shrubs.

Jonathan sighed with satisfaction. Switching on his penlight, he opened the battered notebook and wrote: "11:15—Suspects approach meeting place." Two men got out of the car. One was tall, well-dressed, and carried a briefcase. The other, broad-shouldered and dark, wore the clothing of a construction worker. They looked around, then disappeared into the shrubbery as they made their way toward the live oak.

Jonathan made the next entry, recording the make and model of the car. Just as he closed his notebook, a wavering wail echoed through the graveyard. Corey slammed back against the tree trunk, breathing heavily. Jonathan felt the hair rise on the back of his neck.

"What's that?" Danny asked hoarsely.

Jonathan swallowed, peering into the shadows along the fence. A big cat leaped onto the back gate and howled again before it jumped down and stalked into the Judge's yard. "Just a cat on the prowl," Jonathan said shakily. He watched uneasily as the cat eyed the tree.

"Uh-oh," he whispered. "It's Aristotle!"

The cat sauntered around the tree trunk, sniffing. Then he sat down and looked up, making threatening noises in his throat.

"Go away!" Jonathan hissed.

Aristotle tensed, then sprang to the first low-hanging branch. A few more lithe leaps brought him to the level of the boys.

"Get him away from me!" Corey said loudly.

"Hush!"

"He hates me," Corey said hopelessly as Aristotle stalked him, tail swishing.

"Don't be silly," Jonathan said, watching the cat uneasily. "Besides, what can a cat do?"

Corey, back against the tree trunk, had nowhere to go. Aristotle sensed his helplessness and waited, eyes gleaming.

A twig snapped on the slope; then two figures ducked under the low-hanging branch and stopped in the shadows of the tree. A shaft of moonlight filtered through the leaves, gleaming on the metal edge of a briefcase. The case scraped as the man slid it onto the branch. Then the boys heard two more snaps, metallic this time.

"I don't see why we have to go through all this hanky-panky, Caruthers," the younger man muttered. "Why can't we just take the papers to the old man at his house?"

"I told you before, Joe," his companion said patiently. "The Judge wants to protect his family's name. If we met at the boarding house—or anywhere else in Sweetbriar—the whole town would know about it in less than an hour."

"It's about time this two-horse town woke up anyway," Joe growled. "Just wait until I get my 'dozers rolling! That'll wake them up. How long does the old coot think he can keep this quiet?"

"If you keep your mouth shut, no one will suspect," Mr. Caruthers snapped. "He's worked up the papers to transfer the land to a dairy company. The town council approved the sale—met with the associates of the dairy, went over the site, and found everything in order. Why would anyone suspect that the 'dairy company' is a branch of JPM Development? And if they did, who would know that we intend to put a subdivision on the land?"

"No one but the Judge," the younger man chuckled unpleasantly. "He's making a pretty profit on the deal—five hundred thousand, at least!"

Wide-eyed, Corey and Danny listened as Jonathan scribbled hastily in his notebook. On a branch high above them, Aristotle stretched and decided to make his move. Tail switching, eyes gleaming, he stalked menacingly toward Corey. Corey panicked and stood up, reaching for a higher branch. The branch shook.

"What's that?" hissed the younger man, reaching into the pocket of his jacket.

Jonathan moved quickly. A sideways thrust of his sneaker dislodged Aristotle. The branch trembled, shook again; then twenty pounds of squalling cat

tumbled down at the men's feet. Aristotle crouched, flattened to the ground, then howling in outrage, took off through the graveyard.

"Just a cat, Joe," the tall man said disgustedly. "You're getting jumpy."

"Who wouldn't be? Meeting on the edge of a graveyard! The sooner this deal is over, the better it'll be," the younger man snapped. "One leak, and it could blow up in our faces. I don't want to waste ten years rotting in jail!"

"It's hardly likely since we close the deal tomorrow night at ten," the other responded. "Just take it easy, Joe. Here, stash this folder in the mailbox and let's go." A faint rustle mystified Jonathan. He cautiously peered down through the foliage, but could see nothing in the shadow cast by the tree. In a few minutes the two men emerged from the shadow and started back up the moonlit slope. Their voices faded, but Jonathan caught the last words " . . . who would suspect the Judge, anyway?"

"They're right," Danny whispered. "No one would believe a story as wild as ours without proof—good, solid proof."

"Didn't you hear what the man said?" Jonathan barely suppressed the excitement in his voice. "They stashed something in the mailbox!"

"There's no mailbox here," Corey said, puzzled.

"There's the one we use," Jonathan replied triumphantly.

"The hole!"

Quickly the boys climbed down. Jonathan tucked his notebook into his shirt pocket. "Here goes," he said eagerly, putting his hand inside the hole in the tree trunk.

"Find anything?" Danny asked, trying to look over his shoulder.

"Ahh!"

"What is it?" Corey squeaked.

Jonathan drew his hand out, holding a rolled folder. Corey and Danny crowded close. Jonathan opened the folder and shined his light on the papers. "Look," Jonathan sighed in satisfaction. "Here's our proof!"

"Proof of what?" Corey asked, standing on tiptoe.

"It's a legal paper about the sale of the land," Jonathan replied, flipping through the papers. "It is a development company—and here's where the Judge is supposed to—!"

A scraping sound interrupted their whispered conversation. The scraping sound separated into

taps and footsteps. "It's the Judge!" Jonathan exclaimed. "Up the tree!"

Jonathan thrust the folder back into the hole as the other boys scrambled back up the tree. He was only a few feet behind them when he lost his grip on a branch. He fell spread-eagle across a smaller limb. The limb jerked under the thrust of his weight and slowly began to bob up and down. Peering down, the other two boys saw the slight, thin figure of the Judge emerging from the overgrown shrubbery that separated the boarding house from the fence. Tapping his way across the dark, rough ground with his cane, he reached the shadows of the tree and stopped, looking at the street.

512

The limb bobbed slowly up and down just a few feet above the Judge's wispy white head. Jonathan held his breath. Below him the Judge sighed gustily and turned back to the tree trunk. Thrusting his hand into the hole, he took out the folder. Then the cane tapped again as he moved slowly back toward the boarding house. Jonathan released his death grip on the branch and sat up gingerly.

"You almost got caught!" Danny hissed.

Jonathan answered defensively, "Well, I didn't!" He looked down wistfully. "But there went our proof."

"Proof of what?" Corey asked, exasperated.

"You remember that piece of land outside the town?" Jonathan replied. "There was an article in the newspaper the other day, and I heard my folks talking about it. The Judge negotiated a deal with an out-of-town company. The town sold the land for twenty-five thousand."

"Wow," Danny said.

"Wow, nothing," Jonathan went on. "That paper is a contract giving the Judge five hundred twenty-five thousand for the same land! And from a developing company!"

"Something fishy is going on for sure," Danny muttered. "The town gets twenty-five, he gets five hundred thousand!"

"Who would pay that much for farming land?"

"A development company, that's who," Jonathan said grimly. "The town council wouldn't sell to a developer, so they used the Judge as a go-between. He told them they were selling to a *dairy* company. They were supposed to build a dairy on that land."

"Let's go find the sheriff," Corey said, sliding down to the next branch beside Jonathan. Danny followed, but Jonathan didn't answer. The boys dropped lightly to the ground. Deep in thought, Jonathan almost put his notebook and pencil back into the hole.

"Hey, what if—" Corey began. Jonathan took the notebook and pencil out again and stuffed them into his pocket.

"Come on," he said as he moved quietly to the back gate. It creaked slightly as Corey held it open for the others to ease through. Then they hurried through the graveyard and out to the street.

Jonathan started across Abbey Street. "Aren't we going to the sheriff?" Danny asked.

"Not yet," Jonathan replied thoughtfully. "We still don't have any proof. Maybe," Jonathan's voice took on a dreamy note, "just maybe we can catch them ourselves."

"Uh-uh!"

"Count me out."

Jonathan looked at his friends' determined faces and said rather crossly, "Oh, all right. But let's get one good picture of the three together before we go to the sheriff. Otherwise we may never prove they were in it together."

"How?" Danny asked as they reached the alley behind Mrs. Appleman's house.

"We could get a shot from the tree. They usually stop on the slope when all three of them are talking—and I have a feeling that tomorrow night will be their congratulation night," Jonathan said, eyes gleaming with excitement. "You know, I could borrow my cousin's camera! He works on the newspaper. His flash would be strong enough to work!" He stopped suddenly and looked uncertainly down the dark alley. "Wonder where Aristotle is?" he said, lowering his voice.

"Who knows, but I'm not going down that alley tonight," Danny replied. "That dumb cat thinks he's a dog."

"Yeah, let's go the long way around," Corey suggested nervously.

As a result of the detour, they were a little later getting home than usual. At the first house they parted with only a tired wave.

The next night when they met outside Danny's house, Jonathan was carefully holding a large, professional-looking camera. "I got it," Jonathan crowed quietly. "It's a beauty!"

The boys inspected the equipment with awe. "A *real* camera!"

"OK, hands off," Jonathan warned. "I promised to protect it with my life. Now listen." Quickly he outlined his plan. They were to proceed on to the stakeout. Jonathan and Danny would climb up the tree. Corey would hide behind the fence. When the men arrived, Corey was to go to the phone booth at the corner of Abbey and Church and phone the sheriff. When the men were safely away from the tree, Jonathan would take the picture. The plan was timed to the last second: the run to the phone booth, the time it would take for the sheriff to get from his office to the scene, and even the time required to shinny down the tree to escape.

Fifteen minutes later three dark figures drifted across town toward the cemetery. At the alley behind Mrs. Appleman's house, another dark shadow joined them. Unnoticed, it followed about a half block behind them, tail switching silently.

By nine-thirty the boys were in the live oak, waiting impatiently. Below them, Corey huddled behind the fence. In the shadow of a gravestone, Aristotle crouched, eyes fixed on Corey. Around ten the long car slid smoothly to the curb. The men got out and headed through the bushes toward the tree. "Now, Corey," Jonathan raised his voice slightly, pushing aside the leaves.

Corey stood up and gave him a quick salute. Then he started across the cemetery, darting from gravestone to gravestone. A low growl murmuring in his throat, Aristotle followed. Halfway through the cemetery, Corey glanced uneasily over his shoulder and saw Aristotle. With a frightened yell, he broke into a run. A light went on in the parsonage as Corey charged past, stumbling against a rack of pots. Aristotle leaped over the wreckage in full pursuit. Corey made it to the telephone booth in less than half the allotted time. He slammed the door and leaned against the wall of the booth, panting.

Aristotle circled the booth a few times, then stalked away. Deprived of his prey, he headed back to the stakeout.

"That's the meanest cat I've ever seen," Corey muttered. With shaking fingers, he dialed the sheriff's office. The first and second times, he got a busy signal. Finally he got through, but the sheriff was out on patrol. Corey left a message with the dispatcher and crouched in the booth, waiting. Nothing could have coaxed him back across the cemetery!

Back at the tree, Jonathan and Danny waited tensely. Another shadow detached itself from the

shrubbery and met the two men. All three stopped on the moonlit slope. "Told you!" Jonathan whispered. "Okay, get ready!" Danny climbed down and stood ready to catch the camera. At precisely 10:15, Jonathan edged forward on the limb. Looking through the camera's view finder, he saw the tall man hand the Judge an envelope. The Judge reached inside his coat. Jonathan pushed the button gently.

The night exploded with light. Startled, Jonathan lost his balance and slid down the limb. His foot caught in a fork of the limb. He dangled just above the ground, trying desperately to hold on to both limb and camera.

Danny snatched the camera. "Come on," he shouted as the men turned toward the tree. "Get down!"

"I can't," Jonathan moaned. "My foot's caught!"

Danny gave him an agonized look. Dropping the camera, he yanked Jonathan's foot. Jonathan, hanging upside down, had a full view of the older men's startled faces and of the irate construction worker as he charged down the slope toward the tree.

Just then Aristotle's battle cry split the air. Half dazed and angered by the flash of light, he

launched himself toward the source of his irritation. Unfortunately for Joe, he ran into Aristotle's line of flight.

Even Jonathan winced as the cat landed flat on the man's back. Howling with pain, the man ran back in the direction of his stunned companions. Aristotle rode on his back, growling.

At that moment the sheriff's car drove up. The sheriff and his deputy got out and stood staring in amazement. When the tall man made a break for his car, they collared him easily and herded him back with the Judge.

As the deputy tried to separate the construction worker and Aristotle, the sheriff sauntered over to look curiously at Jonathan. He glanced at Danny's white face and picked up the camera. "This yours, Jonathan?" he asked the dangling boy.

Jonathan nodded, more than a little embarrassed. The sheriff looked at him thoughtfully. "You want to explain before or after we take you down?"

"After," Jonathan said weakly.

An hour later the three men were booked and locked in jail. The sheriff turned his attention to the three boys and the three irate sets of parents who had been brought in to collect their sons. Even a full explanation by Jonathan had not cleared the air. He thought matters couldn't get

any worse until Iona Appleman showed up to collect her cat and his cousin came to collect his camera.

"Sneaking out of the house . . ."

"On a stakeout!"

"My poor tabby."

"You could've been hurt—"

"But we caught—"

"Just you wait until we get home. . . ."

"Jonathan!"

Punctuated by flashes of light from the camera, the noise threatened to overwhelm the boys. "Quiet!" the sheriff boomed. "The men have been booked and charged with fraud. They'll get a trial, then serve their sentences."

The sheriff stopped to look at the crestfallen boys. "Without the boys, all the men would have been long gone before anyone was the wiser. The town owes you its thanks. But don't get excited," he went on as the boys' faces brightened. "You broke a lot of rules, too—your parents' rules. Gallivanting around town like that—interfering with police business—you could have been badly hurt. You, there," he frowned at Jonathan, "if it weren't for Mrs. Appleman's cat, you'd really have been in trouble. Not that he meant to help you out. From now on, if I were you, I'd stay out of that cat's way. Now, maybe your parents would like to take care of your sentences."

After some discussion the parents agreed that the sentence should fit the crime. For the remaining two weeks of summer vacation, the boys were sentenced to work around the house and to be in bed by eight. Not one boy complained. After tonight's disaster all three had decided that detective work was definitely not for them.

As the boys were ushered out, the sheriff said wearily, "Mrs. Conley?"

"Yes sir?"

"Between now and the time school starts, will you *please* keep Jonathan out of the library?"

The next day the boys read about themselves in the paper. Jonathan's cousin got the scoop in both the *Elmstown Gazette* and the *Cross County News.* "Kids Capture Crooks" made a banner headline. Although pleased at the attention he received from the neighborhood kids, Jonathan had dissolved the Crimebusters. Instead, he had taken to wearing a green shade over his brow and had sharpened every pencil in the house. He wanted to run a newspaper.

Mr. and Mrs. Conley were pleased at Jonathan's attentiveness, for he listened carefully to their conversations and those of their friends. "How polite," their visitors murmured. "Jonathan is really a joy to talk to. He's a good listener."

And in his mind, Jonathan had already begun the layout for the newspaper. "*The Sweetbriar Scoop,*" he murmured dreamily, "Jonathan Conley, editor. Has a nice ring to it."

OTHER DAYS

Rufus and the Fatal Four

Eleanor Estes

The following story comes from Rufus M., *a book from the Moffat series, about a family of four children who grew up in the early 1900s. Although they were poor, their family was happy, held together by their own strong sense of family unity. The Moffat children did everything they could to entertain themselves, and the stories of their adventures have entertained readers for forty years. In this story, ten-year-old Janey Moffat and her younger brother Rufus, who is left-handed, take up baseball.*

For some time Rufus had been seeing "The F.F." on all of Janey's notebooks and on the brown covers of her grammar and arithmetic books. He asked Jane what it meant. Jane said it was a secret. However, if Rufus would not tell anybody, the initials stood for the Fatal Four. More than that she would not say. Rufus assumed it had something to do with pirates. Therefore he was really surprised when Jane, in a mood of confidence, further enlightened him to the extent of revealing that the Fatal Four was the name of a baseball team she belonged to that could beat anybody.

"Then," she went on to explain, "if the Fatal Four gets tired of baseball, oh, not gets tired 'cause they'll never do that, but if it should snow, and they couldn't play any more, they'll still be the Fatal Four because it's a good name the members can keep always. Baseball . . . football . . . no matter what. Or it could just be a club to eat cookies and drink punch made out of jelly and water."

This all sounded good to Rufus, particularly the punch. He asked if he could join. Did it cost anything? Jane said she was sorry but the Fatal Four was all girls. However, she would try to bring him a cookie if they ever decided on punch and cookies instead of baseball. So for a time Rufus was not allowed to have anything to do with this team. But sometimes he went across the street to the big empty lot behind the library, sat down on a log, and watched them practice. There were a half-dozen or so silvery gray old telephone poles piled up in one part of the lot. Bleachers, Rufus called them, and that was where he sat to watch the Fatal Four.

Jane and Nancy had organized the Fatal Four baseball team. At first Jane was worried that they were playing baseball in October

when the time for baseball is spring. She thought it would be better if the Fatal Four started right in with punch and cookies on Tuesdays. But once they had begun playing baseball she wondered how she could ever have been so foolish. She loved baseball and could not understand how anybody was happy who did not play it every day.

Naturally, since Jane and Nancy had thought up this whole team, there was no reason why they should not take the two most important roles, the pitcher and the catcher, for themselves. Jane was the catcher. She accepted this position because she thought the name alone would automatically make her a good one. "Yes," she said, "I'll be catcher." And she put her trust in the power of the title and the mitt to enable her to catch anything. Nancy was the pitcher. For a time they were the only members of the team, so they had to be the pitcher and the catcher, for in baseball that is the very least you can get along with. Soon, however, other girls in the neighborhood joined up.

"I'll be the captain," said Nancy. "Let's take a vote."

They took a vote and elected Nancy. Clara Pringle was the outfield to catch all flies. She never really had very much to do because there weren't many flies hit and she sat in the long grass and waited for business. A girl named Hattie Wood was first base. That made four girls they had on the team and that was when they decided to call themselves the Fatal Four.

So far Rufus had had nothing to do with this team except to sit and watch. He did this gladly however, for he considered that anything that called itself the Fatal Four was worthy of being watched, especially if there was that vague possibility of pink punch and cookies in the offing. He used to sit there pounding his fist into one of Joey's old mitts, hoping they'd take him into the Four.

At first the Fatal Four baseball team practiced ardently every day. However, after a week or so Jane grew tired of chasing balls, since she rarely caught one. The mitt and the title of catcher had not produced the desired results.

"A back-stop is what we need," she told Nancy.

None of the girls was willing to be a back-stop. Moreover, they were all needed where they were. Take Hattie Wood off first base and what kind of a team would they have, they asked themselves. An amateur team. The Fatal Four

was anything but that, Nancy assured them. "But if you want a back-stop, why not ask Rufus?" she suggested.

Now there was much arguing back and forth as to whether or not they should invite Rufus to be the back-stop. He was not a girl and this team was supposed to be composed of girls only. But then everybody thought how nice it would be to have Rufus chasing balls for them, so they enthusiastically assented.

"After all," said Jane, "a back-stop is not really part of the team. It's part of the grounds."

So that clinched it and that was how Rufus came to be back-stop for the Fatal Four baseball team. Rufus was happy over the arrangement. When they abandoned baseball for punch and cookies, he might be an accepted member. Moreover, the more practice he had, the sooner the big boys would take him into their team, he thought. Certainly if the pitcher of the boys' baseball team had the same tendencies as Nancy, left-handed Rufus would be a tremendous asset.

Nancy used to be a rather good pitcher. But ever since the girls' baseball team had been organized, Nancy had taken to practicing curves. Somehow these curves always shot the ball way to the left of the batter. The batter would move farther and farther to the left, hoping to catch up with Nancy's curves. But it was no use. No matter how far to the left the batter edged, the farther to the left flew Nancy's balls. Often the bases had to be moved several times during the game to catch up with the home plate. Frequently, by the end of the game, home plate was where the pitcher's box orginally had been, and vice versa. Nancy realized there was a flaw in her pitching which she would have to correct.

Meanwhile, it certainly was lucky the team now had a left-handed back-stop, for Jane had a hard enough time catching just straight pitches, let alone these curves of Nancy's that veered off to the left all the time. But Rufus had only to reach out his left arm farther and farther, and he caught most of them. What he didn't catch he cheerfully ran for, over Mr. Buckle's hen coop or in Mrs. Wood's asparagus patch that had gone to seed, or he hunted between the long silvery logs that lay lined up in a corner of the field.

As a reward for his back-stop duties Nancy pitched Rufus some curves, and since he was a left-handed batter, her balls that veered to the left were just perfect for him and it was only when Rufus was at the bat that Clara Pringle, picking goldenrod in the outfield, had anything to do in the game.

This convinced Nancy that there was nothing wrong with her pitching after all. The trouble lay with the material she was working with. "Slug at 'em, fellas," she said, "Rufe hits 'em all." And the girls, feeling rather ashamed, now tried harder, sometimes even turning around and batting left-handed as Rufus did, hoping to hit Nancy's balls.

One Saturday morning Rufus was sitting in the driver's seat of the old abandoned sleigh that was in the Moffats' barn. He was thinking that if he had a pony next winter he could harness it to this old sleigh and go for a ride. Suddenly Nancy and Janey burst around from the front yard. Nancy was swinging her bat. She had her pitcher's mitt on. Jane was pounding the baseball into Joey's big catcher's mitt, limbering it up.

"Come on, Rufe," they yelled. "This is *the* day!"

"What! Punch and cookies?" exclaimed Rufus.

"No, we're having a real game today. Not just practice," they said.

For a long time Jane and Nancy had thought they were the only girls' baseball team in Cranbury, in the world in fact. Then one day a girl accosted them after school. She said her name was Joyce Allen and that she was the captain of the Busy Bee baseball team, a team composed entirely of girls on the other side of town. She wanted to know whether or not Nancy, the captain of the F.F. team, would accept a challenge from her, the captain of the Busy Bee team, to play next Saturday. Nancy consulted with Jane and said "Yes."

So now today was the day. Rufus climbed off the sleigh, found his old pitcher's mitt that he used to catch Nancy's curves, and they all marched across the street to the big lot behind the library where the game was going to be held. While they waited for the teams to show up, Rufus spit in his mitt, rubbed sand in it, and got it into condition to play.

"I hope we don't have to go all over town and round everybody up," said Jane impatiently.

The Fatal Four had added another team member, Nancy's sister Beatrice, but they still called themselves the Fatal Four because it sounded better than fatal anything else. Since this team had such an excellent name, the F.F., it had plenty of applicants to join. Nancy and Jane were particular, however, saying to join the F.F. you really had to know something about baseball. Most applicants backed away apologetically when Nancy stated this firmly.

At last here came somebody across the lot. It was Joyce Allen, the captain of the Busy Bees.

"The others will be here soon," she said cheerfully. "Some of them hadn't finished washing the breakfast dishes, but they'll be here soon."

"While we're waitin'," said Jane, "since both the captains are here, we can see who's up at the bat first."

Rufus took the bat, threw it, and Nancy caught it. She put her right fist around the end of it, then the other captain put her fist above Nancy's and swiftly placing one fist above the other they measured the length of the bat. The visiting captain's left fist was the last one to fit the bat. It was a tight squeeze but fair, and Rufus said that the visiting team was first up at the bat. Rufus sometimes had to act in the capacity of umpire as well as back-stop.

But where was the visiting team? Or Nancy's, for that matter?

Rufus began to feel impatient.

Here were the captains. All right. Let the teams come then. "Why not have the punch instead?" he asked. But nobody paid any attention to him. It seemed to Rufus as though the game were off, and he decided, Fatal Four or no, to go and find something else to do. Over in a corner of the field some men had started to dig a cellar to a new house. This activity looked interesting to Rufus and he was about to investigate it when along came two girls, arms linked together. So Rufus stayed. There was always the possibility that the Fatal Four might switch from baseball to punch and cookies. Either was worth staying for in Rufus's opinion.

"These girls must be Busy Bees," said Nancy.

They *were* Busy Bees. They both admitted it. However, they said they wished they could join the F.F. instead. They liked the name of it. They had heard many rumors as to what it stood for. Most people thought it stood for Funny Fellows. Did it?

"Of course not!" said Nancy, and Jane clapped her hand over Rufus's mouth before he could say the Fatal Four and give away the secret. No matter what it stood for, the girls wanted to join it and

be able to write the F.F. on all their red notebooks.

While the discussion was going on three more girls arrived, three more Busy Bees. It seemed they too wanted to join the F.F., so they could write the F.F. on their notebooks also. Nancy and Jane looked at the captain. She must feel very badly at this desertion. But she didn't. She said she wished she could join the F.F. too.

"Oh, no," said Nancy. "You all better stay Busy Bees. What team would there be for us to beat if we let you join ours?"

So that settled the matter and Busy Bees remained Busy Bees. Now they lined up at the home plate for they were to be the first at the bat. At last the game began. "Thank goodness, Rufus is here behind me," thought Jane, pounding her fist into the big catcher's mitt. For it really took two Moffats to make one good catcher. If one of them was she, that is.

Nancy's team did not get off to a good start. Nancy had been practicing her curves more than ever, and they swung more and more sharply to the left. If they had not had such a good left-handed back-stop as Rufus, goodness knows where the balls would have landed. In order that they would not crash through a window of the library, the girls rearranged the bases many times.

Of course there was no danger of the balls crashing through the library windows from hits. The danger lay in Nancy's curves. So far she had not been able to strike the Busy Bees out. They were all walking to base on balls. And the balls were flying wild now. Rufus had dashed across the lot to take a look at the men who were digging the cellar to the new house and he was sorely missed. Jane, who had had enough trouble catching in the old days before Nancy cultivated her curves, was becoming desperate.

Right now happened to be a very tense moment. The captain of the Busy Bees was at the bat. There were men on all bases. They'd gotten there on walks. The captain had two strikes against her, however. She had been striking at anything, for she evidently had grown tired of just walking to base. If Nancy could strike her out, it would break the charm and maybe the Fatal Four team would have a chance at the bat. So far the Bees had been at the bat the entire game. The score must be big. They had lost track of it.

Beside wanting to strike Captain Allen out, Nancy was trying especially hard to impress her. She came over to Jane and said in a low voice, "They'll think they have a better team than we have, and I bet that pitcher can't even throw curves! I've just got to strike her out!"

"Yes," agreed Jane, who was anxious to bat herself for a change.

"Watch for a certain signal," Nancy said. "When I hold my two middle fingers up, it means I'm going to throw a curve, a real one. It'll curve out there by the library, and then it will veer back, right plunk over the home plate. She won't strike at it because she'll think it's going over the library. But it won't, and she'll miss it and that's the way I'll put her out."

Jane nodded her head. Another curve! Of course curves made it real baseball and not amateur. She knew that much. All the same she wished she had said, "Why don't you pitch 'em straight for a change?" But she didn't have the courage. Nancy was the captain and the pitcher. She certainly should know how to pitch if she was the pitcher. Nancy wasn't telling Jane how to catch. She expected Jane to know how to catch since she was the catcher. She didn't tell her anything. So neither did Jane tell Nancy anything, and she waited for the signal and wished that Rufus would return and back-stop for this very important pitch.

Now Nancy was winding her arm around and around. Then she stopped. She held up her middle two fingers. The signal! Jane edged over to the left but Nancy frowned her back. Oh, of course.

This curve was really going to fly over home plate. Nancy crooked her wrist and threw! The girl at the bat just dropped to the ground when she saw the ball coming and she let it go. And the ball really did come right over home plate only it was up in the air, way, way up in the air and spinning swiftly toward the library window, for it did its veering later than calculated. Jane leapt in the air in an effort to catch it but she missed.

"Rufus! Rufus!" she yelled, and she closed her eyes and stuck her fingers in her ears, waiting for the crash.

Just in the nick of time Rufus jumped for the ball. He caught it in his left hand before it could crash through the window. He sprinted over with the ball.

"We'd better move the bases again," said Nancy. And they all moved farther away from the library.

"Stay here," said Jane to Rufus, pleadingly. So Rufus stayed and he said since he had caught the ball the girl was out, and why not have punch now? Jane gave him a nudge. This was real baseball and he mustn't think about anything else. The girl said it didn't count that Rufus caught the ball, for he was the back-stop and not on the team. Even so, she graciously permitted Nancy's team a turn at the bat now, because the Busy Bees had had a long enough inning. They had run up such a big score she was sure the F.F. could never come up to it.

"That's the way with baseball," thought Jane. "Whoever is first at the bat usually wins."

Nancy was the first one up of the Fatal Four. The captain of the Busy Bee baseball team did not throw curves. Nancy struck at the first ball. It was a hit. She easily made first base. Now Jane was at the bat. Rufus, who decided to play back-stop for the foreign team as well as Jane's, was pounding his fist into his mitt to get some real atmosphere into this game.

While the pitcher was winding her arm around and around, Jane was busy too. She was swinging the bat, limbering up. At last, she thought. At last she was at the bat. That's all she liked to do in baseball. Bat! And so far she hadn't had a chance. And she swung herself completely around in her enthusiasm. Unfortunately the bat flew out of her hand and it hit Rufus on the forehead.

Rufus was staggered and saw stars. However, he tossed it off saying, "Aw, it didn't hurt," even though a lump began to show. Jane rubbed his forehead, and

thereafter she swung with more restraint. Even so, the catcher and Rufus automatically stepped back a few paces whenever Jane was at the bat, taking no chances with another wallop.

But now the pitcher pitched. Jane, still subdued and repressed, merely held the bat before her. Bang! The ball just came up and hit it and rolled halfway toward the pitcher. Both the pitcher and the catcher thought the other was going to run for the ball. Therefore neither one ran, and Jane made first base easily, putting Nancy on second. Now the bases were full because that's all the bases they had. And it was Clara Pringle at the bat.

The situation was too grave for Clara. She did not want to bat. How could she ever face Nancy if she struck out? Nancy and Jane might never speak to her again if she struck out. Besides, she had hurt her wrist pulling up a stubborn pie-weed when she was in outfield. She looked at Jane, who was dancing toward second, and Nancy, who was dancing toward home, impatiently waiting for the hit that would send them in. Clara gulped at her position of unexpected responsibility. When she joined the Fatal Four she had never envisioned being in a spot like this. She raised her hand to make a request.

"Can Rufus pinch hit for me because I hurt my wrist?" she asked timidly.

Rufus did not wait for anybody to say yes or no. He threw his mitt at Clara and seized the bat, pounding the ground, the home plate, and an old bottle. That's the way he warmed up, and if Jane had been vociferous at the bat, Rufus was nothing short of a tornado.

"Stand still!" yelled the pitcher. "You make me dizzy."

Rufus swung at imaginary balls.

"Hey!" exclaimed the pitcher. "He's left-handed."

"Sure," said Jane. "Why not?"

"You call 'em southpaws," said Nancy. "I pitch good to him myself."

"Well, here goes," said the pitcher. "It just looks funny if you're not used to 'em." And she swung her arm around and around again.

While she was warming up and while Rufus was stomping around, swinging the bat, waiting for the ball, Spec Cullom, the iceman, came along Elm Street. Evidently he saw in an instant that this was a real game and not just practice, for he stopped his team,

threw down the iron weight to anchor his horse, Charlie, and strode into the lot and straddled the nearest log in the bleachers to watch. Rufus saw him and became even more animated with the bat.

At the same moment the twelve o'clock whistle blew. Now all the children were supposed to go home to lunch. The Busy Bees were in favor of stopping, but the Fatal Four protested. Here they were with all bases full and they should certainly play the inning out at least.

So the pitcher pitched and Rufus struck. Crack! He hit the ball! Up and up it sailed, trailing

the black tape it was wound with behind it like the tail of a kite!

As it disappeared from sight in the pine grove, Nancy ran to home plate and Jane ran to second base, and then home, and Rufus tore to first, and then to second and then home. And so it was a home run that had been hit.

"A home run!" everybody yelled in excitement. It was surprising that that hit had not broken a window, and the outfielder of the visiting team ran in search of the ball. But she couldn't find it and Clara joined her, for she was an experienced outfielder, but she couldn't find it either. Then the whole Busy Bee baseball team ran and looked for the ball, but they couldn't find it. So they all went home. The captain, impressed by the home run, yelled to Nancy that the score must have been a tie and they'd come back in a week or so to see who was the champ.

Jane and Nancy ran over to the pine grove to look for the ball. They hunted in the corner of the lot where skunk cabbage grew thick and melon vines covered a dump, covered even the sign that said DO NOT DUMP. They searched through the long field grass on this side of the library,

trying not to get the thick bubbly-looking dew on their bare legs. Was this really snake spit as Joey and Rufus claimed, Jane wondered. If it was, where were all the snakes? She'd never seen a single snake. But where was the ball? That was some home run!

"You don't suppose he batted it clear across Elm Street into that lot, do you?" asked Nancy incredulously.

"Might have," said Jane, not knowing whether to be proud or ashamed. And the two girls crossed the street to take a look, just in case Rufus had swung as mighty an arm as that.

Rufus did not join in the search. He ran around from base to base to home plate, again and again, in ever widening circles until his course led him to the ice-man. The ice-man was one of his favorite people in Cranbury.

"Here," said Spec, "catch." And he threw the missing baseball to Rufus. "I yelled to the team that I caught the ball, but they couldn't hear me, I guess, what with whistles blowing and all the cheers. Some batter!" he said. "Keep it up, fella, and maybe next spring you can be bat boy for the South End baseball team."

The New Colossus

Emma Lazarus, arranged for choral reading by Jan Joss

Key

/ slight pause
// a complete stop
⌣ a continuation of the voice so that the thought is continued to the next line

Readers

Chorus One: light voices
Chorus Two: dark voices
Reader One
Reader Two
Reader Three

All: Not like the brazen giant of Greek fame, ⌣
With conquering limbs/ astride from land to land;//
Reader One :   Here// at our sea-washed,/ sunset gates//
Reader Two: shall stand ⌣
Chorus One: A mighty woman ⌣
Reader Three: with a torch, ⌣
Chorus Two: whose flame ⌣
Is the imprisoned lightning,//

Chorus One: and her name ⌣

Chorus Two: Mother of Exiles. //
From her beacon-hand ⌣
Glows world-wide welcome; //

Chorus One: her mild eyes command ⌣
The air-bridged harbor that twin cities frame. //

Chorus Two: "Keep ancient lands,/ your storied pomp!" //

Reader One: cries she ⌣
With silent lips. //

Reader Two: "Give me your tired,/

Reader Three: your poor,/

Chorus One: Your huddled masses/ yearning to breathe free,/
The wretched refuse of your teeming shore." //

Reader One: cries she ⌣
With silent lips. /

Reader Two: "Give me your tired,/

Reader Three: your poor. /

Chorus One: Send these,/
The homeless,/
Tempest-tost to me," //

Reader One: cries she ⌣
With silent lips. /

Reader Two: "Give me your tired,/

Reader Three: your poor . . . // to breathe free. //

Chorus Two: I lift my lamp // beside ⌣

All: the golden door!" //

Reader One: cries she ⌣
With silent lips. /

Reader Two: "Give me your tired,/

Reader Three: your poor." //

May The Plum Tree Always Blossom

Milly Howard

The following story takes place just before the beginning of World War II when the Japanese were invading China. The setting is Hangchow, a city in occupied China. Refugees from other parts of China where the battles were still raging had to travel through city after city, searching for some place to settle and begin their lives again. As the Japanese army pushed farther into China, the stream of homeless people increased every day. When the city gates of Hangchow opened in the morning, the streets swelled with refugee families. Those who chose to remain in the city went about their business as usual. They tried to ignore the foreign soldiers who occupied their city and the flood of strangers that flowed from the east gate to the west gate.

High summer pressed down on the city of Hangchow with the heat of a thousand feather blankets. Only the slightest of all breezes made its way through the open gates of the orphanage. Just inside the gates, Seventh Plumblossom crouched behind an empty willow basket. Only her straight-cut bangs showed above the pale willow. Unwaveringly her eyes watched the steady stream of people that moved along the dusty street outside the open gates.

As Seventh Plumblossom watched, old women tottered by the orphanage on their way to market, balancing on tiny feet that had been bound in their childhood to prevent growth. Shop workers hurried about on errands, threading their way through the crowd. A peddler pushed his cart, calling for people to stop and eat. The blue smoke of his fire teased Seventh Plumblossom with memories of crisp shrimp and crystallized fruits. She rubbed her nose and swallowed. Blinking her eyes, she renewed her silent watch for her brother, Luang.

At the edge of the mass of people, a gray-bearded man walked along slowly, holding a brightly painted bamboo bird cage. A group of boys rushed by, shouting something. Brushing past the startled old man, they leaped over rubble left by the bombs of December and disappeared into the crowd. The old man lost his balance and fell,

dropping the bamboo cage. It rolled under the peddler's cart and splintered. A flash of red and yellow blurred into the air as the freed bird swept upward into the sky. Muttering, the old man struggled to his feet. Without even brushing off his black silk robe, he thrust his way into the midst of the crowd.

Down the street in the direction from which the boys had come marched a squad of Japanese soldiers. The people glanced backwards over their shoulders and then hurried silently on.

Seventh Plumblossom's eyes widened as the soldiers' strong legs scissored a path through the stream of people and headed for the orphanage gate. She shouted a warning to the children playing behind her and shrank backward into the shadow between the basket and the wall. With sharp, frightened shrieks, the children fled into the buildings. Still, the gathering of the boys old enough to fight took little time. Seventh Plumblossom heard the pounding on the doors, the harsh orders, and the quick shouts. Then seven boys were marched from the orphanage that had been their home—Chang, Lin, Ling Yo, Tau, Dai, Fu, Chin Lo. All of the fifteen-year-old boys marched past the willow basket which hid the frightened Seventh Plumblossom. All of the fifteen-year-olds except her brother Luang.

Seventh Plumblossom trembled. Her movement drew a soldier's attention to the willow basket. Calling sharply in Japanese, he knocked the basket aside, yanking the frightened girl up and thrusting her against the wall. Eyes huge in her pale face, she crouched there, waiting.

"It's only a girl-child. Leave her alone."

The words were spoken quietly but firmly. The soldier who held Seventh Plumblossom released her with a grunt of disgust and turned away.

The one who had spoken knelt beside Seventh Plumblossom. He didn't touch her but looked at her kindly. Still trembling, she stared back into the face of the hated conqueror. Fear shook her as she remembered the men who had stormed into her home at Peking, leaving death and destruction behind them.

"It has passed; you will not be hurt," the man said gently. "What is your name?"

Surprised at his Chinese, she opened her mouth, but no sound came. She tried again. "Seventh Plumblossom," she whispered and swallowed to ease her dry throat.

He looked surprised. "Seventh? Why seventh?"

"Many girls named Plumblossom have come to the orphanage since the war began. We were numbered as we came," she answered falteringly. "I am the seventh."

"How many are here now?"

"Thirteen."

The soldier sat back on his heels, a strange look on his face. If she had not known the conquerors to be unfeeling monsters, she would have said it was a look of sorrow and pity. The years had taught her differently. She and Luang . . .

Her eyes flicked toward the gate. If Luang should return now—the thought filled her with terror. He would be forced to join the ragged line of boys. Like the others, he would be taken to fight in the Japanese army, to fight against his own people. *Go! Go!* Silently she turned her face away from the soldier and willed him to leave. *Go!*

"I have a daughter—" he began, but before he could finish, a harsh command from the gates brought him to his feet. A moment later the soldiers and boys were gone.

The other children gathered hesitantly in the yard. For a while they moved aimlessly from group to group and then slowly returned to their games. Seventh Plumblossom stayed at her post, watching the street.

Another hour passed before she saw Luang. Her fear turned to relief and pride as she watched her tall brother move up the street with an easy stride, stopping to help an overburdened mother with her child. The Japanese invasion of their country had thrust him into responsibility before his time. After the death of their parents, he had become mother and father to Seventh Plumblossom. He was her strength, her hope of life, her only thread to the peaceful existence before the war began.

"Luang! Luang!" she cried,

running to meet him. "They came! They came!"

"The soldiers?" Luang understood her fear. For a moment he didn't ask the question that was in his mind. He knew the answer.

"What happened?"

"They took the boys—Chang, Lin, Ling Yo, Tau—"

Luang's face darkened. He struggled not to speak in front of his sister. When he had regained control, he said quietly, "It will pass. It will pass."

"No, they will come again," Seventh Plumblossom said urgently. "And again, and again. We must hide. We must go away from here!"

Luang frowned, thinking. "You are safer here in the orphanage than you would be on the streets. We must stay here, Plumblossom."

"No! We must go!"

Luang gave her a troubled look. "We will talk to Madame Kai. She will advise us."

Luang knew what Madame Kai's advice would be. It would be safer for Luang to go, for Seventh Plumblossom to stay. But Luang also knew that his sister would never stay in the orphanage without him. He was all she had left, and she clung to him fiercely. Luang felt strongly too. If they were separated, all of their careful planning to stay together would be lost. Each of them would be alone—perhaps never knowing if the other were still alive. He sighed. It was a decision that could not be made quickly.

The weeks went by and the raids on the orphanages increased. No amount of prayers on the prayer wheels, no amount of burning incense could protect Luang forever. Finally even Madame Kai suggested that the two children leave together.

"If you stay, it is certain what will happen. If you go," she hesitated, then continued, "perhaps you will be safe."

Luang and Seventh Plumblossom packed their few belongings—a small ivory fan, a jade hair ornament that had belonged to their mother, a tiny carved figure that had been one of their father's treasures, two bowls, chopsticks, and bedrolls.

Saying good-by took longer. They had been at the orphanage over two years. Luang was a respected older one. Seventh Plumblossom was loved for both her tenderness and her fierceness in protecting the younger ones. The tiny Eleventh Plumblossom had been a special favorite of hers. She took the little orphan in her arms and wiped away the tears.

"I must go," she whispered. "I cannot lose Luang, not to the soldiers, not to time."

Luang motioned for her to come. The sun was low in the sky. Soon the gates would close for the night. The two children left the orphanage and joined the stream of refugees that pushed toward the open gates of the city. Afraid to be seen alone, they walked close

to another family. They were accepted quietly, without question. As they neared the big gates, the people in the crowd began to hurry, jostling against each other. Seventh Plumblossom was swept away from Luang. She struggled against the tide of people, crying out frantically. She was pushed aside and she stumbled, falling against the curb. Dodging the hurrying feet, she scrambled across to one of the wooden stalls that edged the road. She huddled against the side of the stall and waited.

The crowd flowed out the gates, leaving only Seventh Plumblossom and the slow, aged stragglers behind. Then across the street, just inside the gate, she saw Luang. He was anxiously searching the street. She leaped to her feet, but before she could cry out, he saw her. At a quick motion from him to stay away, she moved back against the stall. She watched in disbelief as Luang disappeared down a side street, leaving her alone.

Then a commotion to her right told her why he had gone. A troop of soldiers hurried to the gate, shouting orders to the gatekeepers. Slowly the huge carved gates began to close. Seventh Plumblossom began to weep silently. Through her tears she saw the soldiers separate and begin to search the stalls and buildings

along the street. They were look-ing for someone—who? Fright-ened shopkeepers were herded outside and lined up.

Seventh Plumblossom backed slowly along the side of the stall, trying to move without attracting attention. Once she thought a soldier looked her way, but he made no move toward her. She continued inching her way back-wards. She reached the shadow of the buildings and turned to run. A darker shadow stirred, then slid silently behind her. Suddenly a hand covered her mouth, smoth-ering her startled scream.

"Sh! It is I, Luang," the shadow whispered.

Seventh Plumblossom went limp with relief. Silently Luang guided her down the alley toward an old discarded peddler's cart.

"Under here," he said quietly. He scrambled underneath. Sev-enth Plumblossom followed. Underneath the cart there was only enough room for the two thin bodies to crouch close together. Shattered wood hung low over the

cart, shielding them from sight. They peered through cracks, watching the half-shadowed entrance to the alley. Minutes passed and the street sounds faded. Seventh Plumblossom relaxed and looked up at Luang. Before she could speak, he caught her arm. Fearfully she looked back at the entrance. The shadowy bulk of a soldier, outlined in the red glow of the setting sun, blocked the entrance. Rifle in hand, the soldier entered the alley. Debris crunched under his boots as he walked slowly toward the cart. He stopped in front of the cart. Seventh Plumblossom felt Luang tense beside her and knew that he too was holding his breath.

The listening silence that descended on the alley seemed unbearable. Seventh Plumblossom was suddenly seized by the desire to stand and run. Then one of the broken planks was ripped away, and she shrank back against Luang. He let his breath out in an agonized hiss of defeat as a shadowed face looked down at them.

"Ah, so it is the Seventh Plumblossom from the orphanage," the man said softly. "I thought I recognized you."

Seventh Plumblossom stared blankly. Then the man knelt, and she recognized the soldier who had come to her aid weeks ago. Her heart began to beat again, but her voice was still frozen within her throat.

He looked past her at Luang, who was trapped behind Seventh Plumblossom and could do nothing. Luang said in a thin voice, "I am the one you want. Let Plumblossom go. My sister will return to the orphanage. I will go with you."

The soldier shook his head. "You are not the one we seek," he answered, "We are searching for a spy, not children. But it is not safe for you to move about now. It is past curfew and the streets are empty, except for soldiers. You have chosen a good hiding place. Stay here for now. I will return later and take you to safety."

The board scraped as he lowered it back into place. Stepping back, he paused. Then with a soft sound of satisfaction, he turned and strode away.

"Who was that?" Luang whispered. "Why did a soldier help us?"

"He is one of the soldiers who came to take the boys away," Seventh Plumblossom whispered back. "He helped me then. I don't know why."

"I don't like it. He has gone to get the others."

"No." Seventh Plumblossom shook her head. "He is different. He is kind." She hesitated, then spoke again. "I do not fear him."

Surprised, Luang stayed where he was. For Plumblossom not to fear—this man must be different indeed. They would wait.

Darkness crept into the alley and settled around the cart like an old familiar blanket. Hot and tired, brother and sister slept fitfully. When the light came, they were caught unaware. It blinded their eyes, causing them to blink and stare blankly at the dark forms behind it.

"Come."

It was the Japanese soldier. Someone else was with him. Hope died as they climbed stiffly out and stood up. Luang stepped in front of Seventh Plumblossom.

They could not see the smile on the soldier's face, but they heard it in his voice. "Do not worry. This is Ping, a brother in Christ from your own land. I cannot leave my post to take you to safety. Ping will guide you in my place."

"Where will we go?" Luang asked, distrust still clouding his mind.

"You can trust me," the soldier

said earnestly. "I am a Christian. Several months ago our troop was fighting in the mountains to the west. While there, I attended services in which a foreign missionary woman talked. Some of the villagers told me she also runs an orphanage. Ping will take you to her. You will be safe, and she will teach you about Christ. She will take good care of you."

"But why do you want to help us?"

"You would not understand now, but I hope you will in time." The soldier knelt beside Seventh Plumblossom. "I have a daughter about your age," he said gently. "She is safe in Japan. She was born in the spring when the plum tree bears its blossoms. She, too, is called Plumblossom. I would not like to see fear in her eyes as it is in yours, little sister."

He stood up and placed a hand on Luang's shoulder. "There is much I cannot do, for I am loyal to my country, as you are to yours. But for the sake of my Lord, I can help two children survive the pains of war. You must hurry. Ping will take you to his friends. Tomorrow you will go through the outer gates to the mountains. Now go."

Bewildered, Seventh Plumblossom and Luang followed Ping. The soldier stood still, watching them for a moment. Then he called softly, "Seventh Plumblossom!"

Startled, she turned.

"You no longer need answer to that name," the soldier said quietly. "From now on you are not numbered. Go with God, Plumblossom."

A smile lifted the corners of Plumblossom's lips. "Thank you," she said and turned back to the others.

As the soldier watched, three shadows crossed the entrance to the alley and disappeared around the corner to the street. For a moment the soldier remained in the dark, silently watching. Then his hand went to the pocket that held pictures of his wife and daughter, and he said softly, "May the plum tree always blossom, little one, in your land and in mine."

Literature Lesson:
Making Judgments in Reading

If you've ever laughed over a funny story, you've proved that written stories affect our emotions. Ever since the written story has existed, writers have made readers laugh over ridiculous jokes and adventures or weep over sad stories of hard labor and suffering.

Sometimes fiction can help us understand God's truths better than nonfiction can. Christ Himself used parables to teach truth.

When you as a reader laugh or cry over a story, you're letting your mind draw you into the make-believe world. In other words, even though you *know* that the characters and situations in the story have been made up, you're still reacting as though they were real.

Responses such as laughing or crying over stories stretch our understanding. They help us to know what other people experience, and sometimes they even help us to understand better what we have experienced. It's good to read something that touches our emotions and makes us care about the people in the story. God has made man to be a sensitive being. He wants us to be able to feel the pleasures or sufferings of others.

But you should be aware that some stories can affect your emotions in a wrong way. As you continue reading, you may discover a book that's bad for you. As a Christian reader, you should be on your guard. It is not wrong to read secular stories, but you should quit reading if the story is not wholesome.

Hidden Messages

Some modern authors do not believe in God at all, but they might not state their unbelief directly. Their stories may attack Jesus or Christianity. They may contain bad language or rebellious attitudes. In time, you will know about these authors and why their stories are unsuitable. But if you try to tackle them now by yourself, you might feel like Christian trying to attack Apollyon without wearing any armor.

Usually an author will not boldly state his non-Christian belief but will let his story show it. Readers then unknowingly let the story affect their beliefs. For instance, an author, though wanting to make you doubt that God answers prayer, could create a character that *does* believe in prayer. His story could show that though the character prays and prays, his prayers are never answered. At the end of the story the character might still believe in prayer, but you, the reader, might have doubts.

Too Much Suffering

Many modern stories end in despair. The author may describe suffering in great detail and not offer any hope of relief for a character. When an author does not allow hope to exist in a story, he reflects his own beliefs. He says that no man can hope for joy or peace.

For example, an author might write about a character who breaks a leg in a skiing accident. If the author emphasizes only the pain of the character and tells his

story so that no relief for pain comes, he would be presenting a false view of life. If the story reflects no compassion and ends as it began, with the main character alone and in pain, then the author has shown an ungodly view of life. He is trying to make the reader believe that God is not good. Most suffering in this world is caused because men hurt each other—because of sin. But suffering can be a positive force that causes a person in pain to come to seek God for help.

It is possible for a good story to deal with suffering. "May The Plum Tree Always Blossom" is an example. In this story the author showed the tragedy of war, but she showed that a holy and loving God was in command. A non-Christian writer would not likely show war in the same way.

A Remedy for Bad Books

Sometimes you may feel that what you're reading in a secular book is too violent, too sad, or too odd. If you feel that way, you should not continue to read the book. The author may be communicating a bad message, or you may need to finish the book when you are older. You can always wait to finish a book, or you can talk about the book to people that you trust.

If you read anything that disturbs you, there are three people you can consult. First, you can tell your parents who may be able to glance at the book, find the problem, and help you understand the truth about what the author has said. You might find help from your teacher. Teachers read not only literature, they also read books *about* literature. Their reading helps them know what certain authors are saying. Your pastor can use the Word of God to make things clear for you.

Most of what you read will be pleasant and enjoyable. But as every person grows older, he develops his sense of judgment. If you are a Christian, Christ is developing you into an adult in His image. He wants you to exercise your mind and your conscience to avoid any traps that have been laid for your faith. You can start by using good judgment in what you read.

William Carey: Pioneer of Modern Missions

Karen Wilt and Andy Thomson

The door of the cobbler's workroom opened softly and then closed with a subdued click. John Warr looked up from the shoe he was sewing. It was mounted upside-down on a short post in front of him, and he was driving a sharp steel awl through the sole and into the leather upper. His stitches were neat and tight. Not long from now, he would be free from his apprenticeship.

"Hello, William," he called to the young apprentice standing with head bowed in the doorway. "Why don't you come in? Time's wasting."

Looking sheepish and embarrassed, William shuffled inside, took his apron from a hook on the wall, and prepared for the morning's work. He glanced at John Warr.

"Been talking to Master Nichols, John?" he asked.

"Oh, aye, a little bit. He's in no good mood today."

William looked alarmed. "But not really *angry* though, is he John? He wasn't looking for *me*, was he?"

"No, just his usual self for a Monday morning. He'll be all right after his morning tea," Warr replied easily. "He didn't seem angry with you. Sit down. There's a shoe with a heel to be nailed on there on your bench."

William Carey reluctantly sat down and mounted the shoe on the post in front of him. For a while the two young men worked silently. As William tapped nail after nail into the shoe, he began to relax a little, but he looked as though he had spent a sleepless night and was still unhappy. John whistled cheerfully as he sewed. At last William spoke.

"John."

"Yes, William?"

"Did Master tell you about the shilling?"

"Aye, William, he did. But I'd already heard about it from the ironmonger."

William Carey's face turned red, and for a moment he said nothing. At last he said cautiously, "It's true, John. I stole a shilling from Master Nichols last week."

"Aye," was all that John Warr said. He whistled a few more notes, put the finished shoe down, and took up its partner. Then he said, "Master told me that he forgave you. That was good of him, and I was glad he did it."

"He did. But I suppose the whole town must know about it by now."

"Well—" John slipped some sinewy thread through the eye of the awl. "It's no secret anymore. That's for sure, William."

William sighed heavily. "I'm a hypocrite, John—a thief and a liar, and I didn't deserve to be forgiven."

"No," Warr agreed. "Forgiveness is a thing no man deserves."

"I couldn't even go to church yesterday," William continued. "And I knew that was wrong, too, but how could I come before all those people to worship God

William Carey: Pioneer of Modern Missions   551

when half the town knows that I stole from my own master?"

"That may have been hard," Warr agreed cautiously.

"Even God Himself says that we have to worship with clean hands and a pure heart. But my hands aren't clean, John, and I don't have a pure heart!"

John Warr stopped working and looked at his younger friend. William Carey had never before been concerned about God.

"Even God hates me now. He knows what I've done!" Carey continued. He jumped up and then made himself sit down. "What will I do?" he asked. "I can't find my way to God."

"No," John Warr said quietly. "But God is finding His way to you, William. You're a different man today than you were two days ago."

"Now I know what a sinner I am," William replied.

"That's a good thing for a man to know," he said. "But if you think that stealing that shilling surprised God, you're wrong. A man's sin doesn't take God by surprise, because He knows what we are. You were a sinner long before you stole a shilling, William."

William was silent. "I suppose I was," he agreed at last.

"We all are," John added. "Now that you understand that, what will you do?"

"What can I do? My soul is in danger. What have you done about your soul?"

"I've trusted in Christ's atonement for me. It was hard to understand at first, but at last I came to realize that my only hope was to hold on to the Saviour, just as Peter did when the waves of the ocean nearly overcame him."

"Does the preacher of your dissenting church teach that?" William asked cautiously. He knew that John was a member of a dissenting church—a church that had separated from the official Anglican Church.

"Aye," John said.

"Well," Carey turned back to his shoe. "Since I'm too ashamed to go to my own established church, John, I may as well cut the cord and go to your dissenting church. No one could think any worse of me than he does now, and I'd like to hear more of your kind of preaching."

William Carey visited John Warr's small church several times. Eventually he repented with faith in Christ and was saved. He joined the dissenting church and began studying Greek and Latin

earnestly, reading borrowed books in his spare time. He soon started his own small church and supported himself and his wife by making shoes and teaching in the evening. Busy as he was, he made time to study. A new dream was in William Carey's heart—to spread the gospel to all men. He urged other preachers to consider sending missionaries to other countries that didn't have the gospel.

But Carey found to his dismay that few preachers were interested in foreign missions. Most of the dissenting preachers at this time believed that the Great Commission of Christ to go into all the world and preach the gospel had been a command given only to the apostles, not to the Church. They thought that countries that had

centuries ago rejected the gospel had been left in heathen darkness by God as judgment. Therefore, it was not man's responsibility to go to a foreign country to preach the gospel.

"You are an enthusiast!" one preacher rebuked Carey. "When God pleases to convert the heathen, He'll do it without consulting you or me!"

Even though he was rebuked and ignored, Carey continued to urge that churches consider sending out missionaries. He published a pamphlet on the Church's great opportunity and obligation to obey the Great Commission. At last he began to win friends for his cause. But others were still skeptical. One learned preacher scornfully asked Carey how successful he thought an unschooled cobbler would be in attempting to translate the New Testament into the languages of Bengali, Sanskrit, and all the other tongues of Asia.

But Carey would not be daunted. When the ministers of nearby churches met at Nottingham for prayer and preaching, Carey preached on missions. His text was Isaiah 54:2-3:

> Enlarge the place of thy tent, and let them stretch forth the curtains of thine habitations: spare not, lengthen thy cords, and strengthen thy stakes; For thou shalt break forth on the right hand and on the left; and thy seed shall inherit the Gentiles, and make the desolate cities to be inhabited.

He urged the preachers to recognize that God wanted to glorify His name by bringing heathen nations to the light of the gospel. He urged the men to "expect great things from God; attempt great things for God." This slogan lived long after his death, but at the time he preached it, his listeners ignored it. They still were skeptical. After his sermon was over, they merely filed out of the church building.

"Are we still to do nothing?" Carey asked his friend Andrew Fuller. Fuller was much older than Carey and was respected by the other ministers. Carey's message had touched him. He stopped the ministers and asked that a mission society be formed.

Four months later the Baptist Missionary Society met at Kettering, another small town north of Nottingham.

The men present raised a small sum of money at this meeting. It was not enough to send a man to a foreign country, but Carey was hopeful that more money could be raised. The Mission Society decided to support Dr. John Thomas, a physician who had lived in India and was planning to return there as a missionary. Carey volunteered to take his family and accompany Dr. Thomas. Andrew Fuller, now head of the Society, pledged that he and the other members would seek to raise enough money to support the new missionaries.

In 1793 the small group set sail for Calcutta, India. But both Carey and Thomas were almost penniless, and when they arrived in India, they spent their first day walking the streets, preaching, and looking for a place to stay.

The Indians were fascinated by the gospel. They enjoyed listening to the two Englishmen preach, but they had no desire to believe in Christ.

Meanwhile, Carey had to move his family from place to place as he looked for work. Although he had been promised financial help from those back home, the journey from England to India was long and dangerous. The tiny mission society could not send much money, and what they sent arrived only after several months had passed.

Disease was common in India. During their first several years there, the Careys suffered recurring attacks of dysentery, malaria, and fever. William's son Peter died of dysentery, and Mrs. Carey never fully recovered from the illness nor from her child's death. At last William found work and a healthful place for his family to live. He hired a *punjab,* or teacher, to help him learn Bengali. But the death of his son and the seemingly unsuccessful work depressed him. Seven long years passed with not one convert. Worse yet, most of his own children were not saved.

During these years Carey learned Bengali. He also studied Indian society. Most people thought that Hinduism was a non-violent religion, but Carey discovered that the Hindus had not totally discarded ancient beliefs in child sacrifice. The Hindus also believed that it was good for a widow to permit herself to be burned alive with her dead husband. At first none of the

English authorities in India would listen to Carey when he protested these practices. When people in England heard of his failure to make converts or to effect any change at all, they wondered if Carey should return home. Some doubted that he had really been called as a missionary.

But Carey refused to believe that God had deserted him. He continued his preaching and his translating. Already he had learned that the Bengali language and most other Indian tongues were derived from Sanskrit. He planned to learn Sanskrit next to make it easier to learn the other languages. And at last the ice began to break when Felix, Carey's oldest son, was saved.

One day while Carey was struggling over his Bengali grammar, the sharp cries of an Indian boy startled him. He ran out to the street to see what was wrong.

"*Sahib, Sahib!* Please come quickly. My father needs medical attention. His arm, it is broken. He has fallen on the slippery *ghat* at the river." The dark-skinned child grabbed Mr. Carey's arm. "Please, great *Sahib,* come."

"I am not the doctor. Let me find Dr. Thomas," Mr. Carey said.

With the child running alongside, Mr. Carey sprinted through the house, calling for Doctor Thomas. Finding him in the garden, the Indian boy explained the accident again in a high-pitched flow of Bengali that neither man could completely understand. Taking two minutes to check his medical bag, Dr. Thomas rushed with Carey and the boy to the river.

The injured man lay on the slippery steps that led down to the sacred Hindu River. The man's children had gathered round him, wide-eyed with worry. As the white doctor and his friend approached, they stepped back, almost falling into the muddy water.

"My arm!" the man moaned.

Dr. Thomas pulled back the loose cloth draped on the man's shoulder. Near the shoulder the upper bone of the arm swelled outward in the wrong direction.

"The bone has popped out of joint; it is not broken," Dr. Thomas said.

He lifted the man off the *ghat* and carried him to the shade of a tree. Raising the useless arm, he instructed Mr. Carey to hold it at shoulder level. Then he tied the trembling Indian man to the thick tree trunk. With a quick jerk at

the elbow, he popped the bone back into its socket.

"Save me!" the man cried in pain. He wiggled his fingers and bent his elbow. His face lit up. "It is healed."

"Come with us to the mission compound, and we will give you medicine for the pain," Dr. Thomas said. "Let us tell you how Christ can heal your soul as well as your body."

"You are the English Christians?" the man asked.

"Yes."

"People have spoken often of you." The man's eyes were curious. "They say that your God forgives men of their sins."

"He does. Christ is our Redeemer."

"I would like to hear more of this," the man said. "My name is Krishna Pal. For years I have carried a burden in my soul. I joined the Kharta-bhojas of the Hindus to find release from my sins. They give my soul no rest. What can your Christ do?"

"Christ has said in His Word, 'He that covereth his sins shall not prosper: but whoso confesseth and forsaketh them shall have mercy,' " Dr. Thomas quoted.

Krishna Pal repeated the words. "I will hear more of this," he said.

Dr. Thomas gave him the pain medicine, and Krishna Pal walked home, thinking over the words of Christ.

Krishna Pal returned, leading his friend Gokul to the mission station. Mr. Carey and Dr. Thomas searched the Bengali Scriptures for verses that might open the eyes of the Indian men.

"Christ said this," Mr. Carey opened the Bible to John 3:16. "'For God so loved the world, that he gave his only begotten Son, that whosoever believeth in him should not perish, but have everlasting life.'"

"If I believe Christ, I can become immortal?" Gokul asked. "Have you done this, Sahib? How old are you?"

For hours the men explained the Word of God. The Indian men listened and questioned, but to believe—they knew that in turning to Christ alone they would be turning away from all their Indian customs and ways. They must break caste. Their relatives would throw them out or kill them. These English men had been in India seven years, and no Indians had yet turned to follow Christ.

The burden of sin weighed more and more heavily on the soul of Krishna Pal. The words of the missionaries promised release.

558

Dr. Thomas had told Krishna Pal that a truer *gayatri* (sacred saying) than any of the Hindu prayers was "He that confesseth his sins, and forsakes them, obtaining the righteousness of Jesus, is free."

One cool night after the sun had retreated over the horizon, Krishna Pal watched his children playing in the warm sand. He thought over the promises of the Bible, and he knew in his heart that Carey had been telling him the truth. Silently he prayed to Christ, confessing his sin and accepting Christ as Saviour. The burden lifted, and Krishna Pal became a new creature.

Early the next morning he set off for the mission compound. In the bustling street of the town he caught sight of a tall figure bargaining at a market stall.

"Dr. Thomas, Dr. Thomas," he called. "Oh Sahib, I am a great sinner, but I have confessed my sin . . . and I am free!"

Dr. Thomas dropped the sack of rice he had bought. "You are now my brother," he said.

Krishna Pal's family followed their father to Christ. Gokul also believed. But Carey and Dr. Thomas were careful. They knew that the two Indian men had many spiritual battles to fight. Would they discard all their beliefs in luck and the need to appease the minor gods? Would they break caste? Hinduism was not just a religion in India. It was a way of life. Everything from eating and dressing to marrying and earning a living was governed by Hinduism, especially the belief in caste. The two missionaries thought that if they urged the men too much, the converts would shrink back. They decided to answer the questions of the two men, lead them through the Bible, and allow God to bring them out of superstition and the bondage of the caste.

One day at noon the two men decided to stay at Mr. Carey's home to eat the luncheon meal called *tiffin*, thus breaking the laws of the caste by eating with non-caste members. The hired servants of the missionaries spread the word during the meal. "Krishna Pal and Gokul have become Europeans. How horrible!" People ran from their mud houses and wooden shacks. They lined the roads shouting disapproval. Some of the people flung mud at the new Christians, but they were too afraid of British authority to harm them.

After several weeks of learning Scripture, Krishna Pal spoke to the missionaries about his desire to follow Christ regardless of the consequences. He was eager to guide his family carefully in the Christian faith.

"Will you be baptized, Krishna Pal?" Mr. Carey asked.

"I will follow my Lord," Krishna Pal said.

"I will also," Gokul said.

Krishna Pal urged his family to be baptized. They agreed. The following Sunday afternoon, the Indian converts forsook Hinduism completely.

The morning dawned cloudless and blue. The missionaries had discussed the baptism for days. They decided to go to the Hooghly River. The Hooghly was formed at the mouth of the Ganges River, which the Indians considered sacred and holy. When the Indians saw the new Christians baptized there, what would they think?

"The testimony of Krishna Pal and Gokul will show the Indians that they truly believe Christ," Mr. Carey said.

At the river Gokul and the family of Krishna Pal held back. "We cannot," they said. A crowd had gathered, and the converts were afraid of being attacked.

"Baptize me," Krishna Pal said.

"And me," young Felix Carey said.

Mr. Carey led his oldest son and Krishna Pal into the water. "These two have forsaken the world to be disciples of Christ. By following Christ in the waters of baptism, they testify publicly their belief in Him." Mr. Carey turned to his son and said in English, "By your testimony of new life in Christ I baptize you in the name of the Father, and of the Son, and of the Holy Ghost." He lowered Felix into the water and raised him up. Repeating the same words in Bengali, he lowered Krishna Pal into the river.

Holding their hands, he prayed for God's blessing on each life. The words he had repeated for seven fruitless years in India went through his mind:

"Expect great things from God; Attempt great things for God."

He had attempted the impossible and expected God to work miracles. The next day Krishna Pal started plans for a Christian church building. Within a year, the little church swelled with one hundred Indian converts. The miracle had come.

In later years more missionaries came, and William Carey

established outposts in several other towns. He also translated the entire Bible into Bengali, Sanskrit, Marathi, Punjabi, Telegu, and Kanarese. He produced dictionaries in Bengali, Sanskrit, and Marathi, and he also wrote several books of India's folklore and translated ancient poems into English. In fact, William Carey is credited not only with his mission work but also with helping to begin modern Indian literature.

The preacher who had tauntingly asked Carey if a cobbler could translate the Scripture had unwittingly prophesied just what William Carey would do in India—translate Scripture so that millions could read it for themselves or have it read to them in words they would know.

In his boldness to attempt a great thing for God, William Carey pioneered the way for modern missions. He found that translating Scripture into native tongues was the quickest way to win converts. He also discipled and trained the people he had won so that they could become preachers to their own people. His methods are still used today by missionaries opening up foreign fields.

Skill Lesson: Map Projections

William Carey left England to preach the gospel in faraway India. If you look at a globe, you can see that he had to sail around Africa to reach the city of Calcutta in India. His trip was long, often uncomfortable, and sometimes dangerous. He and his family braved terrible storms that almost swamped the ship. They endured days of killing heat that made the tar between the planks bubble.

Whenever he could, Carey kept himself too busy to notice his discomfort. Although he didn't have much formal schooling, he taught himself as much as he could. On his voyage he learned how important globes and maps could be. The globes back in England were accurate because they matched the spherical shape of the earth. On land the merchants and captains used globes to plan voyages, but at sea the sailors used maps. Flat maps were easy to carry and store.

The reason that the maps were not as accurate as globes was that it is impossible for a flat piece of paper to be a correct copy of the surface of a sphere. You can compare the earth to an orange with its skin on. The oceans and continents could be drawn on this skin to make the orange a small globe. But if you wanted to convert it to a flat map, you might have a problem. You would find that even if you could open the skin with one cut all the way around, you still couldn't lay it out flat like a map. It would make two half-spheres, forming two "mounds" or "bowls." If you flattened them, then the edges of each half-sphere would split in many places. You could make the half-spheres into square maps only if you stretched them.

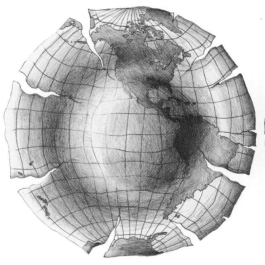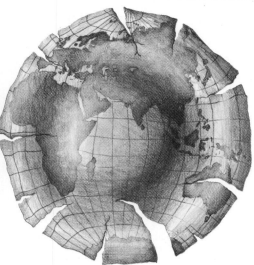

In their drawings mapmakers tear or stretch parts of the earth. The many methods they use to cut, stretch, or reduce the areas of land on their maps are called map projections.

When mapmakers use an *interrupted projection,* they draw the map with several cuts. These cuts break the map into a strange shape, but they leave the size and shape of the continents fairly accurate.

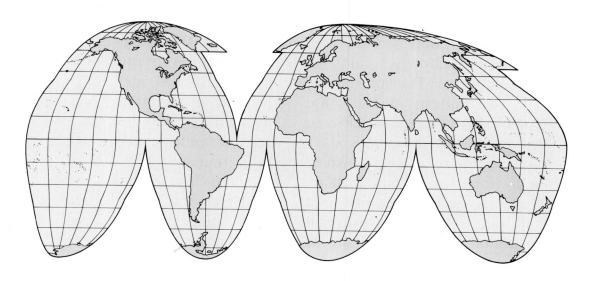

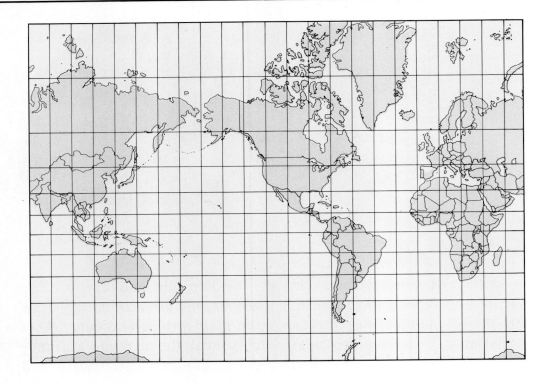

Another projection called the *Mercator projection* stretches the earth's surface instead of cutting it. On a Mercator map, the land along the equator is accurate in size and shape. The lands at the top and bottom of the map, however, have been stretched to enormous sizes in comparison.

If you look at a map instead of a globe to see how William Carey reached India, you would not want to use an interrupted projection. His route might be through one of the map's cuts. A Mercator projection is better for tracing ocean voyages. If you want to compare the size of England to that of India, however, a Mercator projection would not be as good as an interrupted projection. Land areas on an interrupted projection map are more accurate than on a Mercator projection.

Once Carey reached India, he used maps for guidance. He had taught himself to read maps and was able to use his skills in the service of the Lord.

Master of the Skies

Tim Davis

It was a beautiful day. Fluffy, billowing clouds filled the sky south of Paris, and Monsieur Dubois's balloon awaited him in the meadow. He and La Salle, his faithful valet, approached on horseback, anticipating a day of adventure.

"The weather," began La Salle, "it's quite charming, is it not, Monsieur?"

"Suitable at best, La Salle, suitable," replied Monsieur Dubois. He stroked the fat, sleepy cat that lounged in his arms. "Were it not for my calling, I'd find it far less than satisfactory."

"No doubt, Monsieur."

Dubois continued, "Such are the harsh inconveniences of a cartographer—braving the elements to master the skies—but master them I will, La Salle, that I will. I, Jean Louis Philippe Dubois, balloonist par excellence, shall become the first man in all France to map the clouds."

"*Oui,* Monsieur," nodded La Salle.

"Ah, my maps, once completed, shall guide men through the skies throughout all the civilized world. No cloud shall escape my cartographic pen."

La Salle stifled a chuckle and nodded as the two men dismounted. There before them floated the ornate balloon that Dubois adored. On the threshold of the nineteenth century, man's invention had certainly soared to new heights.

"La Salle, you shall follow me the best you can on horseback."

"*Oui,* Monsieur." La Salle pulled a large sack off the horse's saddle and extended it to Dubois. "Your lunch, Monsieur."

"*Oui, oui,* and quite so. Hand me a chicken leg or some such thing before I faint from hunger, La Salle," demanded Dubois.

The valet quickly obeyed. Dubois daintily lifted the drumstick to his mouth and took a small bite.

"Eeyew!" he cried suddenly and threw the chicken leg to the ground. "Why, what sort of chef do you take yourself for, La Salle? This chicken is seasoned heavily enough for . . . for a peasant! How often must I remind you that the taste buds of Jean Louis Philippe Dubois are like finely-tuned instruments—sensitive to the most subtle tones of taste."

"Oh . . . *oui,* Monsieur, I'm very sorry, Monsieur," stammered La Salle.

"Only my great generosity permits me to pardon you. And thus I shall excuse you of your off—OH!"

Dubois's attention was suddenly distracted as a hungry field mouse started nibbling on the discarded drumstick.

"Get away, you vermin! La Salle, get it! Catch that rodent! Get him away from my chicken leg!"

La Salle started in clumsy pursuit around the startled horse, through the grass, around the balloon ropes—ooof! The portly valet tripped, allowing the frantic mouse to escape.

Meanwhile, Dubois was practically beside himself. "Oooh, can you imagine it, La Salle? Food once touched by the lips of Jean Louis Philippe Dubois actually being nibbled by a common rodent of the field! How indignantly insulting!"

Brushing himself off, La Salle replied, "Monsieur, I imagine the mouse was merely hungry."

"Indeed, La Salle," Dubois answered coldly. "Well, it shall not happen again." He turned to the fat, lazy cat in his arms. "Charlemagne, you may have the pleasure . . . if you can stand La Salle's seasoning, that is."

Soon Charlemagne had reduced the drumstick to a small,

clean bone. The field mouse looked on sorrowfully, but soon his eyes spotted the tempting lunchbag by the balloon. Meanwhile, Dubois and La Salle had managed to prepare for the ascent. Everything—the charts and compass, quill pens and paper, and finally the bag of lunch—was loaded with the passengers: Dubois, Charlemagne, and one uninvited guest, a hungry field mouse.

"Cut the ropes! Jean Louis Philippe Dubois must be off, conquering the heights of cartography for the glory of France!"

The obedient valet cut the cords, releasing the balloon to the skies. They were off!

Only a few hundred feet up Dubois commenced his mapmaking. Feverishly he sketched the clouds around him, checking them with his compass and rechecking them.

"My dear Charlemagne, it almost seems as though the clouds are changing before my very eyes," Dubois said to his sleepy pet. "It's a most frustrating condition to a cartographer such as myself. How can I master the skies under such circumstances?"

Charlemagne merely rolled onto his back on the balloon-basket floor.

"Hmmm, perhaps a spot of lunch will do me good. That is, if I can find something not too highly seasoned." Dubois reached into his lunch bag for a bite—and that's exactly what he got. It was the mouse!

"Aaahhh!" screamed Dubois, jumping up and down and waving his injured little finger.

Charlemagne woke up as if he'd been shot. The frightened mouse scampered up a rope to the side of the balloon. Unnoticed by Dubois, the hungry mouse stead-ily nibbled at the rope. Below them all, on horseback, La Salle noticed the commotion.

He yelled up, "Monsieur, is everything all right?"

Dubois turned red in the face and yelled, "All right? All right? I got a bite!"

"You got it right?" replied La Salle. "Wonderful!"

"Oooh," yelled back Dubois. "Not right, bite! I said I got a bite from that whining rodent!"

La Salle had his hand cupped to his ear, but it was no use. "Monsieur, what did you get right from that winding road? I can't see any winding roads."

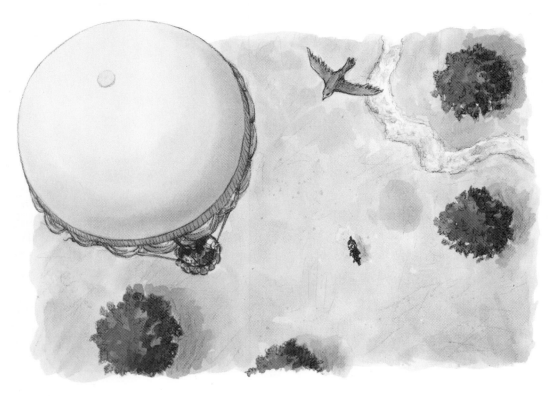

Dubois stamped his feet furiously, rocking the balloon and making Charlemagne nervous. "There is no winding road, La Salle! I'm talking about that rat!"

"No, Monsieur, I can't see where it is at," replied the valet, scratching his bald head. He looked down again and whispered to himself, "All upset about some winding road." He shook his head.

Meanwhile Dubois squealed in frustration as Charlemagne cowered on the basket floor. "That La Salle, why do I keep him? I, the great Jean Louis Philippe Dubois, master of the skies. I tell you, Charlemagne, I don't know how I maintain my composure with him. A man of lesser manners than I wouldn't, I tell you. And that horrible mouse—eeeyew, there it is! Charlemagne, climb up that rope and kill it immediately!"

Seeing his master in such a state of mind, Charlemagne dared not disobey. Timidly he began inching his way up the rope toward the mouse.

But the little mouse had nibbled ravenously at the rope. Just as Charlemagne was about to strike—snap! The rope broke. Whoosh—down swung the fat cat below the basket, clinging to every

strand of rope that he could get a claw into.

"Charlemagne!" screamed Dubois, peering over the edge. "Hold on!"

"Monsieur," shouted up La Salle, "What's happening?"

Dubois nearly burst his voice box. "IT'S THAT MOUSE!"

"Oh, the mouse," chuckled La Salle to himself. "So *that's* what he's so upset about. How dare the rodent trifle with *the* Jean Louis Philippe Dubois?"

Meanwhile the hungry mouse had taken a liking to the taste of rope and had commenced nibbling on another.

"My darling Charlemagne," urged Dubois, "don't be frightened. I shall save you." Slowly the Frenchman pulled his terrified pet back toward the basket.

Then—snap! A second rope broke. Dubois grabbed the edge of the basket, letting Charlemagne fall again with a claw-wrenching jerk.

Several of Dubois's maps fluttered past the cat and down toward the ground. The balloon dropped a little from the force of the basket's jerk.

"LA SALLE!"

"Don't worry, Monsieur. I'll retrieve them!" shouted back the faithful valet.

"In the meantime, this ferocious mouse will chew us loose!" screamed Dubois.

"Hmmm . . . I suppose he might," thought La Salle. Then he shouted back, "Monsieur, I shall try to think of a solution!"

"Think quickly, La Salle!" replied the frantic balloonist. The basket was hanging down, held by only two ropes now. More papers slowly sifted out. Looking up, Dubois snarled, "You silly rat! Don't you realize that you are toying with Jeanne Louis Philippe Dubois, the most distinguished balloonist-cartographer in all of France, master of the skies?" As he spoke, he couldn't help noticing a sparkle in the mouse's eye as it began chewing on the next rope.

Snap! There went another rope. There was only one left.

Dubois, holding on for his life, screamed, "La Salle!"

The valet had been thinking and thinking some more. At last he responded. "Monsieur, your lunch!"

"My lunch?" cried Dubois. "I'm hanging by a thread up here and you're telling me to eat my lunch?"

"No," shouted back La Salle. "The mouse . . . offer your lunch to the mouse!"

"To that murderous creature?"

"*Oui,* Monsieur, I'm afraid it's your only hope of survival," replied the valet. He was pleased with himself for thinking of such a plan.

"Oooh," moaned Dubois to himself. "Debasing!" But the desperate look in Charlemagne's eyes—not to mention his own desperate situation—convinced him of the necessity. He reached carefully for the sack of food lying snug in a corner of the dangling basket above him, pulled out a sandwich, and held a quarter of it up toward the little mouse, the master of the balloon.

Down the rope the mouse climbed, quickly snatching the snack in his teeth and scurrying back again. Then he savored every bite of that sandwich, much to the embarrassment of Jean Louis Philippe Dubois.

"Is it working?" cried La Salle. But Dubois could only moan in humiliation as the balloon continued to descend.

"Mee-oooowww!" came a sudden cry. It was Charlemagne rubbing across the top of an evergreen tree. The balloon was coming in for a woodsy landing. La Salle could hear the ripping noise from the ground.

"Ooof! La Salle!"

"Mee-oooww!"

Charlemagne and Dubois tumbled through the branches. They landed with a thud on the pine-needle floor.

La Salle urged the horse to a gallop toward the place where Dubois had landed in the midst of the trees. He called out, "Monsieur, are you all right?"

There was Dubois with a black eye, tattered suit, dirty face, and ruffled sleeves deruffled. Beside him was Charlemagne, with tangled fur and a queasy look on his face. It was a funny sight to behold, but La Salle knew better than to laugh. He jumped off the horse and ran over to his master. "Is Monsieur all right?"

"Is Monsieur all right?" Dubois whined. Then he exploded, "No, Monsieur is not all right! Just look at these clothes, La Salle! And this dirt—how revolting! Why, why it's even on my face! Don't just stand there. Help me get up!"

La Salle reached for Dubois's hand and pulled him to his feet.

"My little finger!" cried Dubois. "La Salle, how *do* I tolerate you? I, Jean Louis Philippe . . ."

On and on went the stuffy Frenchman as La Salle helped him to his horse and handed him a bleary-eyed Charlemagne. The portly valet gathered together as many things as he could and mounted his horse too.

Dubois was talking too much to notice the rustling La Salle heard in the pine needles. It was the mouse! The valet checked slyly to see whether Dubois was looking. Then he tossed a chicken leg in the direction of the rustling and watched to see the little field mouse come out and start nibbling. It looked in his direction, and its beady little eyes sparkled.

La Salle winked and then rode away with Jean Louis Philippe Dubois, master of the skies.

ABOVE THE CLOUDS

Jeri Massi

For centuries most men believed that flight was limited to birds and angels. Every now and then an optimistic inventor would develop some kind of contraption to help him fly. Leonardo da Vinci once sketched a primitive type of helicopter, but he had to give up his idea when he realized that there was no way to make the propeller turn quickly enough to lift a man. Motorized engines would not be invented for several centuries. Other inventors built huge wing contraptions. Those men brave enough to try their experiments were rewarded with broken bones and disappointment. The Marquis de Bacqueville launched himself in his wings from a hill overlooking a river. He had predicted that he would glide over the waves, but instead he dove into the waters and took a long swim.

Then in the 1700s, two brothers in France began experimenting with hot air. Joseph and Etienne Montgolfier had noticed that both smoke and steam rise. Joseph made small paper balloons and filled them with smoke. These bags floated for a few seconds. The brothers realized that if they could produce their experiments on a big scale, they might enable man to travel by air.

They experimented with more balloons until they made one big enough to carry two men. At a public exhibition of the powers of the balloon, they sent two men into the air. The flight lasted less than a half hour, but ballooning was born.

Meanwhile, Professor Jacques Charles and two mechanics started work on a hydrogen-filled balloon. Two months later they sent it up at a public demonstration. The balloon traveled fifteen miles before several leaks brought it down. It descended on a French

peasant village. When the superstitious farmers saw it, they thought it was a monster. They attacked it with pitchforks and knives and tore it apart. After that the king issued edicts to assure all people that balloons were merely machines designed for the good of society.

Throughout most of the 1800s the French people were first in ballooning. French scientists in the wealthy upper class used balloons for experiments in the air. Although some of these men were hopelessly wrong in their concepts of the atmosphere, others conducted careful tests and kept objective records of what they found. Their tests helped them to define certain laws of air pressure and gravity. The French also used balloons for pleasure, sightseeing, and daredevil stunts. When engaged in war, they were the first to send manned balloons up to gain information on territory and the enemy armies.

For almost two centuries the hydrogen-filled balloon replaced the hot air balloons. Hot air cooled too quickly for long flights, and it was dangerous to keep a fire burning in the wicker basket of the balloon. Hydrogen was more dependable for flight, but if it were ignited it would blow a

balloon and its cargo to shreds. Static electricity in the air, a lightning storm, or any stray spark could destroy a hydrogen balloon. Then in the twentieth century a compact and safe propane air-heater was developed for ballooning, and once again the hot air balloon became the people's choice. Some balloonists still use hydrogen with great care, and some use helium, which is safer than hydrogen but more expensive.

Today balloon racing is a sport enjoyed throughout the world. Balloonists also compete to set world records. In 1978 three Americans became the first people to cross the Atlantic Ocean in an unpropelled balloon. Countless other people had tried and failed throughout the last two hundred years to reach this goal.

Although many people engage in competition, others see the balloon as a symbol of tranquillity. They enjoy a simple and silent ride up through the clouds, drifting wherever the wind takes them.

The Store-Bought Dress

Milly Howard

In the 1950s the Palmers were sharecroppers on Evan Grant's farm. By late fall of every year, the ripe cotton stretched in long rows of white across the Alabama hills. Gathering the fluffy cotton became important to the Palmers and to most of the county; even schools let out so the children could help in the final weeks of picking. In this way the children could earn money for the luxuries their families might not be able to afford otherwise.

Merrilee Palmer put her hand on her back as she straightened wearily. She tugged at the strap of her half-filled cotton sack and groaned.

"Only ten o'clock and I'm already tired," she said aloud.

Her older sister looked across the two rows of cotton plants that separated them. "You only have three weeks to earn enough money to buy that bike you want," she warned. "It takes a lot of cotton to make that much money."

Merrilee sighed. Josie was right, of course. Not having a bike meant that she had to walk everywhere. And Alice, her best friend in the whole fifth grade, had a shiny new bike.

Josie was pulling ahead of her, moving slowly but steadily. Merrilee watched her slender fingers pull the fluffy white cotton balls from the dry plants and stuff them into the sack trailing behind her.

"What are you going to buy with your money, Josie?"

Josie looked back at Merrilee. "More than you are, if you don't come on," she answered, smiling.

"Here, I'll help you catch up, and then we'll go empty these sacks into the ones by the cotton wagon."

She let her sack fall to the ground and stepped over the low rows. The two sisters worked up the row, stuffing the cotton into Merrilee's sack.

"Thanks, Josie," Merrilee said as they reached Josie's sack.

"It will be strange, not riding together on the same bus this year," Merrilee said as she walked to the wagon with her sister. Josie was four years older than Merrilee, and this was her first year in high school.

"I know," Josie said. "I'm half of one mind, half of another about moving up. At least I know most of the kids in the ninth grade."

"You wouldn't have any trouble even if you didn't know any of them," Merrilee said affectionately. "You don't have trouble talking to people."

Daddy said that Josie was a word spinner, weaving words like Mama wove cloth. He was right, too. That was Josie's gift. No one had been surprised when she was chosen to give a speech at the Thanksgiving fair this year.

After returning, Merrilee pushed her straggling hair out of her eyes. Right now she wished she could grow a little and move as fast as the older pickers. Behind her the younger children were strung out across the field. Ahead of her the boys worked, shouting back and forth across the rows. The men had already pulled out of sight over the hill, and a group of slower moving women were reaching the top now. Merrilee shaded her eyes, looking for her mother's pink-flowered sunbonnet. Yes, it was there, the one closest to them.

"Reckon Mama's going to be okay?" she asked Josie.

"It appears so," Josie replied, casting an anxious look in her mother's direction. "She's keeping up, but just barely."

"Doc said she was well," Merrilee said.

"Doc didn't say anything about picking cotton," Josie said. "Daddy wanted her to stay at home, but she convinced him she was all right. I think Mama's worried about all the doctor bills that piled up when she was sick. Mr. Grant says cotton's not selling too high this year."

"Aw, Mr. Grant always says that," Merrilee scoffed. Josie smiled. That was true. If prices were higher, Mr. Grant was well pleased. If they were low, he said, "I told you."

"He's a fair man, though," Josie said. "He always gives Daddy his rightful share."

"Mm-hmm," Merrilee mumbled, keeping a wary eye on the boys picking a couple of yards ahead of her. They were slowing down now that the adults were out of sight. Slowly Merrilee and Josie drew closer to the boys. A boy from Merrilee's class was on her right. He had quit picking and was lying on his sack, watching a hawk circle in the blue sky.

"Travis Benton," Merrilee warned as she passed him, "you'd better not!"

"Not what?" he said innocently.

"Throw that hairy caterpillar on me!" Merrilee snapped.

"Me?" Travis exclaimed indignantly.

Merrilee frowned and reached behind to yank her sack closer. The boy behind Travis flipped something across the rows. Her fingers touched the fat worm that landed on the shoulder strap. "Yuck!" she muttered under her breath. She knew that one satisfactory scream could bring on a flock of practical jokes. Steeling herself, Merrilee flicked the caterpillar away and continued to pick.

"Aw, you're no fun," Travis grumbled.

"Too bad," Merrilee sniffed. She grinned as the boys lagged behind them, waiting on the next group of girls to come closer.

Only Randall Farley and Josie kept working. He was picking the rows next to Josie. Picking at the same pace, they began to pull ahead of Merrilee. She heard the quiet murmur of Randall's voice and Josie's silvery laughter. After seeing them together, Merrilee first thought about teasing her older sister. Then she saw how happy Josie was as she talked with Randall. She forgot her mischievous thoughts and suddenly feared that Josie would grow up and leave her behind. The four years between them had widened suddenly into a gulf.

Then she shook her head. "She's only thirteen," Merrilee told herself. "She's not going anywhere yet."

The noontime sun drove the pickers into the shade of the cotton wagon. A dipper from the barrel of cool water was passed around. Merrilee drank deeply and sat down beside her mother.

"You okay?" she said, looking at her mother's pale face.

"Just a little hot," Mrs. Palmer answered. "You wouldn't think it would be this hot in October." She fanned herself with the pink sunbonnet and smiled at Merrilee. "They're weighing now."

Merrilee looked at the group clustered around the scale. Sack after sack was weighed and recorded in Mr. Grant's little book. She watched eagerly as her sack was lifted to the scale. "Merrilee Palmer," Mr. Grant called out. "Eighty pounds."

Merrilee flushed with pleasure. That was fifteen pounds more than she had been able to pick in one morning last year. Mrs. Palmer patted her hand.

"You're doing great, honey," she said. "Keep it up, and you'll have that bike."

Mr. Palmer grinned at Merrilee as he stopped beside them. "A hundred pounds next year, maybe?"

Merrilee grinned back. Suddenly the morning's work didn't seem so hard.

Mr. Palmer looked at his wife's face. "You're going back to the house this minute," he said sternly. "Merrilee, Josie, I'm going to take your mother home and get her to lie down. You can go back to the field after you eat lunch. I'll be back in a little while."

The girls nodded and settled down with their paper bags. Josie unfolded her napkin as Merrilee hungrily bit into a chicken leg. "Slow down, Merrilee," Josie said, "you're going to get sick."

Merrilee swallowed carefully. "I hope Mama isn't going to get sick again."

"I think she's still tired. We can help her do the housework when we get home," Josie said.

"Mm-hmm," Merrilee nodded, mouth full again. It didn't seem long before one of the pickers called "Let's go!"

Groaning, Merrilee crawled to her feet. The afternoon stretched on, hot and dry. The children often sought the shade of nearby trees, trying to keep cool. Every trip back to the wagon to empty the full sacks was a relief. In the late afternoon a cool breeze sprang up, making work easier. Everyone began to pick a little faster. By the time the setting sun had turned the sky pink, the wagon was full.

"The first day is always hard," Daddy said, looking at the tired girls. "How about a ride home?"

"On the wagon?"

"On the wagon."

"Whoopee," Merrilee yelled, swinging herself over the sideboard. Josie landed beside her

on the soft cotton, bouncing slightly, then rolling over to look at the reddening sky.

"This is the best part of the day," Josie said dreamily. "Look, Merrilee, there's the evening star."

"Where?" Merrilee popped out from under the cotton she had piled over herself. "Where?"

Josie took one look at the cotton stuck to Merrilee's flushed face and laughed. Evening star forgotten, the girls began to sing.

When Mr. Palmer stopped the wagon outside the barn, the girls slid off and raced into the house.

Mrs. Palmer was sitting up, leaning against the pillows and reading.

"Are you feeling better, Mama?" Merrilee asked.

Her mother put down the book and held out her arms. "I'm much better," she said hugging her and starting to get up. "I was just a little tired."

"Don't get up, Mama," Josie said. "We're going to fix supper."

"That's right," Daddy said from the doorway. "And I'm going to help."

Mama threw up her hands and began to laugh. "All right, you three, I know when I'm beaten."

Sounds of running water and clattering pots soon came from the kitchen, along with giggling as Papa sang his favorite songs loudly and more than slightly off-key.

After supper the girls did the dishes and went off to take their baths. "I feel better," Merrilee said, bouncing on the bed and shaking her wet hair.

"Don't get water on the bed," Josie said absently. She was standing in front of the window, brushing her hair and looking out at the brilliant stars. The breeze lifted her hair and spread it across her shoulders.

Merrilee lay watching for a moment. "I bet I know what you're going to buy," she said suddenly.

Josie smiled.

"That dress in Carlson's window," Merrilee said triumphantly.

Josie's smiled faded, and she swung around to look at Merrilee. "How did you know? I didn't tell anyone."

"You stand outside that window every Saturday when we go to town," Merrilee replied. "It had to be something in the window, and I knew it wasn't the furniture."

"Well, what do you think?" Josie asked. "Isn't it beautiful?"

"Yes," Merrilee answered, remembering the swirls of white eyelet embroidered in a green the exact color of Josie's eyes. "But a store-bought dress? All that money for just a dress?"

Josie flinched. "Well, I need shoes, too." She hesitated for just a moment. "I know Mama could make me one, but she's not feeling well—and when I saw this one . . . ."

Merrilee nodded, thinking of the speech Josie was going to make at the fair. Half the county would be there, and that dress would look beautiful on Josie.

"Uh-huh. It's a pretty dress, Josie. You'll look nice in it."

Josie brightened. "You don't think I'm wasting my money?"

"Well," Merrilee teased, "you'd be better off with a basketball, or a rope."

She broke off as Josie jumped for the bed. Giggling, Merrilee slid off the other side, hitting the floor with a bump.

"Get to sleep in there, girls. Tomorrow's another day of hard work," their father called.

"Yes sir," the girls called back, straightening the bed. Then the only sound was night noises stealing in the open windows.

The next day was easier. Merrilee began to catch the rhythm of the other workers. Dragging behind her, the sack became less of a burden. Then too, whenever she began to drop behind, Josie stopped and helped her catch up.

"You're losing money," Merrilee said. "You could have emptied your sack twice more today if you hadn't helped me."

"A bike costs a lot of money," Josie smiled. "We'll do all right together."

And so the days passed by, clear and beautiful. None seemed as hot as that first day had, and the chatter back and forth among the workers made the picking seem easier. Mr. Palmer didn't let his wife pick again, but she was soon up working around the house. The days melted into weeks. November arrived, and Merrilee was half surprised when the last field was picked.

Josie and Merrilee stood in line with the others to get their brown pay envelopes. Merrilee ripped hers open to count the crisp green bills. Hugging herself in delight, she looked over at Josie. Josie had already resealed her envelope, but the brightness of her eyes told Merrilee that the dress and shoes were as good as bought.

After the picking was finished, Mr. Grant always gave a wiener roast for the workers. That night they roasted hot dogs and marshmallows over a bonfire. After-

wards the children played hide-and-seek in the dark, and Mr. Grant settled the accounts with Mr. Palmer.

Merrilee was racing wildly around a bush when Josie suddenly reached out and grabbed her arm. "You scared me!" Merrilee yelled.

"Hush," Josie said sharply. "I just heard Mr. Grant talking. The cotton did sell for less this year. I don't think Daddy made enough money."

"What are we going to do?" Merrilee said, startled.

"We can give him ours," Josie said. "You know he'd never ask for it."

Merrilee gave a fleeting thought to her disappearing bike before nodding. "Okay."

The next morning the girls put their pay envelopes on the breakfast table. "We want you to have these, Daddy," Josie said.

Mr. Palmer's eyes misted as he looked at his daughters. "Thanks, girls. Every bit helps. I'll give as much as I can back to you."

The next day was Saturday. Josie and Merrilee finished their chores early and were waiting beside the old Ford when their mother and father came out. Money or no money, they weren't going to miss a trip to town.

"Ready, girls?" Mr. Palmer asked as Josie reached up to straighten his tie.

When they reached town, Mr. Palmer parked in front of the doctor's office. "We'll meet you girls at Watkins' Drugstore in about an hour. Everything should be settled by then, and we can get some hamburgers."

The girls walked down the street to the dime store. Merrilee noticed that Josie didn't look across the street to Carlson's Department Store. They looked at just about everything in the dime store before Josie said, "It's time."

When they reached the drugstore, Mr. and Mrs. Palmer were just driving up. "Let's eat, girls," he said.

Merrilee had finished her hamburger and was gently blowing bubbles through her straw when Mr. Palmer put two envelopes on the table. "We had some left. I thought you two would like to go shopping."

"Oh, boy!" Merrilee said, reaching for her envelope. "Can we go now?"

He grinned and said, "Take off!"

Merrilee was the first one out the door. She waved at her mother

and father and turned toward the department store. Josie followed more slowly. Inside the store Merrilee headed for the sporting goods department, counting her money as she went. "Enough for a volleyball," she thought, "and a net and maybe something else."

Merrilee found the ball and balanced it in her hands. "I wonder if Josie likes volleyball," she thought. Putting the ball down, she walked back to the door. Josie stood outside on the sidewalk, looking at the dress in the window.

Merrilee stood for a moment watching her. She twisted the envelope in her hands, thinking of how Josie had helped her. Josie couldn't have more than Merrilee had. If Josie had worked on her own, she might have had enough money left over for the dress. Merrilee took one last look at the sporting goods section and walked outside.

"Well, come on in! Someone may buy that dress while you're looking," she said.

Josie just shook her head. "I don't have enough money. I can't get the dress."

"Sure you can," Merrilee said, handing Josie her pay envelope. "It'll be our dress. After all, I get it next, don't I?"

And she did. Josie wore the white dress with the pretty shoes to the Thanksgiving fair. Merrilee sat on the grass below the platform, listening to her sister with pride. Three years later, an older, taller Merrilee stood on another platform wearing the same dress. She looked across at Josie, seated with the others who had come to the eighth-grade graduation, and knew that she was remembering too.

Eli Whitney
and the
Cotton Gin

Beki Gorham

Cotton, cotton! Even at the Greenes' dinner party, cotton was the main topic of conversation. The women stopped to listen as the men discussed the problems of getting their valuable crops to market.

"Just about every family in the South grows cotton in their back yard. After all, cotton fiber can be made into strong cloth for clothing. But planting whole plantations in cotton! Foolish, gentlemen, foolish!" Dr. Ashley tapped his glass with his fork to emphasize his remark.

Two chairs down from him, Evangeline Charles murmured in agreement. "Just think about picking all that cotton in the hot sun. Then it has to be stored until the seeds can be picked out. Why, it takes a small family all winter to clean enough cotton to weave their own clothes and stockings!"

Mr. Tremayne coughed, "Some large plantations *do* invest chiefly in cotton, but the workers have to pick out the seeds by hand, Evangeline. The longer it takes, the less profitable it is. We need something to make the work go faster."

Mrs. Greene leaned forward. "Gentlemen," she exclaimed, "You simply must meet the young man from New York who has been staying with our family. He's extremely intelligent, and he is always working on better ways to do things. He'll be an inventor someday, I'm sure. In fact, he made me a beautiful loom after mine broke."

She put down her napkin and motioned to the servant at the door. "Louisa, set up the loom that Mr. Whitney made for me in the parlor." Turning back to her guests, she said, "If you are all finished, please join me in the parlor, and we will take a look at the loom."

The ladies and gentlemen gathered in the parlor. As they admired the workmanship of the loom, Mrs. Greene slipped out of the room. She returned shortly with a lanky young man.

"Ladies and gentlemen," she said, motioning toward her companion, "I'd like you to meet Mr. Eli Whitney."

Mr. Whitney was besieged with questions about the loom;

then he and the men talked about cotton and the difficulty of removing the seeds.

"If we could only process the cotton more quickly," Mr. Tremayne said, "we could increase our production and exportation to other countries. Why, cotton could become the moneymaker of the South!"

Interested, Mr. Whitney nodded. "I'll see what I can do," he said. "I'll have to give it some thought first."

He went out to the field to look at the small crop and took some of the cotton with him when he went back to the house. When he asked for a place to work, Mrs. Greene had a workshop set up for him in the basement. For ten days he worked behind the closed doors of the basement workshop. The banging and squeaking drew curious people from all over the plantation. As rumors of the secret project spread, people from all over Savannah came to see what the young Northerner was making. Eli turned everyone away from the door—servants, visitors, even his hostess. "It's a machine that will remove seeds from cotton," he told them. "That's all you need to know. The rest will remain secret until it is finished."

And no one knew any more until ten days later. Eli had completed a small model. He showed it to a few people, but they still kept the secret. Then six months later the cotton gin was ready. Eli obtained a patent for his machine in March of 1794. The secret was finally out. Eli Whitney had invented the cotton gin!

Eli Whitney's cotton gin consisted of a roller with wire teeth that projected through slits of an iron guard. The slits were smaller than the cotton seeds. When the roller turned, it pulled cotton fibers through the slits, leaving the larger seeds to fall into a box. The one-horsepower machine could separate seeds from the cotton fibers faster than fifty men working by hand. The cotton gin increased cotton exportation twentyfold and made cotton the staple crop of the South.

The Size of Service

Alicia Petersen

Glitter. So much glitter. It was everywhere—all around her. That was what she thought of life in Damascus. This great house in which she served seemed to twinkle, shine, and gleam everywhere. She was surrounded by the cool shine of marble floors; the warm gleam of brass adorning the walls; silver glistening from slender pitchers and vases; the shimmer of beautiful silken garments; and, of course, the lovely, deep luster of gold. Yes, there was much glitter in this beautiful place.

When she thought of her present home and its glitter, she always thought, too, of her other home—that small, poor house so far away in the land of Israel.

Sometimes it seemed her earlier life had been only a dream. But no, it had been real: the tiny single-roomed dwelling where she had lived with her grandmother. She recalled the days of sun and childish play but also the unhappy times when the children of the village had teased her.

"Did your mother and father desert you?" they taunted. "They probably decided you were just *too small* to matter!"

Hearing what was happening outside, Grandmother had called her into the house and wrapped her in loving arms. As she was comforted in her grandmother's warm embrace, Nahmi's heart was also comforted by the old woman's gentle-voiced talk of Jehovah. No person was small who trusted Jehovah! What a great God watched over Israel. And most wonderful of all, Jehovah cared even for *her*—an orphan. Always Grandmother ended by saying, "Wherever the path of your life may lead, Nahmi, *serve the Lord God Jehovah. Serve Him well!*"

Nahmi had wondered about her grandmother's challenge. She wondered exactly how a person—especially such a small person as she—could serve the mighty Jehovah God. Surely one must need to be like the prophet Elisha to be of true use to the Lord. Elisha's miracles were the talk of all Israel's common people.

Nahmi's life with her grandmother in the little house had ended suddenly one warm spring night. Nahmi had been jolted from sleep by the sound of pounding hooves, thundering chariot wheels, the shouts and curses of men, and the screams of women and children. That awful night a marauding band of Syrian soldiers had swept into the village! Nahmi would never forget the moment when she was torn from her grandmother's arms. As the tall soldier carried the girl from the house, the old woman stumbled after him, sobbing and calling, "Serve well, Nahmi; serve Jehovah well!"

Nahmi sighed as she remembered it all. But her sigh and her sad memories did not slow her hands in their task of polishing. Her mistress loved to have everything in the house gleaming. Oh, her fine mistress! How fortunate she was to have such a mistress. Surely Jehovah had been gracious.

She remembered that in the first terror-filled days after her capture, she had feared she would be chosen to serve one of the crude, disorderly soldiers. But though she could not then understand the harsh Syrian tongue, she saw that none of the soldiers was at all interested in claiming her for a servant. In fact, they seemed to be vying to see who would *not* have to take her. All the other captured villagers had been spoken for. "It's true, then, what the boys of my village said," thought Nahmi. "I'm too small to be even a servant to a Syrian!"

As the sun rose the third day of the journey, the raiders and their captives had come within sight of Damascus. As she marveled at the city's size, Nahmi heard a chariot draw near behind her. Moving aside quickly to let it pass, she was startled to see it stop. Standing tall and proud in the chariot was the leader of her Syrian captors! She had only caught glimpses of him from a distance until then. Nahmi's heart raced. What did the expression on his face mean? He spoke quietly but firmly to two soldiers who were nearby. Responding to what had obviously been a command, the two came toward Nahmi. They picked her up and swung her into the captain's chariot! Terrified, Nahmi crouched as close to the side of the chariot as she possibly could. Her trembling

stilled as the captain gently placed his hand on her head, smiled, and tried to show her that he would not hurt her.

So it was that Nahmi had made her entrance into Damascus. Riding in the captain's chariot, she sensed the affection and admiration the people of the city had for this military leader. The press of the crowd slowed progress through the streets. The people smiled, waved, and tried to touch the chariot and its driver. To the tired Israelite girl, it seemed a very long time before the chariot stopped. As the horses were drawn to a halt, she could only stare in wonder. This was the biggest

dwelling place she had ever seen! Dazed, she was helped from the chariot and across the threshold. The captain then gave Nahmi over into the care of several women. They in turn led her through a seemingly endless maze of rooms. Finally she was taken into a small, clean room where she was bathed, shampooed, scented, and then dressed in what seemed to her unbelievably beautiful garments. And at last she was taken to a room alive with rich glitter. In the middle of the room, reclining on a couch, was the most beautiful lady Nahmi had ever seen. It was not the silken garments, the golden jewelry, the milk-white skin, or the raven hair of the woman that drew Nahmi's heart. Instead, it was a spirit of sweetness which shone from her face. But there was something about this lovely woman which made Nahmi feel sorry for her: there seemed to be a strange sadness about her. But surely that first impression was wrong—how could such a lovely woman, surrounded by wealth, possibly be sad?

Thus Nahmi's life and service in Damascus had begun. For some unknown reason, the great Syrian captain, Naaman, had chosen her as a special maid for his wife. And from that first sight of her mistress, Nahmi served not just with hard-working hands but also with a loving heart. Slowly the strange Syrian sounds became recognizable speech to her; slowly Nahmi learned her way about the great house in which she served; slowly, too, she came to realize that the sadness she had sensed in her mistress was real.

So much glittered here. But so much was sadness, too. That mysterious air of unhappiness was explained one day as Nahmi stood dressing the luxurious long black locks of her mistress's hair. As Nahmi reached forward to sweep back the hair from her mistress's temples, her fingers felt dampness. Her mistress was *crying*! Nahmi moved quickly around to kneel in front of the stool, looking up into the lovely face. She knew it was bold of her, but she had to try to help. She asked, "Mistress, what is it? What is wrong? Please do not cry. Can I help?"

"Help?" echoed her mistress. "Thank you, little one, but there is no help for my sadness. Look around you, Nahmi. Is it not impressive? Is it not lovely, all the shining ornamentation of our

riches?" Her tears flowed more freely as she went on: "But what is wealth? Or this great house or my dear husband's place as captain of the Syrian hosts and the favorite of King Benhadad? All of it is as nothing, Nahmi, nothing! For Naaman is. . . . Naaman has. . . . My husband is a *leper*, Nahmi."

Shocked, Nahmi replied, "A leper, Mistress? But he seems so strong and well."

Raising her face from her hands, her mistress replied, "His leprosy is slight. I thank the gods of Syria each day for that fact. It does not keep him from the military service he loves or from the court where he is so popular. Not yet, that is. But the physicians warn that the disease will soon become much worse. When that happens, we must . . . Naaman will become . . . an *outcast!* "

Looking up into the sad, beautiful face, Nahmi felt her own eyes fill with tears. "Oh, Mistress," whispered Nahmi broken-heartedly, "if my dear master were in the land of Israel, his disease could be cured!"

"Cured? You speak foolishly, child," replied her mistress gently.

"Nothing is impossible to the great Jehovah, God of Israel," Nahmi persisted. "He has a

mighty prophet, Elisha by name, who works miraculous things among the people. And this great man of God sometimes dwells in Samaria. If, while he were there, my lord Naaman could. . . ."

"Samaria—so close. A god of miracles? And E-li-sha, his prophet? If only such a thing might truly be! But the very thought is as a dream."

"Could you not at least *speak* of the matter to Master Naaman, Mistress? If there were some way—any way—my master could reach Elisha. . . ."

"Your love and desire to help are sweet to me, Nahmi. Even in the midst of hopelessness, they bring comfort to my heart."

"I want to bring help to my master and lift the burden of your heart, Mistress," protested Nahmi. "But only the great hand of Jehovah can do those things. So, I shall pray."

"Many, many prayers have been offered to our god, Rimmon! See—there in the niche—the flowers I take every day, begging his help for my beloved husband. But the months have passed, and Naaman's trouble worsens."

"I know nothing of stone gods, Mistress. But I do know of the living God, Jehovah. To Him I will go in prayer. And if you could speak of Elisha to my Master Naaman—"

"Hush now, Little One," the mistress murmured. "The sun sinks low. Naaman will be coming home from the court soon. It is hopeless even to think, and yet—perhaps—just perhaps I will speak to my husband of these things."

Days passed, and weeks. Their passing was marked by Nahmi's faithful, earnest praying for Jehovah's help.

But the first part of her prayer was answered. Captain Naaman went to Samaria to seek the Prophet Elisha's help! It seemed to Nahmi that her whole world held its breath while he was gone. All Damascus whispered the news of Naaman's petition to King Benhadad and the wealth of silver and gold he took to Samaria to purchase Elisha's cooperation.

And so they waited: all those in Damascus and those in the lovely, glittering dwelling of Captain Naaman. Nahmi's prayers were constant now. Her every thought was with her absent master, and she begged Jehovah to work through His prophet. The others of the household prayed, too, but their prayers were unlike Nahmi's silent communication with her God. Instead, they prayed with offerings of flowers and fruits and the smoky burning of sacrifices to little statues of the Syrian god Rimmon. They moaned and cried aloud. "How terrible," Nahmi thought, "to worship a god whose ears and heart are stone!"

At last Naaman returned home. But neither the city nor most of his own household knew of his coming, for it was quiet in the dark of night.

In the early morning hours of the new day, Nahmi was shaken awake by Sulla, the overseer of the household servants. "Nahmi. Nahmi, wake up! You must hurry: Master Naaman returned during the night. He commands your presence at once in the mistress's bedchamber."

Shaking with fear and excitement, Nahmi dressed, drew her sleep-tumbled hair into a tidy knot, and ran to her mistress's quarters. Reaching the doorway, she stopped suddenly. Master and mistress turned together at the sound of her arrival. As she silently beckoned Nahmi to come to her, the mistress's eyes overflowed with tears. At sight of the tears, Nahmi was dismayed. It had all been in vain then! Master Naaman had returned as he had gone—what would lie ahead for her?

But then Nahmi saw that although both her mistress and master were crying, the tears wetting their cheeks came from eyes that shone like stars: eyes expressing infinite joy!

Master Naaman's voice was husky and hesitating as he spoke: "Your mistress and I wanted you here to tell you . . . to tell you at once . . . that your Jehovah God has heard your prayers, little one. The thanks we owe to you can never be properly expressed. For see—the spots, those dread spots—all of them are gone!"

The mistress's arm went about Nahmi's shoulders. "Come, let us sit together while the master tells the tale. I myself still cannot take it in."

As the tiny Nahmi sat between her master and mistress, the words Captain Naaman spoke transported her to the soil of Samaria, and in her mind she saw the drama he described: mighty Naaman's arrival at the prophet Elisha's residence . . . the disbelief the captain felt when the prophet would not even see him but instead sent a servant out to

deliver an unbelievable instruction: "Go and wash seven times in the Jordan River, and your flesh will be made new."

"I confess that my anger knew no bounds!" snorted Naaman. "Imagine it—all the time spent, the petitioning of both the kings of Syria and Israel—only to have some unseen prophet send word by his servant that I should wash in Jordan's waters! Who could have thought such a thing! Why, there should have been great drama in the moment! The man of Jehovah should have come out to me himself, made loud supplications to heaven; or he might at least have struck the spots of my leprosy with his hand,

that the miracle of healing could be accomplished! But no—nothing but a ragged servant and a ridiculous instruction. I thought the rivers of Syria were certainly far better than Israel's muddy Jordan. The prophet's servant did well to leap out of the way, for I turned my horses, shouted to my men, and wheeled my chariot away from that lowly place in a great cloud of dust!"

"But Master, how then came your healing?" Nahmi asked in a quavering voice.

Naaman responded slowly: "It came only as I cast away my anger and my pride. As I first heard of Jehovah's prophet Elisha through you—a servant—so too did I obey the prophet, because my servants who rode with me begged me to reconsider. Slowly, at their urging, I slew my anger and buried my pride. It was a different, a humble Naaman who entered a foreign river in obedience to a foreign God's command, and it was a healed Naaman who came forth from the water!"

"Master, oh my dear Master, how my heart rejoices!"

"And so it should. For my body has been cleansed of that which would have made me an outcast. But, too, there is cause for other, yea even greater rejoicing," Naaman's sun-bronzed hand touched his chest as he spoke. "Here, too, there has come healing. Mine was a sickly heart— a heart scarred with the fatal worship of a stone god. No more. This heart is now new, alive, joyful. None but the Lord God Jehovah shall be worshiped by my heart and my house from this time forward!"

"Oh, Master, I . . ."

"Ah yes, *you*, little one. To you I owe unspeakable gratitude. What great service you have rendered!" Naaman exclaimed.

"Great service? Oh no," protested Nahmi. "I'm far too small."

Naaman gently laid a finger across Nahmi's lips, stilling her speech. "What size is service, Nahmi? You have proven that what is smallest in itself holds the greatest potential for serving others and for serving God."

Glitter. So much glitter. It was everywhere—all around her. But now, there was a difference. Now there was the rich gleam that comes only from hearts aglow with the golden love of the God of Heaven.

Glossary

This glossary contains information about selected words found in this reader. You can find meanings of words as they are used in the stories. Certain unusual words such as foreign names are included so that you can pronounce them correctly when you read.

The pronunciation symbols below show how to pronounce each vowel and several of the less familiar consonants.

ă	pat	ĕ	pet	î	fierce
ā	pay	ē	be	ŏ	pot
â	care	ĭ	pit	ō	go
ä	father	ī	pie	ô	paw, for

oi	oil	ŭ	cut	zh	vision
ŏŏ	book	û	fur	ə	ago, item, pencil, atom, circus
ōō	boot	hw	which		
yōō	abuse	*th*	the	ər	butter
ou	out	th	thin		

aard·vark (ärd′ värk′) —*noun* A South African burrowing mammal.

aardvark

a·bort (ə bôrt′) —*verb* To cancel before completing.

a·buse (ə byo͞oz′) —*verb* To hurt or injure by treating in a cruel way.

ac·ces·so·ry (ăc sĕs′ ə rē) —*noun* An extra item that goes with or improves a main item.

ac·ti·vate (ăc′ tə vāt′) —*verb* To set in operation or motion.

ad·re·nal (əd rē′ nəl) —*adjective* Having to do with a stimulating chemical produced by the body.

ae·ro·sol (âr′ ə sôl′) —*noun* A mass of tiny drops of a liquid or pieces of solid material suspended in air or another gas.

af·front (ə frŭnt′) —*noun* A deliberate insult.

ag·gie (ăg′ ē) —*noun* A marble used in playing games.

a·ghast (ə găst′) —*adjective* Shocked or terrified.

a·gile (ăj′ əl) or (ăj′ īl′) —*adjective* Capable of moving quickly and easily; nimble.

a·gue (ā′ gyo͞o) —*noun* A sickness with periods of chills and fever.

al·cove (ăl′ kōv′) —*noun* An inset or recessed part of a room.

alms (ämz) —*noun* Money or food given to the poor.

a·loof (ə lo͞of′) —*adjective* Cool and distant; not very friendly.

am·ble (ăm′ bəl) —*noun* An easy, unhurried walk.

am·pu·tate (ăm′ pyo͞o tāt′) —*verb* To cut off all or part of an arm, leg, or finger.

a·nal·y·sis (ə năl′ ĭ sĭs) —*noun* Any careful study of a subject and its details.

an·cient (ān′ shənt) —*adjective* Very old.

a·nes·the·tize (ə nĕs′ thə tīz′) —*verb* To give someone a numbing drug.

angst (ängkst) —*noun* A vague feeling of fear.

animist (ăn′ ĭ mĭst) —*noun* One who believes that objects and animals have living souls.

ap·pren·tice·ship (ə prĕn′ tĭs shĭp′) —*noun* The time a person spends learning a trade or job skill while working for a master craftsman.

ap·pro·pri·ate (ə prō′ prē ĭt) —*adjective* Suitable; proper.

a·ro·ma (ə rō′ mə) —*noun* A pleasant smell; fragrance.

ă pat	ā pay	â care	ä father	ĕ pet	ē be	ĭ pit	ī pie	î fierce	ŏ pot	ō go
ô paw, for	oi oil	o͝o book	o͞o boot	yo͞o abuse	ou out	ŭ cut	û fur	hw which
th the	th thin	zh vision	ə ago, item, pencil, atom, circus	ər butter

602

ar·ray (ə rā′) —*noun* An orderly arrangement; an impressive display or collection.

array

ar·ro·gant (ăr′ ə gənt) —*adjective* Proud; haughty.

as·sas·sin (ə săs′ ĭn) —*noun* A murderer.

as·say (ăs′ ā′) or (ă sā′) —*verb* To try to do something.

a·stride (ə strīd′) —*adjective* With one leg on each side of.

au·di·ence (ô′ dē əns) —*noun* A formal hearing or a conference.

au·thor·i·ta·tive (ə thôr′ ĭ tā′ tĭv) —*adjective* Coming from proper authority; official.

a·venge (ə vĕnj′) —*verb* To take revenge.

awl (ôl) —*noun* A pointed tool that is used to make small holes in wood or leather.

az·ure (ăzh′ ər) —*noun* A light to medium blue, like that of the sky on a clear day.

balm·y (bä′ mē) —*adjective* Mild, pleasant.

ban·ish (băn′ ĭsh) —*verb* To force someone to leave the country.

bar (bär) —*noun* The ruling association of lawyers.

barge (bärj) —*noun* A boat with a flat bottom used to carry freight.

bar·ri·cade (băr′ ĭ kād′) or (băr′ ĭ kād′) —*noun* A quickly built fence set up for defense.

base (bās) —*adjective* Not honorable; shameful, mean, or low.

bawl (bôl) —*verb* To cry out or call in a loud, strong voice; bellow.

bay (bā) —*verb* To bark with long, deep cries.

bea·con (bē′ kən) —*noun* A fire, light, or radio signal used to guide or warn.

bear·ings (bâr′ ĭngz) —*noun* A person's position in relationship to surroundings; a geographical location.

beat (bēt) —*verb* To strike an opponent's blade with a single sharp blow of the fencing foil.

beech (bēch) —*noun* A tree with light, smooth bark and edible nuts enclosed in prickly hulls.

beech

be·siege (bĭ sēj′) —*verb* 1. To surround in order to capture. 2. To crowd around and hem in.

be·sought (bĭ sôt′) —*verb* Asked in a serious way; begged.

be·wil·dered (bĭ wĭl′ dĕrd) —*adjective* Confused or puzzled.

bil·low·y (bĭl′ ō ē) —*adjective* Surging like waves.

bond·age (bŏn′ dĭj) —*noun* The condition of being a slave; slavery.

book (bŏŏk) —*verb* To record police charges against a person.

boom (bŏŏm) —*noun* A long pole used to stretch out the bottom of a sail.

boot camp (boōt cămp) —*noun* A camp for training military recruits.

bout (bout) —*noun* A contest.

bow·line (bō′ lĭn) or (bō′ līn′) —*noun* A rope used to control a sail.

bow net (bō′ nĕt′) —*noun* A special bowed net used for trapping wild birds.

bram·ble (brăm′ bəl) —*noun* A prickly plant or shrub, like a raspberry bush.

bran·dish (brăn′ dĭsh) —*verb* To wave in a threatening way.

brawn·y (brô′ nē) —*adjective* Muscular; very strong.

bra·zen (brā′ zən) —*adjective* Brass-colored or made of brass.

breach (brēch) —*noun* A hole or blank space in something.

break (brāk) —*verb* To train a horse to respond to human commands.

break·er (brā′ kər) —*noun* A wave that breaks into foam when it reaches shore.

breech·es (brĭch′ ĭz) —*noun* Short trousers that are fastened at or just below the knees.

brig·and (brĭg′ ənd) —*noun* One of a group of robbers.

broach (brōch) —*verb* To bring up a subject in a roundabout way.

bronc (brŏngk) —*noun* Also *bronco*. A small, wild or partly tamed horse of the West.

brute (broōt) —*adjective* Physical or muscular.

bu·bon·ic plague (boō bŏn′ ĭk plāg′) —*noun* A contagious, usually fatal, disease.

buck·le (bŭk′ əl) —*verb* To bend or twist.

bulk·head (bŭlk′ hĕd′) —*noun* One of the partitions that divide a ship or plane into compartments.

bulk·y (bŭl′ kē) —*adjective* Having great size or volume.

bur·lap (bûr′ lăp′) —*noun* A coarse cloth woven of thick fibers of hemp, jute, or flax.

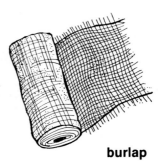

burlap

cal·is·then·ics (kăl′ ĭs thĕn′ ĭks) —*noun* A series of exercises to build muscles and endurance.

ca·nal (kə năl′) —*noun* A man-made body of water that connects two or more points. Canals are used for travel, shipping, irrigation, or drainage.

can·is·ter (kăn′ ĭ stər) —*noun* An airtight container.

cap·tor (kăp′ tər) —*noun* One who keeps a person or thing as prisoner.

car·a·van (kăr′ ə văn′) —*noun* A group traveling together in a long line.

ca·reen (kə rēn′) —*verb* To lurch, lean, or swerve while in motion.

car·go (kär′ gō) —*noun* The freight carried by a ship, airplane, or other vehicle.

/ ă pat / ā pay / â care / ä father / ĕ pet / ē be / ĭ pit / ī pie / î fierce / ŏ pot / ō go /
/ ô paw, for / oi oil / ŏŏ book / ōō boot / yōō abuse / ou out / ŭ cut / û fur / hw which /
/ *th* the / th thin / zh vision / ə ago, item, pencil, atom, circus / ər butter /

car·niv·o·rous (kär nĭv′ ər əs) —*adjective* Feeding on the flesh of other animals.

car·tog·raph·er (kär tŏg′ rəf ər) —*noun* One who maps or charts regions.

case·ment (kās′ mənt) —*noun* The frame of a window that swings outward on hinges.

caste (kăst) —*noun* Strictly enforced class divisions of Hindu society. Marriage and occupations are determined by one's caste classification.

cast·ing (kăs′ tĭng) —*noun* The indigestible part of a bird's food that the bird forms into a ball and spits out.

cat·a·mount (kăt′ ə mount′) —*noun* Mountain lion.

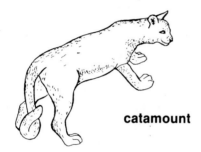

catamount

cat·a·ract (kăt′ ə răkt′) —*noun* A huge waterfall.

cat·e·chism (kăt′ ĭ kĭz′ əm) —*noun* Basic knowledge presented in a question-and-answer format.

ce·les·tial (sə lĕs′ chəl) —*adjective* Having to do with the sky or heaven.

chafe (chāf) —*verb* To bother or annoy.

chan·de·lier (shăn′ də lîr′) —*noun* A hanging lamp holding many separate lights.

chan·nel (chăn′ əl) —*verb* To form a passageway in or through something.

cha·rade (shə rād′) —*noun* A foolish attempt at deception.

cher·ish (chĕr′ ĭsh) —*verb* To care for tenderly and affectionately; to love.

chil·blain (chĭl′ blān′) —*noun* Itchy, irritated skin that has been exposed to moist, cold air.

cho·ral (kôr′ əl) or (kōr′ əl) —*adjective* Performed by a choir of voices.

chro·mi·um (krō′ mē əm) —*noun* A hard steel-gray metal that resists tarnishing.

churn (chûrn) —*verb* To move or swirl violently.

cinch (sĭnch) —*verb* To fasten firmly to a saddle with a strap.

ci·pher·ing (sī′ fər ĭng) —*noun* The figuring of basic math equations.

clam·ber (klăm′ bər) —*verb* To climb on all fours with some trouble.

cla·mor (klăm′ ər) —*noun* Loud, confused noise.

clench (klĕnch) —*verb* To grasp or grip tightly.

clus·ter (klŭs′ tər) —*noun* Tightly grouped items of a group.

cob·bler (kŏb′ lər) —*noun* A person who makes or repairs shoes.

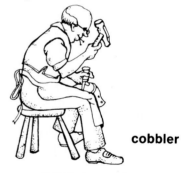

cobbler

cob·ble stones (kŏb′ əl stōnz′) —*noun* Round stones once used to pave streets.

cof·fer (kô′ fər) or (kŏf′ ər) —*noun* A strong-box or treasury.

com·mence (kə mĕns′) —*verb* To begin; to start.

com·mu·nism (kŏm′ yə nĭ′ zəm) —*noun* A social system in which there are no social classes and little or no private property. The governments of some countries, such as Russia, are based on this idea. These countries actually have a small privileged and powerful ruling class and very little freedom for anyone else.

com·pa·ny (kŭm′ pə nē) —*noun* A group of soldiers commanded by a captain.

com·plex (kəm plĕks′) or (kŏm′ plĕks′) —*adjective* Made up of many parts.

com·po·sure (kəm pō′ zhər) —*noun* Control over one's emotions; a calm manner; self-control.

com·put·er graph·ics (kəm pyoo′ tər grăf′ ĭks) —*adjective* Having to do with a detailed image created by a computer.

con·fer (kən fûr′) —*verb* To gather to discuss a specific matter.

con·i·cal (kŏn′ ĭ kəl) —*adjective* Shaped somewhat like a cone.

conical

con·se·quence (kŏn′ sĭ′ kwĕns) —*noun* Something that happens as a result of another action.

con·sign (kən sīn′) —*verb* To give over to the trust or care of another.

con·ster·na·tion (kŏn′ stər nā′ shən) —*noun* Amazement, confusion.

con·su·late (kŏn′ sə lĭt) —*noun* The office of a government official when he represents a foreign country.

con·sult (kən sŭlt′) —*verb* To go to for advice, an opinion, or information.

con·tend·er (kən tĕnd′ ər) —*noun* One who participates in competition.

con·tor·tion (kən tôr′ shən) —*noun* A position that is twisted or bent severely out of shape.

con·vict (kən vĭkt′) —*verb* To persuade someone of his sinfulness.

co·or·din·a·tion (kō ôr′ də nā′ shən) —*noun* Harmonized functioning of the muscles.

cope (kōp) —*verb* To struggle with and overcome some problem.

cor·on·a·tion (kôr′ ə nā′ shən) or (kŏr′ ə nā′ shən) —*noun* The ceremony of crowning a king or a queen.

Corps (kôr) or (kōr) —*noun* A group of men assigned to a specific job in the army.

corps-à-corps (kôr′ ə kôr′) —*noun* Literally, a "body-to-body" position.

cor·ri·dor (kôr′ ĭ dər) —*noun* A narrow hallway or passage in a building with doors opening onto it.

coun·ter·at·tack (koun′ tər ə tăk′) —*noun* A return attack.

cow·er (kou′ ər) —*verb* To withdraw or shrink away because of fear.

crab ap·ple (krăb′ ăp′ əl) —*noun* A small, sour fruit that looks like an apple.

crag (krăg) —*noun* A steep portion of rock that juts out of a cliff.

crag·gy (krăg′ ē) —*adjective* Resembling or similar to rugged cliffs.

crane (krān) —*verb* To strain or stretch one's neck.

cray·fish (krā′ fĭsh′) —*noun* A water animal that looks like a lobster but is much smaller.

crest (krĕst) —*verb* To come to the top of something, such as a hill or a wave.

crest·fall·en (krĕst′ fôl′ ən) —*adjective* Depressed; deflated.

cringe (krĭnj) —*verb* To shrink back fearfully.

cro·chet (krō shā′) —*verb* To make by connecting loops of thread with a hooked needle.

/ ă pat / ā pay / â care / ä father / ĕ pet / ē be / ĭ pit / ī pie / î fierce / ŏ pot / ō go /
/ ô paw, for / oi oil / oo book / oo boot / yoo abuse / ou out / ŭ cut / û fur / hw which /
/ *th* the / th thin / zh vision / ə ago, item, pencil, atom, circus / ər butter /

crop (krŏp) —*noun* A small pouch in a bird's digestive system that stores partly digested food.

crow (krō) —*verb* To utter a cry of delight.

crow·hop (krō′ hŏp′) —*noun* A stiff-legged jump in which the horse has all four hooves off the ground at the same time.

crys·tal·lized (krĭs′ tə līzd′) —*adjective* Covered with sugar.

cu·bi·cle (kyōō′ bĭ kəl) —*noun* A small room.

cu·bit (kyōō′ bĭt) —*noun* A unit of measure about eighteen inches long.

cur (kûr) —*noun* A lowly breed of dog.

cur·few (kûr′ fyōō) —*noun* A regulation forbidding people to be in the streets after a certain time.

cur·ry (kûr′ ē) or (kŭr′ ē) —*noun* A blend of several very powerful spices.

cur·tail (kər tāl′) —*verb* To stop or cut off unexpectedly.

cut·o·ver (kŭt′ ō′ vər) —*verb* To circle the blade over the opponent's foil.

cut·ter (kŭt′ ər) —*noun* A lightly armed motorboat used by the coast guard.

cy·press (sī′ prəs) —*noun* An evergreen tree that has small needles that look like scales; it is commonly found in swamps.

D

dachs·hund (däks′ hŏont′) or (dăk′ sənd′) —*noun* A small dog with a long body, drooping ears, and very short legs.

dachshund

darn (därn′) —*verb* To mend cloth by interweaving long stitches of thread or yarn across the hole.

daw·dling (dôd′ lĭng) —*verb* Taking more time than is needed.

day sail·er (dā′ sā′ lər) —*noun* A small sailboat for day trips.

de·base (dĭ bās′) —*verb* To lower in quality.

de·ceive (dĭ sēv′) —*verb* To make a person believe something that is not true; to mislead.

de·con·tam·i·nate (dē′ kən tăm′ ə nāt′) —*verb* To destroy impurities or pollution.

de·coy (dē koi′) or (dĭ koi′) —*noun* A person who leads another person into danger.

deft (dĕft) —*adjective* Quick and skillful.

de·fy (dĭ fī′) —*verb* To resist or challenge authority.

de·jec·tion (dĭ jĕk′ shən) —*noun* Sadness, depression.

de·lir·i·ous (dĭ lîr′ ē əs) —*adjective* Out of one's senses; raving.

del·ta (dĕl′ tə) —*noun* A mass of sand, mud, and soil that settles at the mouth of a river.

de·mol·ish (dĭ mŏl′ ĭsh) —*verb* To tear down completely; wreck.

de·pres·sur·ize (dē prĕsh′ ər īz′) —*verb* To release from pressure.

de·prive (dĭ prīv′) —*verb* To take something away from a person.

de·sert (dĭ zûrt′) —*verb* To abandon or forsake.

des·ti·na·tion (dĕs′ tə nā′ shən) —*noun* The end goal of a journey.

des·ti·tute (dĕs′ tĭ tōōt′) or (dĕs′ tĭ tyōōt′) —*adjective* Utterly lacking; poor.

de·tach (dĭ tăch′) —*verb* To separate or disconnect.

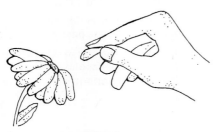

detach

de·tain (dĭ tān′) —*verb* To slow down or delay someone.

de·tour (dē′ tōōr′) —*verb* To take a path other than that originally planned.

de·vi·ate (dē′ vē āt′) —*verb* To go astray from a certain path.

de·vice (dĭ vīs′) —*noun* A machine that is designed to do several different jobs.

di·ag·nose (dī′ əg nōs′) —*verb* To identify or distinguish clearly, especially a disease.

di·a·lect (dī′ ə lĕkt′) —*noun* A way of speaking a language in different places or parts of a country.

di·a·logue (dī′ ə lôg′) or (dī′ ə lŏg′) —*noun* The words spoken by characters in a play or story.

dig·ni·ty (dĭg′ nĭ tē) —*noun* Worthiness or honorableness.

di·min·ish·ing (dĭ mĭn′ ĭsh ĭng) —*adjective* Gradually getting smaller.

di·plo·ma·cy (dĭ plō′ mə sē) —*noun* Tact in helping people.

dis·card (dĭs cärd′) —*verb* To throw away.

dis·cern (dĭ sûrn′) or (dĭ zûrn′) —*verb* To recognize differences; to judge.

dis·charge (dĭs chärj′) —*verb* To release from work, service, or jail; dismiss.

dis·con·so·late (dĭs kŏn′ sə lĭt) —*adjective* Hopelessly discouraged.

dis·dain·ful (dĭs dān′ fəl) —*adjective* Feeling or showing contempt or scorn.

dis·en·gage (dĭs′ ĕn gāj′) —*verb* To circle one's blade under an opponent's foil.

dis·mount (dĭs mount′) —*verb* To get off or down.

dis·patch·er (dĭs păch′ ər) —*noun* One who sends out messages.

dis·pel (dĭ spĕl′) —*verb* To send away or scatter.

dis·sent (dĭ sĕnt′) —*verb* To think or feel differently; to disagree.

dis·tinct·ly (dĭ stĭngkt′ lē) —*adverb* Clearly, definitely.

dis·tin·guished (dĭ stĭng′ gwĭsht) —*adjective* Excellent; famous; important.

do·jo (dō′ jō) —*noun* A school for learning martial arts.

do·main (dō mān′) —*noun* An area controlled by a person or animal.

domain

down·cast (doun kăst′) —*adjective* Depressed; low in spirits.

draft (drăft) or (dräft) —*noun* Selection for duty in the military.

/ ă pat / ā pay / â care / ä father / ĕ pet / ē be / ĭ pit / ī pie / î fierce / ŏ pot / ō go / / ô paw, for / oi oil / ŏŏ book / ōō boot / yōō abuse / ou out / ŭ cut / û fur / hw which / / *th* the / th thin / zh vision / ə ago, item, pencil, atom, circus / ər butter /

drone (drōn) —*verb* To make a low humming noise.

du·bi·ous (dōō′ bē əs) or (dyōō′ bē əs) —*adjective* Skeptical, reluctant, undecided.

dug·out (dŭg′ out′) —*noun* A boat made by hollowing out a special type of log.

dys·en·ter·y (dĭs′ ən tĕr′ ē) —*noun* A disease of the lower intestine usually associated with poor sanitation.

ear·nest (ûr′ nĕst) —*noun* Money paid in advance to bind an agreement.

e·dict (ē′ dĭkt′) —*noun* A decree of royalty.

el·e·ments (ĕl′ ə məntz) —*noun* The forces that produce weather.

e·lim·i·nate (ĭ lĭm′ ə nāt′) —*verb* To leave out; omit; reject.

em·bank·ment (ĕm băngk′ mənt) —*noun* A mound of earth or stone surrounding a body of water.

e·merge (ĭ mûrj′) —*verb* To come into view; appear.

em·er·y stone (ĕm′ ə rē stōn′) or (ĕm′ rē stōn′) —*noun* A fine-grained stone used for grinding or polishing.

em·is·sar·y (ĕm′ ə sĕr′ ē) —*noun* An agent or messenger.

em·phat·i·cal·ly (ĕm făt′ ĭk lē) —*adverb* Forcefully, definitely.

en·act (ĕn ăkt′) —*verb* To act out as in a drama.

en·coun·ter (ĕn koun′ tər) —*verb* To come upon or meet.

en·gage·ment (ĕn gāj′ mənt) —*noun* A battle.

en·sure (ĕn shŏŏr′) —*verb* To make certain of.

en·thu·si·ast (ĕn thōō′ zē ăst′) —*noun* A person possessed with an idea; a fanatic.

e·phah (ē′ fə) —*noun* An ancient measurement nearly equal to a bushel.

es·sen·tial (ĭ sĕn′ shəl) —*adjective* Of the greatest importance; basic; fundamental.

et·i·quette (ĕt′ ĭ kĕt′) or (ĕt′ ĭ kĭt′) —*noun* A set of rules for behaving properly in different situations.

e·va·sion (ĭ vā′ zhən) —*noun* Avoiding or getting away from something or someone.

ev·er·glade (ĕv′ ər glād′) —*noun* A large area of marshland covered with tall grass.

everglade

ev·o·lu·tion (ĕv′ ə lōō′ shən) —*noun* The imagined processes by which living things supposedly formed by themselves without a Creator and somehow kept improving by themselves.

ex·act (ĭg zăkt′) —*verb* To demand the payment of.

ex·hi·bi·tion (ĕk′ sə bĭsh′ ən) —*noun* A public display.

ex·ile (ĕg′ zīl′) —*noun* One who has been forced to leave his home or country.

ex·ot·ic (ĭg zŏt′ ĭk) —*adjective* Unusual; foreign.

ex·por·ta·tion (ĕk′ spôr tā′ shən) —*noun* Shipment to another country for sale.

ex·tend (ĭk stĕnd′) —*verb* To reach or stretch.

ex·tinct (ĭk stĭngkt′) —*adjective* No longer in existence.

fac·tu·al (făk′ chōō əl) —*adjective* Based on or including facts.

fal·ter (fôl′ tər) —*verb* To move unsteadily; to stumble.

fam·ished (făm′ ĭsht) —*adjective* Extremely hungry.

fare (fâr) —*verb* To get along, survive.

far·thing (fär′ *th*ĭng) —*noun* A British coin worth less than a penny.

feint (fānt) —*verb* To pretend to attack in order to draw an opponent's defense away.

fer·ry (fĕr′ ē) —*noun* A boat used to carry people back and forth across a body of water.

fer·vent (fûr′ vənt) —*adjective* Showing warmth or enthusiasm.

fer·vor (fûr′ vər) —*noun* Heated emotion.

fet·ish (fĕt′ ĭsh) —*noun* An object believed to have supernatural power.

feud (fyōōd) —*noun* A long, bitter quarrel between two people or groups.

fil·tered (fĭl′ tərd) —*adjective* Passed through a porous substance to remove impurities.

fi·nan·cial (fə năn′ shəl) —*adjective* Having to do with the management and use of money.

fit·ful (fĭt′ fəl) —*adjective* Irregular or interrupted.

flail (flāl) —*verb* To swing wildly about.

fledg·ling (flĕj′ lĭng) —*noun* A young bird just learning to fly.

fleet·ing (flē′ tĭng) —*adjective* Quickly passing.

flinch (flĭnch) —*verb* To pull back quickly in pain or fear; to wince.

flitch (flĭch) —*noun* A side of bacon cured and salted to preserve it.

foil (foil) —*noun* A long, light, thin sword used in fencing. A red plastic tip on the foil prevents injuries.

fore·see (fôr sē′) or (fōr sē′) —*verb* To see, imagine, or realize in advance.

for·sake (fôr sāk′) —*verb* To give up, abandon, leave behind.

fran·tic (frăn′ tĭk) —*adjective* Very excited with fear or worry.

fren·zy (frĕn′ zē) —*noun* Wild, energetic excitement.

fret (frĕt) —*verb* To worry.

friv·o·lous (frĭv′ ə ləs) —*adjective* Not serious, unimportant.

frock (frŏk) —*noun* A smocklike garment worn by women in olden times.

frock

fruit·less (frōōt′ lĭs) —*adjective* Unsuccessful.

fur·tive·ly (fûr′ tĭv lē) —*adverb* Quietly and sneakily like a thief.

fu·se·lage (fyōō′ sə′ läzh) or (fyōō′ zə′ läzh) —*noun* The main body of an airplane.

fu·tile (fyōōt′ l) or (fyōō′ tīl′) —*adjective* Having no useful result; ineffective.

fu·tur·is·tic (fyōō′ chər ĭs′ tĭk) —*adjective* Describing a time yet to come.

/ ă pat / ā pay / â care / ä father / ĕ pet / ē be / ĭ pit / ī pie / î fierce / ŏ pot / ō go /
/ ô paw, for / oi oil / ŏŏ book / ōō boot / yōō abuse / ou out / ŭ cut / û fur / hw which /
/ *th* the / th thin / zh vision / ə ago, item, pencil, atom, circus / ər butter /

ga·la·bi·a (gə lā′ bē yə) —*noun* A smock-like robe worn by Egyptian natives.

gal·li·vant (găl′ ə vănt′) —*verb* To roam about in search of amusement.

gape (gāp) —*verb* To stare at something with one's mouth open.

gar·ble (gär′ bəl) —*verb* To disorder; to scramble.

gawk (gôk) —*verb* To stare rudely.

gay·a·tri (gā′ yə trē) —*noun* A sacred saying.

ga·zelle (gə zĕl′) —*noun* A very swift, deer-like animal of Asia and Africa.

gazelle

ges·ture (jĕs′ chər) —*noun* A movement of a body part, made to help express a feeling.

ghat (gôt) or (gät) —*noun* A broad flight of steps leading down to a river.

gi (gē) —*noun* A uniform used in the martial arts made up of loose cotton pants, a tunic, and a belt.

gib·let (jĭb′ lĭt) —*noun* The heart, liver, or gizzard of a bird.

glide (glīd) —*verb* In fencing, to exert pressure on an opponent's blade with the foil and slide it across to score on the opponent's jacket.

glow·er (glou′ ər) —*verb* To glare angrily.

gnome (nōm) —*noun* A fairy-tale dwarf.

gnome

gob·lin·ish (gŏb′ lĭn ĭsh) —*adjective* Like a goblin (an ugly, fearful, fairy-tale character).

goi·ter (goi′ tər) —*noun* A disease characterized by swelling of the thyroid gland.

good·man (gŏŏd′ mən) —*noun* A courteous old-time title for a man who was not a noble.

Grand Vi·zier (grănd′ vĭ zîr′) —*noun* A high government official especially in Moslem countries.

grave (grāv) —*adjective* Extremely serious; important.

grav·el·ly (grăv′ ə lē) —*adjective* Rough or low-sounding.

greaves (grēvz) —*noun* Leg armor worn below the knee.

grim (grĭm) —*adjective* Gloomy.

grim·ace (grĭm′ ĭs) or (grĭ mās′) —*noun* A facial expression of pain or discomfort.

groom (grŏŏm) —*verb* To make neat.

grope (grōp) —*verb* To feel about; to search blindly or uncertainly.

grove (grōv) —*noun* A group of trees without underbrush among them.

gruff (grŭf) —*adjective* Unfriendly; harsh.

guild·er (gĭl′ dər) —*noun* A coin used in ancient times.

gul·ly (gŭl′ ē) —*noun* A ditch cut in the earth by flowing water.

gust (gŭst) —*noun* A sudden, strong breeze.

ha·bi·ta·tion (hăb′ ə tā′ shən) —*noun* The place one lives.

hack·a·more (hăk′ ə môr′) or (hăk′ ə mōr′) —*noun* A rope halter used to break horses into wearing a bridle.

hag·gard (hăg′ ərd) —*adjective* Weary; exhausted.

hand·guard (hănd′ gärd′) —*noun* A rounded shield between the handgrip and blade on a fencing foil or actual sword.

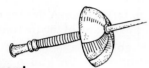

handguard

han·ker·ing (hăng′ kər ĭng) —*noun* A desire to have something or to do something.

ha'pen·ny (hā′ pə nē) —*noun* A British coin worth half a penny.

har·dy (här′ dē) —*adjective* Strong and healthy; robust.

har·row (hăr′ ō) —*verb* To break up and level off plowed ground.

har·vest (här′ vĭst) —*noun* The crop that is gathered.

hasp (hăsp) —*noun* The metal loop to which a padlock is secured to lock a door.

haught·y (hô′ tē) —*adjective* Too proud of oneself; superior in one's own mind; arrogant.

haunch·es (hônch′ ĭz) or (hŏnch′ ĭz) —*noun* The upper thighs of an animal.

hay·wire (hā′ wīr′) —*adjective* Not working properly; broken.

heave (hēv) —*verb* To raise, lift, or throw with effort of force; hoist.

he·li·um (hē′ lē əm) —*noun* A nonflammable, lighter-than-air gas used to float balloons.

herd (hûrd) —*verb* To gather, keep, or drive together.

her·e·tic (hĕr′ ĭ tĭk) —*noun* One who disagrees with established religion; literally, one whose religious beliefs condemn his soul.

her·i·tage (hĕr′ ĭ tĭj) —*noun* Something passed down from preceding generations.

her·ring (hĕr′ ĭng) —*noun* A salt water fish well liked for its taste.

hi·bis·cus (hī bĭs′ kəs) —*noun* A bush with large colorful flowers.

hill·ock (hĭl′ ək) —*noun* A small hill.

hilt (hĭlt) —*noun* The handle of a sword.

hitch (hĭch) —*noun* A delay or difficulty.

hoard (hôrd) or (hōrd) —*noun* A hidden supply of goods or valuables.

hob·ble (hŏb′ əl) —*noun* A rope or strap used to prevent free movement of an animal.

hob·by·horse (hŏb′ ē hôrs′) —*noun* A child's toy made of a stick with a toy horse's head on one end.

hobbyhorse

/ ă pat / ā pay / â care / ä father / ĕ pet / ē be / ĭ pit / ī pie / î fierce / ŏ pot / ō go /
/ ô paw, for / oi oil / o͝o book / o͞o boot / yo͞o abuse / ou out / ŭ cut / û fur / hw which /
/ *th* the / th thin / zh vision / ə ago, item, pencil, atom, circus / ər butter /

hoist (hoist) —*verb* To lift a heavy object, often with mechanical help.

hold·ing (hōl' dĭng) —*noun* A tract of land one possesses.

hol·low (hŏl' ō) —*noun* An indented surface or area.

holt (hōlt) —*noun* An otter's den.

host (hōst) —*noun* A large number; multitude.

hub·bub (hŭb' ŭb') —*noun* Confused noise.

hu·mid·i·fi·er (hyōō mĭd' ə fī' ər) —*noun* A device for adding moisture to the air.

hu·mil·i·a·tion (hyōō mĭl' ē ā' shən) —*noun* Extreme embarrassment.

hwa·rang·do (hwä răng' dō') —*noun* A Korean martial art whose name literally means "the way of the flower of manhood." It was studied by the royal bodyguard of the emperor.

hy·ae·na or **hy·e·na** (hī ē' nə) —*noun* An Asian or African animal that looks rather like a large dog.

hy·drau·lic (hī drô' lĭk) —*adjective* Operated or moved by pressure.

hy·poc·ri·sy (hĭ pŏk' rĭ sē) —*noun* The act of pretending what one is not; lack of sincere feelings.

hys·ter·ics (hĭ stĕr' ĭks) —*noun* Excited or frightened behavior.

ig·nite (ĭg nīt') —*verb* To set fire to; to catch fire.

ignite

il·lu·mi·nate (ĭ lōō' mə nāt') —*verb* To light an area.

im·mense·ly (ĭ mĕns' lē) —*adverb* Very much; greatly.

im·per·ti·nent (ĭm pûr' tn ənt) —*adjective* Improper, rude, or insolent.

im·pulse (ĭm' pŭls') —*noun* A sudden urge or desire; a whim.

in·aud·i·ble (ĭn ô' də bəl) —*adjective* Too quiet to be heard.

in·den·ta·tion (ĭn' dĕn tā' shən) —*noun* A dent or hole in the surface of something.

in·den·ture (ĭn dĕn' chər) —*noun* A contract binding one person into the service of another for the payment of a debt.

in·dif·fer·ent (ĭn dĭf' ər ənt) or (ĭn dĭf' rənt) —*adjective* Apathetic; careless.

in·di·gest·i·ble (ĭn dĭ jĕs' tə bəl) or (ĭn dī jĕs' tə bəl) —*adjective* Inedible; unable to be used by the body.

in·dig·nant (ĭn dĭg' nənt) —*adjective* Showing anger about something that is unfair or bad.

in·dis·posed (ĭn' dĭ spōzd') —*adjective* Mildly ill.

in·ex·pli·ca·ble (ĭn ĕk' splĭ kə bəl) or (ĭn' ĭk splĭk' ə bəl) —*adjective* Unable to be explained.

in·fa·mous (ĭn' fə məs) —*adjective* Having a bad reputation; notorious.

in·fi·nite (ĭn' fə nĭt) —*adjective* Having no limit.

in·fu·ri·ate (ĭn fyŏŏr' ē āt') —*verb* To make extremely angry.

in·hab·it·ed (ĭn hăb′ ĭ tĭd) —*adjective* Lived in; made to be home.

in·let (ĭn′ lĕt′) or (ĭn′ lĭt′) —*noun* A bay or other recess along the coast.

in·sight (ĭn′ sīt′) —*noun* The ability to see hidden truth.

in·stinc·tive (ĭn stĭngk′ tĭv) —*adjective* Coming from natural impulse.

in·tense·ly (ĭn tĕns′ lē) —*adverb* With strong emotion or concentration.

in·tent (ĭn tĕnt′) —*adjective* Focused; concentrated.

in·ter·com (ĭn′ tər kŏm′) —*noun* A device used for talking between two parts of a building, ship, or aircraft.

in·ter·ject (ĭn′ tər jĕkt′) —*verb* To put in between two other things.

in·ter·val (ĭn′ tər vəl) —*noun* A period of time between two events.

in·vest (ĭn vĕst′) —*verb* To spend in order to gain more.

in·vol·un·tar·y (ĭn vŏl′ ən tĕr′ ē) —*adjective* Not subject to the control of the will.

i·rate (ī rāt′) or (ī′ rāt′)—*adjective* Angry, furious.

i·ron·mon·ger (ī′ ərn mŭng′ gər) or (ī′ ərn mŏng′ gər) —*noun* A merchant who deals in hardware.

jack·al (jăk′ əl) —*noun* An African or Asian animal that looks like a dog. It often feeds on what is left of animals that lions or leopards have killed as prey.

jess (jĕs) —*noun* A short strap attached to the leg of a bird. A leash may be attached to the jess.

jest (jĕst) —*noun* Something said or done for fun; joke; prank.

jet·ti·son (jĕt′ ĭ zən) —*verb* 1. To cast overboard. 2. To eject into outer space.

john·ny·cake (jŏn′ ē kāk′) —*noun* A pancake made with cornmeal.

joust (joust) —*noun* A combat between two knights on horses.

jump·master (jŭmp′ măs′ tər) —*noun* The man who coordinates the efforts of a skydiving team.

ka·ra·te (kə rä′ tē) —*noun* A kind of self-defense in which the person does not use weapons.

keel (kēl) —*noun* A fin attached to the bottom of a sailboat that keeps it upright.

keen (kēn) —*adjective* Having a sharp edge or point.

ken·nel (kĕn′ əl) —*noun* A street gutter.

kin·dle (kĭn′ dl) —*verb* To stir up or arouse.

kin·dling box (kĭnd′ lĭng bŏks′) —*noun* A box used for the storage of small firewood.

/ ă pat / ā pay / â care / ä father / ĕ pet / ē be / ĭ pit / ī pie / î fierce / ŏ pot / ō go /
/ ô paw, for / oi oil / o͝o book / o͞o boot / yo͞o abuse / ou out / ŭ cut / û fur / hw which /
/ *th* the / th thin / zh vision / ə ago, item, pencil, atom, circus / ər butter /

la·ment (lə mĕnt′) —*verb* To regret deeply; mourn.

lank (lăngk) —*adjective* Long, straight, and limp in texture.

la·ser (lā′ zər) —*noun* A highly focused beam of light.

league (lēg) —*noun* A group of teams that compete with each other.

lib·er·ate (lĭb′ ə rāt′) —*verb* To set free.

liege (lēj) —*noun* A respectful term for a king.

lieu·ten·ant (lo͞o tĕn′ ənt) —*noun* An officer in the military who ranks below a captain.

light·ed (lī′ təd) —*verb (archaic)* Arrived unexpectedly.

limb (lĭm) —*noun* A jointed extension of the body, such as an arm or leg.

list·less (lĭst′ lĭs) —*adjective* Lacking energy or enthusiasm; apathetic.

lithe (līth) —*adjective* Gracefully flexible.

live·li·hood (līv′ lē ho͝od′) —*noun* The way a person earns a living.

lodg·ing (lŏj′ ĭng) —*noun* A temporary place to sleep.

loin·cloth (loin′ klôth′) —*noun* A piece of cloth worn around the midsection.

loll (lŏl) —*verb* To recline in a relaxed or lazy way.

loom (lo͞om) —*noun* A machine or frame for weaving threads to make cloth.

lull (lŭl) —*verb* To cause to sleep or rest; soothe.

lum·ber (lŭm′ bər) —*verb* To move or walk in a clumsy or noisy way.

lu·na·tic (lo͞o′ nə tĭk) —*noun* An insane or foolish person.

lunge (lŭnj) —*noun* In fencing, a sudden, thrusting attack.

lurch (lûrch) —*verb* A violent jerk.

lure (lo͝or) —*verb* To attract in order to capture.

lurk (lûrk) —*verb* To sneak about in order to ambush.

lush (lŭsh) —*adjective* Thick and plentiful.

lust (lŭst) —*noun* A desire that is too strong and leads to sin.

lynx (lĭngks) —*noun* A large wildcat with thick, soft fur.

ma·che·te (mə shĕt′ ē) —*noun* A large, broad-bladed knife.

machete

mack·in·tosh (măk′ ĭn tŏsh′) —*noun* A raincoat.

mag·is·trate (măj′ ĭ strāt′) —*noun* A local governmental official.

main·te·nance (mān′ tə nəns) —*noun* The act of caring for something.

make·shift (māk′ shĭft) —*adjective* Something used as a temporary substitution.

mal·a·dy (măl′ ə dē) —*noun* An illness or disease.

ma·lar·i·a (mə lâr′ ē ə) —*noun* An infectious disease that causes spells of chills, fever, and sweating.

mal·let (măl′ ĭt) —*noun* A sports tool with a wooden head and a long handle.

mal·nu·tri·tion (măl′ nōō trĭsh′ ən) or (măl′ nyōō trĭsh′ ən) —*noun* A weakness that comes from eating poorly.

ma·neu·ver (mə nōō′ vər) or (mə nyōō′ vər) —*verb* To move or guide in a clever, planned way.

man·go (măng′ gō) —*noun* A tropical fruit with a smooth rind and sweet, juicy, yellow-orange flesh.

man·grove (măn′ grōv′) or (măng′ grōv′) —*noun* A tropical tree or shrub that has many roots growing above the ground. Mangroves form dense thickets in marshes and along shores.

man·gy (mān′ jē) —*adjective* Dirty, filthy, or shabby.

man·tel (măn′ tl) —*noun* The shelf above the fireplace.

mantle (măn′ tl) —*noun* A cloak.

maraud (mə rôd′) —*verb* To raid or invade in search of plunder.

mar·i·on·ette (măr′ ē ə nĕt′) —*noun* A puppet operated by strings.

marionette

ma·roon (mə rōōn′) —*verb* To leave a person helpless and alone in a deserted place; to strand.

marred (märd) —*adjective* Spoiled or blemished.

mar·tial art (mär′ shəl ärt′) —*noun* An oriental art of combat, usually studied as a sport or recreation.

mean (mēn) —*adjective* Lowly.

med·dle (mĕd′ l) —*verb* To interfere in other people's business without being asked.

mem·brane (mĕm′ brān′) —*noun* A thin wall of tissue in living things.

mesh (mĕsh) —*noun* A solid material with many small open spaces.

met·a·phor (mĕt′ ə fôr′) —*noun* A figure of speech that compares one thing with another kind of thing without using the word *like* or *as*.

mid·dy blouse (mĭd′ ē blous′) —*noun* A child's loose blouse with a collar like a sailor's.

mill (mĭl) —*verb* To move around in a confused way.

mince·meat (mĭns′ mēt′) —*noun* A mixture of finely chopped fruit, spices, suet, and sometimes meat; used as a pie filling.

mink (mĭngk) —*noun* An animal with a slender body and thick, soft brown fur.

mis·hap (mĭs′ hăp′) or (mĭs hăp′) —*noun* An unfortunate accident.

mite (mīt) —*noun* An extremely small amount.

mod·i·fy (mŏd′ ə fī) —*verb* To change, alter.

mo·lest (mə lĕst′) —*verb* To bother or destroy.

mol·ly·cod·dle (mŏl′ ē cŏd′ əl) —*verb* To be overprotective or indulgent.

mon·arch (mŏn′ ərk) or (mŏn′ ärk′) —*noun* A king, queen, or emperor.

Mon·sieur (mə syŭ′) —*noun* The French title for an adult man. Used as the English word *Mr.* is used.

/ ă **pat** / ā **pay** / â **care** / ä **father** / ĕ **pet** / ē **be** / ĭ **pit** / ī **pie** / î **fierce** / ŏ **pot** / ō **go** / ô **paw, for** / oi **oil** / ŏŏ **book** / ōō **boot** / yōō **abuse** / ou **out** / ŭ **cut** / û **fur** / hw **which** / / *th* **the** / th **thin** / zh **vision** / ə **ago, item, pencil, atom, circus** / ər **butter** /

moor·ing line (mŏŏr′ ĭng lĭn′) —*noun* A line used to tie up or anchor a boat.

mor·tal (môr′ tl) —*adjective* Having to do with death.

mot·ley (mŏt′ lē) —*adjective* Composed of a strange combination of people or things that make up a group.

mul·let (mŭl′ ĭt) —*noun* A type of edible fish.

mur·ky (mûr′ kē) —*adjective* Stirred up; muddy.

musk·rat (mŭs′ krăt′) —*noun* A North American animal that lives in or near water. The muskrat has thick brown fur and a narrow, flat, scaly tail.

mus·lin (mŭz′ lĭn) —*noun* A cotton cloth with a plain weave.

mus·ter (mŭs′ tər) —*verb* To gather; assemble.

mu·ti·ny (myōōt′ nē) —*noun* Open rebellion against leaders, especially by sailors.

naught (nôt) —*noun* Nothing.

nav·i·gate (năv′ ĭ gāt′) —*verb* To plan, guide, and control the course of a ship or aircraft.

nee·dle (nē′ dəl) —*verb* To tease, annoy, or provoke.

niche (nĭch) or (nēsh) —*noun* A small place set into the wall to hold a statue.

ob·so·lete (ŏb′ sə lēt′) or (ŏb′ sə lēt′) —*adjective* No longer used; out of date.

ob·struc·tion (əb strŭk′ shən) —*noun* Something blocking the path of another thing.

oc·cu·pied (ŏk′ yə pīd′) —*adjective* Taken over by another country.

off·side (ôf′ sīd′) —*adjective* Illegally ahead of the ball in soccer or football.

off·spring (ôf′ sprĭng′) or (ŏf′ sprĭng′) —*noun* Children or descendents.

o·paque (ō pāk′) —*adjective* Not reflecting light; not shiny; dull.

op·ti·mis·tic (ŏp′ tə mĭs′ tĭk) —*adjective* Tending to take a cheerful view of a situation.

o·rang·u·tan (ō răng′ ə tăn′) or (ə răng′ ə tan′) —*noun* A large ape that lives on islands south of Asia.

or·nate (ôr nāt′) —*adjective* Made with much decoration; fancy or elaborate.

out·post (out′ pōst′) —*noun* A settlement in an outlying area.

pa·gan (pā′ gən) —*noun* One who worships many gods or no god at all rather than the one true God as revealed in the Bible.

pal·met·to (păl mĕt′ ō) —*noun* A palm tree with leaves shaped like fans.

pan·ni·kin (păn′ ĭ kĭn) —*noun* A small saucepan or cup made of metal.

parched (pärcht) —*adjective* Dried or roasted.

Par·lia·ment (pär' lə mənt) —*noun* The governing body of England. It is much like the American Congress.

pa·role (pə rōl') —*noun* An early release from prison. A paroled person must stay on good behavior for a certain period of time.

par·ry (păr' ē) —*verb* To ward off an attack.

par·son·age (pär' sə nĭj) —*noun* The house provided by a church for its pastor.

pas·sion (păsh' ən) —*noun* A powerful or very strong feeling.

pa·thet·ic (pə thĕt' ĭk) —*adjective* Causing one to feel pity or sorrow; sad; pitiful.

pau·per (pô' pər) —*noun* A poor person.

paw-paw (pô' pô) —*noun* A tropical evergreen tree with a large yellow fruit.

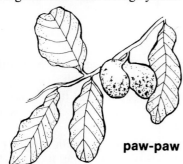

paw-paw

peas·ant (pĕz' ənt) —*noun* A poor farmer.

pe·des·tri·an (pə dĕs' trē ən) —*noun* A person who travels on foot.

peeved (pēvd) —*adjective* Annoyed; resentful.

pelt (pĕlt) —*noun* An animal skin with the fur still on it.

pe·nal·ize (pē' nəl īz') —*verb* To punish for breaking a rule.

per·il (pĕr' əl) —*noun* The chance of harm or loss; danger.

pes·ti·cide (pĕs' tĭ sīd') —*noun* A chemical used to kill harmful insects.

pe·ti·tion (pə tĭsh' ən) —*noun* A special request to someone in charge.

pheas·ant (fĕz' ənt) —*noun* A large bird with a long tail.

pheasant

pi·ous (pī' əs) —*adjective* Very religious or holy.

pitch (pĭch) —*verb* To plunge back and forth.

plank (plăngk) —*noun* A thick, wide board.

pla·toon (plə tōōn') —*noun* A group of military men commanded by a lieutenant.

plea (plē) —*noun* An urgent request.

pledge (plĕj) —*noun* A delivery of goods in payment of a debt.

plumb (plŭm) —*adjective* Completely; totally.

plum·met (plŭm' ĭt) —*verb* To fall swiftly; plunge.

pneu·mo·nia (nōō mōn' yə) or (nyōō mōn' yə) —*noun* A serious disease of the lungs.

poise (poiz) —*noun* Balance; muscular control.

pome·gran·ate (pŏm' grăn' ĭt) or (pŭm' grăn ĭt) —*noun* A tree whose fruit has a tough, reddish rind and many small seeds.

por·ce·lain (pôr' sə lĭn) or (pōr' sə lĭn) —*noun* A brittle kind of fine china.

/ ă pat / ā pay / â care / ä father / ĕ pet / ē be / ĭ pit / ī pie / î fierce / ŏ pot / ō go /
/ ô paw, for / oi oil / ōō book / ōō boot / yōō abuse / ou out / ŭ cut / û fur / hw which /
/ *th* the / th thin / zh vision / ə ago, item, pencil, atom, circus / ər butter /

port (pôrt) or (pōrt) —*noun* The left side of a ship as one faces forward.

port·ly (pôrt′ lē) or (pōrt′ lē) —*adjective* Fat or stout in a dignified way.

po·ten·tial (pə těn′ shəl) —*adjective* Not yet real or definite, but possible in the future.

pre·cip·i·ta·tion (prĭ sĭp′ ĭ tā′ shən) —*noun* Water droplets or ice crystals, such as rain or snow, that fall from the sky to the earth.

pre·cise (prĭ sīs′) —*adjective* Accurate; definite.

pred·a·tor (prĕd′ ə tər) or (prĕd ə tôr′) —*noun* An animal that lives by catching and eating other animals.

pre·dic·a·ment (prĭ dĭk′ ə mənt) —*noun* A troublesome or embarrassing situation.

preen (prēn) —*verb* To smooth or clean with the beak or bill.

pre·oc·cu·pied (prē ŏk′ yə pīd′) —*adjective* Lost in thought.

press (prĕs) —*verb* In fencing, to exert pressure on an opponent's blade. It is usually followed by a quick release.

pre·vail (prĭ vāl′) —*verb* To be greater in strength or influence; triumph.

prey (prā) —*noun* An animal hunted or caught by another for food.

prim·er (prī′ mər) —*noun* An undercoat of paint used to prepare a surface for paint.

pro·ba·tion (prō bā′ shən) —*noun* A period of time for testing a person's behavior.

pro·ces·sion (prə sĕsh′ ən) —*noun* A group of persons walking or riding along in an orderly line.

pro·long (prə lŏng′) —*verb* To extend or lengthen.

pros·trate (prŏs′ trāt′) —*adjective* 1. Physically or emotionally exhausted. 2. Flat on the ground.

pro·trud·ing (prō trōōd′ ĭng) —*verb* Jutting out; projecting.

prov·ince (prŏv′ ĭns) —*noun* A political territory of a country.

pry (prī) —*verb* To raise or move with a lever or wedge.

punc·tu·ate (pŭngk′ chōō āt′) —*verb* To interrupt at intervals.

pup·pet·eer (pŭp′ ĭ tîr′) —*noun* One who operates puppets.

py·thon (pī′ thŏn′) —*noun* A very large, nonpoisonous snake of Africa, Asia, and Australia. Pythons coil around and crush the animals they eat.

quag·mire (kwăg′ mīr′) —*noun* A marsh-like area with a soft, muddy surface.

qualm (kwäm) or (kwôm) —*noun* A feeling of doubt.

quar·an·tine (kwôr′ ən tēn′) or (kwŏr′ ən tēn′) —*noun* An enforced isolation of disease-exposed people to stop the spread of infectious diseases.

quartz (kwôrts) —*noun* A milk-white mineral found commonly in rock around the world.

quea·sy (kwē′ zē) —*adjective* Uneasy; slightly ill.

quench (kwĕnch) —*verb* To satisfy.

quern (kwûrn) —*noun* A hand-turned grain mill used in olden times.

que·ry (kwîr′ ē) —*noun* A question; an inquiry.

quick·sil·ver (kwĭk′ sĭl′ vər) —*adjective* Unpredictable; spontaneous.

quill (kwĭl) —*noun* A writing pen that is made from a long, stiff feather.

rack (răk) —*verb* To strain or try very hard.

ram·rod (răm′ rŏd′) —*noun* A straight metal rod used to ram the ammunition into the barrel of a gun.

ranks (răngks) —*noun* All soldiers who are not officers.

rau·cous (rô′ kəs) —*adjective* Boisterous; disorderly.

ra·ven (rā′ vən) —*adjective* Black and shiny as a raven's feathers.

raven

rav·en·ous (răv′ ə nəs) —*adjective* Greedily hungry.

rav·ing (rā′ vĭng) —*adjective* Wild; uncontrolled.

re·cline (rĭ klīn′) —*verb* To lie back in relaxation.

rec·on·cile (rĕk′ ən sīl′) —*verb* To re-establish friendship between; to forgive.

re·con·nais·sance (rĭ kŏn′ ə səns) —*noun* Exploration of an area to gather military information.

re·count (rĭ kount′) —*verb* To tell or tell again.

re·cruit (rĭ krōōt′) —*verb* To get a person to join or help.

re·duce (rĭ dōōs′) or (rĭ dyōōs′) —*verb* To make smaller; to pulverize.

ref·u·gee (rĕf′ yōō jē′) —*noun* A person who flees from his own home or country to find safety.

ref·use (rĕf′ yōōs) —*noun* Something useless or worthless; trash; rubbish.

re·gain (rē gān′) —*verb* To get again.

reg·u·late (rĕg′ yə lāt′) —*verb* To control or direct according to certain rules.

reg·u·la·tion (rĕg′ yə lā′ shən) —*noun* A law or set of rules by which something is ruled.

re·gur·gi·tate (rē gûr′ jĭ tāt′) —*verb* To bring back up after chewing and swallowing.

re·lay (rē′ lā′) —*verb* To pass or send along.

re·lent (rĭ lĕnt′) —*verb* To become softer or gentler in attitude.

rel·ic (rĕl′ ĭk) —*noun* Something that survives from the distant past.

re·morse (rĭ môrs′) —*noun* Sorrow or regret.

ren·der (rĕn′ dər) —*verb* To perform; to give or make available.

ren·e·gade (rĕn′ ĭ gād′) —*noun* An outlaw.

re·pri·sal (rĭ prī′ zəl) —*noun* A counterattack intended to make up for previous damages made by the enemy.

re·proach (rĭ prōch′) —*noun* A shame, dishonor.

rep·u·ta·tion (rĕp′ yə tā′ shən) —*noun* The general worth of someone as judged by others.

re·sent (rĭ zĕnt′) —*verb* To feel angry or bitter about.

res·er·voir (rĕz′ ər vwär′) —*noun* A body of water collected and stored for later use.

/ ă pat / ā pay / â care / ä father / ĕ pet / ē be / ĭ pit / ī pie / î fierce / ŏ pot / ō go /
/ ô paw, for / oi oil / ōō book / ōō boot / yōō abuse / ou out / ŭ cut / û fur / hw which /
/ *th* the / th thin / zh vision / ə ago, item, pencil, atom, circus / ər butter /

res·ig·na·tion (rĕz′ ĭg nā′ shən) —*noun* The act of giving up or quitting a position or job.

res·o·lute (rĕz′ ə lo͞ot′) —*adjective* With strong will and determination.

re·solve (rĭ zŏlv′) —*verb* To decide with determination.

re·sour·ces (rĭ′ sôr′ sĭz) or (rĭ sōr′ sĭz) or (rē′ sôr′ sĭz) or (rē′ sōr′ sĭz) —*noun* Supplies for a task.

re·spect (rĭ spĕkt′) —*noun* A particular feature or detail.

re·sponse (rĭ spŏns′) —*noun* An answer or reply.

re·strain (rĭ strān′) —*verb* To hold back by physical force.

re·sume (rĭ zo͞om′) —*verb* To begin again after a break; continue.

rev·el (rĕv′ əl) —*verb* To make merry; to enjoy something.

re·vive (rĭ vīv′) —*verb* To bring back or return to life.

re·volt·ing (rĭ vōl′ tĭng) —*adjective* Causing offense or disgust.

rick·et·y (rĭk′ ĭ tē) —*adjective* Shaky, unfirm, likely to fall apart.

rig (rĭg) —*verb* To fit out; equip; prepare.

rig·ging (rĭg′ ĭng) —*noun* Masts, sails, lines, and other equipment on a boat.

ri·ot (rī′ ət) —*verb* To take part in a wild, violent disturbance.

ri·poste (rĭ pōst′) —*noun* In fencing, a thrusting attack made after deflecting an opponent's blow.

ri·val (rī′ vəl) —*noun* A competitor.

ro·dent (rōd′ nt) —*noun* Small animals like mice, rats, squirrels, or beavers.

rodent

ro·de·o (rō′ dē ō′) or (rō dā′ ō) —*noun* A public show in which cowboys display their skills in horseback riding and compete in riding broncos or steers, roping cattle, and similar events.

rogue (rōg) —*noun* A dishonest person; a cheat.

rud·dy (rŭd′ ē) —*adjective* Having a healthy pink or reddish color.

rue·ful·ly (ro͞o′ fə lē) —*adverb* Sorrowfully; regretfully.

ruf·fi·an (rŭf′ ē ən) —*noun* A villain.

Rug·by (rŭg′ bē) —*noun* A British game similar to football.

rum·mage (rŭm′ ĭj) —*verb* To search thoroughly by moving things around.

sag (săg) —*noun* A drooping area or depression.

sa·lute (sə lo͞ot′) —*verb* To greet with polite or friendly words or gestures.

saun·ter (sôn′ tər) —*verb* To stroll or walk leisurely.

sa·vor (sā′ vər) —*verb* To relish or enjoy something.

scal·a·wag (skăl′ ə wăg′) —*noun* A reprobate; rascal.

scav·en·ger (skăv′ ən jər) —*noun* An animal that feeds on decaying material.

sche·mat·ic (skē măt′ ĭk) —*adjective* Having to do with a simplified diagram.

schol·ar (skŏl′ ər) —*noun* A person who has a great deal of knowledge.

score (skôr) or (skōr) —*noun* A group of twenty items.

scourge (skûrj) —*verb* To punish by beating.

scrab·ble (skrăb′ əl) —*verb* To climb in a struggling way, usually on all fours; to scramble.

scraw·ny (skrôn′ ē) —*adjective* Thin and bony.

scrip (skrĭp) —*noun* A small bag or satchel used for carrying money.

scum (skŭm) —*noun* Refuse; trash.

scur·ry (skûr′ ē) —*verb* To run or move about quickly.

seal (sēl) —*noun* An instrument used to imprint a design on wax.

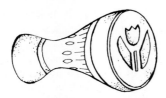

seal

sed·i·men·ta·ry (sĕd′ ə mĕn′ tə rē) —*adjective* Formed from the particles left by muddy water.

seize (sēz) —*verb* To take hold of suddenly and quickly; grab.

self-re·li·ance (sĕlf′ rĭ lī′ əns) —*noun* Confidence in one's own ability.

sen·tence (sĕn′ təns) —*noun* A penalty passed by a court.

sen·ti·men·tal (sĕn′ tə mĕn′ tl) —*adjective* Easily moved by feeling or emotion.

sen·ti·nel (sĕn′ tə nəl) —*noun* A guard; a sentry.

se·vere (sə vîr′) —*adjective* Hard or harsh; stern.

share·crop·per (shâr′ krŏp′ ər) —*noun* A farmer living on and farming another person's land. He gives part of his crop as rent.

sheaf (shēf) —*noun* A collection of papers.

sheep·ish (shē′ pĭsh) —*adjective* Embarrassed or self-conscious.

shek·el (shĕk′ əl) —*noun* A Hebrew coin weighing about a half ounce.

shil·ling (shĭl′ ĭng) —*noun* A coin in the old British currency. It was worth about fifty cents if compared to today's dollar.

shin-donnegan (shĭn′ dŏn′ ə gən) —*noun* A leap of joy.

shin·ny (shĭn′ ē) —*verb* To climb by gripping and pulling with the hands and legs.

shoal (shōl) —*noun* A shallow place in a body of water.

shroud·ed (shroud′ ĭd) —*verb* Concealed; partially hidden.

shut·tle·cock (shŭt′ l kŏk′) —*noun* A piece of cork with feathers in it, used to play badminton.

shuttlecock

sig·ni·fy (sĭg′ nə fī′) —*verb* To signal or give a silent suggestion.

sil·hou·et·ted (sĭl′ ōō ĕt′ ĭd) —*verb* Shown as a dark outline.

sin·ew·y (sĭn′ yōō ē) —*adjective* Made of animal sinew or tendon.

skep·ti·cal (skĕp′ tĭ kəl) —*adjective* Scoffing or doubtful.

skit·ter (skĭt′ ər) —*verb* To skip, glide, or move rapidly along a surface.

skulk (skŭlk) —*verb* 1. To walk stealthily; lurk. 2. To avoid work.

slay (slā) —*verb* To kill violently.

sleight (slīt) —*noun* Cleverness; skillfulness.

slough (slou) or (slōō) —*noun* A swampy pit or bog.

slug·gish (slŭg′ ĭsh) —*adjective* Moving slowly as if from sleepiness.

/ ă pat / ā pay / â care / ä father / ĕ pet / ē be / ĭ pit / ī pie / î fierce / ŏ pot / ō go /
/ ô paw, for / oi oil / ōō book / ōō boot / yōō abuse / ou out / ŭ cut / û fur / hw which /
/ *th* the / th thin / zh vision / ə ago, item, pencil, atom, circus / ər butter /

smirk (smûrk) —*verb* To smile in a knowing, superior way.

smol·der (smōl′ dər) —*verb* To burn with little smoke and no flame.

smote (smōt) —*verb* Hit; struck.

snipe (snīp) —*verb* To shoot at people from a hiding place.

sol·i·tar·y (sŏl′ ĭ tĕr′ ē) —*adjective* Existing or living alone.

sow (sou) —*noun* A female pig that is fully grown.

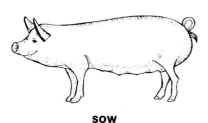

SOW

span (spăn) —*noun* Formerly, a unit of measure equal to about nine inches.

spar (spär) —*verb* To practice fighting techniques.

spit (spĭt) —*verb* To pierce as if to cook on a rotating rod over a fire.

spread·eagle (sprĕd′ ē′ gəl) —*adjective* With the arms and legs stretched out.

spruce (sprōōs) —*noun* An evergreen tree with short needles and soft wood.

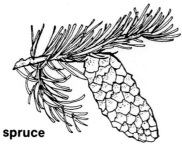

spruce

stag·nant (stăg′ nənt) —*adjective* Foul or stale from standing still.

stake·out (stāk′ out′) —*noun* A close watch kept on an area or person suspected of criminal activity.

stalk (stôk) —*verb* To move in a quiet, cautious way.

stance (stăns) —*noun* A position of readiness assumed by a fencer.

sta·ple (stā′ pəl) —*noun* A major product grown or produced in a region.

star·board (stär′ bərd) —*noun* The right-hand side of a ship as one faces forward.

stark (stärk) —*adjective* Utterly; completely.

stash (stăsh) —*verb* To hide or store away in a secret place.

sta·tis·tics (stə tĭs′ tĭks) —*noun* Facts and figures gathered together and analyzed for informaton on a particular subject.

stave (stāv) —*noun* A staff or club.

stick·ball (stĭk′ bôl′) —*noun* A type of baseball played with a rubber ball and a stick or broom handle for a bat.

stile (stīl) —*noun* A ladder over a fence.

stir·rup (stûr′ əp) or (stĭr′ əp) —*noun* A loop or ring with a flat bottom, hung by a strap from either side of a horse's saddle. It is used to support the rider's foot.

stocks (stŏks) —*noun* A timber frame with holes used to confine the ankles or wrists. A form of punishment in earlier times.

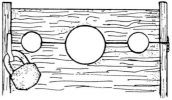

stocks

stow (stō) —*verb* To put or place; store.

strat·e·gy (străt′ ə jē) —*noun* A scientifically researched plan of action.

strut (strŭt) —*noun* On an airplane, a metal rod bracing the wing against the body of the plane.

stu·por (stōō′ pər) or (styōō′ pər) —*noun* Mental confusion; daze.

sub·dued (səb dōōd′) or (səb dyōōd′) —*adjective* Quiet; under control.

sub·merge (səb mûrj') —*verb* To place or go beneath the surface of the water.

sub·tle (sŭt' l) —*adjective* So slight as to be difficult to detect or recognize.

suf·fice (sə fīs') —*verb* To fulfill current needs.

suit·or (soo' tər) —*noun* A man who is courting a woman.

sum·mon (sŭm' ən) —*verb* To call together; to gather.

sup (sŭp) —*verb* To eat the evening meal.

su·per·vi·sion (soo' pər vĭzh' ən) —*noun* The act of watching over or inspecting an action, work, or performance.

sup·pli·ca·tion (sŭp' lĭ kā' shən) —*noun* Humble asking or begging.

surge (sûrj) —*noun* A sudden increase.

sur·mount (sər mount') —*verb* To top, to overcome.

sus·pend (sə spĕnd') —*verb* To forbid attendance for a period of time.

sus·pen·sion bridge (sə spĕn' shən brĭj') —*noun* A bridge suspended from cables that are stretched over a wide canyon or deep gulf.

su·ture (soo' chər) —*noun* Surgical material used to join two edges of a wound in a sewing manner.

swash·buck·ler (swŏsh' bŭk' lər) —*noun* A showy sword fighter.

swatch (swŏch) —*noun* A small sample strip of cloth taken from a larger piece.

swin·dle (swĭn' dl) —*verb* To cheat someone.

swine (swīn) —*noun* A pig or hog.

tack (tăk) —*noun* A change of direction to bring the sailboat into the wind in order to change direction.

tal·on (tăl' ən) —*noun* The claw of a bird that seizes other animals as prey.

talon

tang·y (tăng ē) —*adjective* Sharp; pungent; penetrating.

Tao·ism (tou' ĭz əm') or (dou' ĭz əm') —*noun* A Chinese religion founded in the sixth century before Christ.

tar·get (tär' gĭt) —*noun* A small round shield.

tarp (tärp) —*noun* A large waterproof sheet of canvas used to protect things from moisture.

taunt (tônt) —*verb* To tease or mock.

tech·ni·cian (tĕk nĭsh' ən) —*noun* A person trained in a specific type of technical work.

teem (tēm) —*verb* To be full of; abound or swarm.

ten·don (tĕn' dən) —*noun* The tough fiber that connects muscle to bone.

teth·er (tĕ*th*' ər) —*noun* A restraining rope that allows an animal some limited movement.

thatch (thăch) —*noun* Straw, reeds, or palm fronds used to cover a roof.

thong (thông) or (thŏng) —*noun* A thin strip of leather used to fasten something.

thor·ough·bred (thûr' ō brĕd') —*noun* A purebred animal.

thrash (thrăsh) —*verb* 1. To beat or whip. 2. To move wildly or violently.

thresh·old (thrĕsh' ōld) or (thrĕsh' hōld) —*noun* The piece of wood or stone placed at the base of or beneath a door.

thy·roid (thī' roid) —*noun* A body organ that produces necessary chemicals.

tick·er tape (tĭk' ər tāp') —*noun* A thin strip of paper that reported the latest stock market information by telegraph before the invention of computers.

tif·fin (tĭf' ĭn) —*noun* A luncheon.

til·ler (tĭl' ər) —*noun* A lever or handle used to turn a rudder and steer a boat.

tin·ker (tĭng' kər) —*noun* A traveling salesman of various household supplies.

tog·gle switch (tŏg' əl swĭch') —*noun* A switch with a projecting lever mounted with a spring.

toll (tōl) —*noun* A heavy demand.

top·i·cal (tŏp' ĭ kəl) —*adjective* Concerning a particular topic or subject.

tote (tōt) —*verb* To carry.

tran·quil·li·ty (trăng kwĭl' ĭ tē) or (trăn kwĭl' ĭ tē) —*noun* The condition of being peaceful or calm.

trans·ac·tion (trăn săk' shən) or (trăn zăk' shən) —*noun* A piece of business conducted between two parties.

trap (trăp) —*noun* A light, two-wheeled carriage equipped with springs.

trawl·er (trô' lər) —*noun* A boat used for a special kind of fishing.

treach·er·ous (trĕch' ər əs) —*adjective* Deceptively dangerous.

trea·son (trē' zən) —*noun* A crime against one's country.

trel·lis (trĕl' ĭs) —*noun* A decorative latticework frame for climbing plants and bushes.

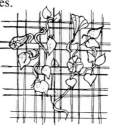

trellis

tres·pass (trĕs' pəs) or (trĕs' păs') —*verb* To invade someone's property without permission.

tri·fle (trī' fəl) —*noun* A small, unimportant thing. —*verb* To play with something in a careless way.

tripe (trīp) —*noun* The stomach lining of a cow, sometimes served as food. It is considered a delicacy.

truce (troos) —*noun* A short halt in a battle or war.

tur·bid (tûr' bĭd) —*adjective* Muddy, heavy, or dense.

turn·pike (tûrn' pīk') —*noun* A toll highway.

tu·tor (too' tər) or (tyoo' tər) —*noun* A private teacher.

ty·phus (tī' fəs) —*noun* An infectious disease.

ty·rant (tī' rənt) —*noun* A ruler who is unjust and cruel.

ul·ti·mate·ly (ŭl' tə mĭt lē) —*adverb* Finally.

un·der·study (ŭn' dər stŭ' dē) —*noun* A person who learns a part in a performance so that he can replace the regular performer if called on to do so.

un·done (ŭn dŭn') —*adjective* Destroyed.

un·fal·ter·ing (ŭn fôl' tər ĭng) —*adjective* Steady, unwavering.

un·fath·om·a·ble (ŭn fă*th*′ ə mə bəl) —*adjective* Unable to be measured.

un·pro·pelled (ŭn prə pĕld′) —*adjective* Free-floating; not powered by an engine.

up·hol·ste·ry (ŭp hōl′ stə rē) or (ŭp hōl′ strē) —*noun* The materials used in padding and decorating furniture.

up·lands (ŭp′ ləndz) or (ŭp′ lăndz′) —*noun* The higher parts of an area, usually inland.

up·per (ŭp′ ər) —*noun* The top portion of a shoe.

ut·most (ŭt′ mōst′) —*adjective* Of the highest or greatest degree.

ut·ter (ŭt′ ər) —*adjective* Complete or total.

va·cant (vā′ kənt) —*adjective* Having no expression on the face; blank.

vague (vāg) —*adjective* Not clear or distinct.

val·et (vă lā′) —*noun* A personal servant for a man.

van·ity (văn′ ĭ tē) —*noun* Emptiness, foolishness, worthlessness.

van·tage point (văn′ tĭj point′) —*noun* A strategic position that provides a commanding view.

var·mint (vär′ mĭnt) —*noun* A troublesome or obnoxious animal.

veer (vîr) —*verb* To swerve suddenly to avoid something.

ven·ti·late (vĕn′ tl āt′) —*verb* To allow fresh air to circulate.

ven·ture (vĕn′ chər) —*noun* A task or action that involves risks and possible danger.

ver·dict (vûr′ dĭkt) —*noun* The decision made by a jury at the end of a trial.

ver·min (vûr′ mĭn) —*noun* Small animals that are annoying or harmful.

vex (vĕks) —*verb* To annoy; to irritate.

vice (vīs) —*noun* A bad character trait or sin.

vig·or (vĭg′ ər) —*noun* Strength, energy, or enthusiasm for a task.

vir·tue (vûr′ cho͞o) —*noun* Goodness; purity.

vi·sor (vī′ zər) —*noun* The front projection of a cap that protects the eyes.

vi·tal signs (vīt′ l sīnz′) —*noun* The heart rate, breathing, and temperature of a person.

vul·gar (vŭl′ gər) —*adjective* Having very poor taste or manners; crude; coarse.

vy·ing (vī′ ĭng) —*verb* Competing.

wal·low (wŏl′ ō) —*verb* To roll around lazily in mud.

war·y (wâr′ ē) —*adjective* Watchful; careful.

wa·ver (wā′ vər) —*verb* To be uncertain; to tremble or flicker.

wedge (wĕj) —*verb* To fasten in place firmly.

weight·y (wāt′ ē) —*adjective* Very important.

wench (wĕnch) —*noun* A young woman or peasant girl.

| / ă pat / ā pay / â care / ä father / ĕ pet / ē be / ĭ pit / ī pie / î fierce / ŏ pot / ō go / |
| ô paw, for / oi oil / o͝o book / o͞o boot / yo͞o abuse / ou out / ŭ cut / û fur / hw which / |
| *th* the / th thin / zh vision / ə ago, item, pencil, atom, circus / ər butter / |

wharf (hwôrf) —*noun* A landing place or pier at which ships may tie up and load or unload.

wheedle (hwēd′ l) or (wēd′ l) —*verb* To persuade by flattery or deceit.

whence (hwĕns) or (wĕns) —*adverb* From where.

whet (hwĕt) or (wĕt) —*verb* To sharpen.

whim (hwĭm) or (wĭm) —*noun* A sudden wish, desire, or idea.

will (wĭl) —*verb* To desire something deeply and stongly.

wince (wĭns) —*verb* To pull back quickly in pain; flinch.

wit (wĭt) —*noun* The ability to describe things in a clever, funny way.

wraith (rāth) —*noun* A ghost.

wrath (răth) or (räth) —*noun* Anger.

wrench (rĕnch) —*verb* A sudden, hard twist or turn.

wretched (rĕch′ ĭd) —*adjective* 1. Miserable; full of remorse. 2. Inferior in quality.

writhe (rīth) —*verb* To twist, struggle, or squirm in pain or embarrassment.

wroth (rôth) —*adjective* Angry.

yearn (yûrn) —*verb* To desire something desperately.

yield (yēld) —*verb* To give forth; produce; provide.

Zen (zĕn) —*noun* A form of Buddhism, a major religion in China and Japan.

zinc (zĭngk) —*noun* A shiny bluish-white metal that is not affected by air and moisture.

zith•er (zĭth′ ər) or (zĭth′ ər) —*noun* A musical instrument made of a shallow, flat box with thirty to forty strings stretched over it. It is played by plucking the strings.

Photo Credits

Basketball Hall of Fame page 440

George Collins pages 209, 244, 245, 393, 576

Creation Research Society page 297

Greenville News-Piedmont: Photo by Fletcher W. Ross, pages 93, 94

Steve Hicklin pages 95, 99-100

Library of Congress page 28

Morton Salt, Division of Morton Thuckol page 243

National Archives page 575 (bottom)

National Park Service: Photos by Richard Freer, pages 101, 521; Photo by Fred Mang, Jr., page 388

National Zoological Park: Photo by Jessie Cohen, page 385

S.C. Wildlife Marine Resource Department: Photo by Phillip Jones, page 391

Texas Tourist Development Agency: Photo by Richard Reynolds, page 190

Unusual Films pages 1, 30, 31, 333, 390, 415, 417-22, 442-43, 547

U.S. Fish and Wildlife Service: Photo by Robin Hunter, page 330; photo by Alan Jenkins, page 331 (top); photo by Craig Koppie, pages 331 (bottom), 335 (right); photo by Don Pfitzer, page 336; photo by Gary Zahm, page 329, 335 (left)

Virginia Division of Tourism page 575 (top)